Y0-BCR-471

The Child Protection Team Handbook

The Child Protection Team Handbook

A Multidisciplinary Approach to Managing Child Abuse and Neglect

Edited by Barton D. Schmitt

Department of Pediatrics,
University of Colorado Medical Center,
Denver, Colorado

 Garland STPM Press
New York & London

15 14 13 12 11 10 9 8 7 6 5 4 3 2 1

Library of Congress Cataloging in Publication Data

Main entry under title:

The Child protection team handbook.

   Bibliography: p.
   Includes index.
   1. Child abuse—Handbooks, manuals, etc.
2. Child abuse—Prevention—Handbooks, manuals, etc.
3. Social service—Team work—Handbooks, manuals, etc.
I. Schmitt, Barton D., 1937–
HV713.C3827   362.7'3   77-78700
ISBN 0-8240-7000-3

Printed in the United States of America

To C. Henry Kempe, M.D.,
*in recognition of his pioneer efforts in
the field of child abuse, and in appreciation
for the personal impact he has had
on the lives and careers of this
book's contributors.*

Contributors

BEEZLEY, PATRICIA J., M.S.W., Assistant Director, National Center for Child Abuse and Neglect; Instructor, Department of Pediatrics, University of Colorado Medical Center, Denver, Colorado 80262.

BERDIE, JANE W., M.S.W., Doctoral Program, Department of Family Social Science, University of Minnesota, St. Paul, Minnesota 55455.

BOCKMAN, HARLAN R., LL.B., Judge, District Court, Adams County, Colorado; Former Assistant District Attorney; Former member of Adams County Multidisciplinary Team.

BOGGESS, PAMELA J., M.D., Child Development Specialist/Pediatrician, National Center for Child Abuse and Neglect; Assistant Professor of Pediatrics, University of Colorado Medical Center, Denver, Colorado 80262.

BOND, JOHN R., Ph.D., Clinical Psychologist; Consultant, Child Protective Services Unit, Honolulu, Hawaii.

BREAKEY, GAIL F., M.P.H., Project Coordinator, Hawaii Family Stress Center, Honolulu, Hawaii.

BRIDGES, CAROLE L., R.N., School Nurse Practitioner; Assistant Head Nurse, Pediatric Outpatient Department, University of Colorado Medical Center, Denver, Colorado 80262.

CARROLL, CLAUDIA A., M.S.W., Child Protection Team, University of Colorado Medical Center, Denver, Colorado 80262.

CROSS, SHARON L., R.N., M.S., P.N.A., Instructor, Public Health Nursing, School of Public Health, University of Minnesota, Minneapolis, Minnesota 55455.

FRASER, BRIAN G., J.D., Executive Director, National Committee for Prevention of Child Abuse, Chicago, Illinois; Formerly, Staff Attorney, National Center for Child Abuse and Neglect, Denver, Colorado.

GRAY, JANE D., M.D., Pediatrician, Child Protection Team, University of Colorado Medical Center, Denver, Colorado 80262.

GROSZ, CANDACE A., B.A., Coordinator, Child Protection Team, University of Colorado Medical Center, Denver, Colorado 80262.

KEMPE, C. HENRY, M.D., Professor of Pediatrics and Microbiology, University of Colorado Medical Center, Denver, Colorado 80262; Director, National Center for the Prevention and Treatment of Child Abuse and Neglect, Denver, Colorado 80262.

LENHERR, MARILYN R., M.S., Coordinator, Child Protection Team, University of Colorado Medical Center, Denver, Colorado 80262.

LOY, LEIMALAMA LEE., M.S.W., Supervisor, Child Protective Services Unit, Department of Social Services and Housing, Honolulu, Hawaii.

SCHMITT, BARTON D., M.D., Associate Professor of Pediatrics, University of Colorado Medical Center; Director, Child Protection Team, Colorado General Hospital, Denver, Colorado 80262.

STERN, HARRIET C., M.D., Clinical Instructor, Pediatrics and Psychiatry, University of Colorado Medical Center; Consultant Psychiatrist, Child Protection Team, Colorado General Hospital, Denver, Colorado 80262.

Contents

III. Child Protection Team Conferences

IV. Treatment Tasks

Appendix A: PROTOCOLS AND POLICIES FOR THE MANAGEMENT OF CHILD ABUSE AND NEGLECT AT COLORADO GENERAL HOSPITAL

Appendix B: A CHART AUDIT ON CHILD ABUSE AND NEGLECT CASES INVESTIGATED IN JANUARY AND MAY OF 1974 BY THE CHILD PROTECTIVE SERVICES UNIT IN HONOLULU, HAWAII—BARTON D. SCHMITT AND GAIL F. BREAKEY

Appendix C: COMPREHENSIVE QUESTIONNAIRES ON BEHAVIOR AND DEVELOPMENT—BARTON D. SCHMITT

Appendix D: SOCIAL WORKER EVALUATION FORMS—CLAUDIA A. CARROLL

Foreword

Hospital-based child protection teams came into being 25 years ago through the efforts of Betty Elmer, M.S.W., of the Pittsburgh Children's Hospital; Helen Boardman, M.S.W., Children's Hospital in Los Angeles; and C. Henry Kempe, M.D., of the Department of Pediatrics at the University of Colorado Medical Center in Denver. In the past 20 years, child protection teams have expanded from having two or three members (generally a social worker, a pediatrician, and a nurse) to include a variety of professionals from the fields of psychology, psychiatry, law, and education. Most importantly, in recent years, representatives from the child protective services of welfare departments have become permanent members of hospital-based teams.

During this time, we have also seen the growth of community-based child protection teams. These are generally under the leadership of the child protection services of the welfare department, but they invariably include broad representation of the above disciplines. Obviously, there is a place for both kinds of teams. We estimate that in urban communities a team is required for each 300,000 to 400,000 inhabitants; and, in a city such as Denver, two hospital-based teams and two community-based teams make sense. It is vital, in the case of hospital-based teams, that the child protection service of the welfare department delegate a decision-making member to the team so that joint recommendations can be formulated.

The development of a treatment plan must take into consideration the availability of treatment services in the community and represent a unified professional view to the families and the courts. It is equally essential that the same team originally involved in decision making and the formulation of a treatment plan be brought into the case when a change of disposition (e.g., the return of a child from foster care to a home) is considered by the court. All too often hospital-based teams are poorly integrated into the welfare system, work in isolation, and have their recommendations ignored, and their expertise and detailed knowledge of the case overlooked when the family is reevaluated once treatment has begun.

It is not difficult to appoint team members; but it is quite another matter for such a diverse group to begin functioning as a team. Clearly, there are many situations in which the variety of professionals are a hindrance, rather than a help; and the participants' individual skills are submerged in a general, vague coalescence. This may make for unanimous recommendations, but it doesn't really make for good recommendations.

In child abuse and neglect, we are in a situation similar to the management of cleft palate and harelip. It is believed throughout the world that a great variety of professionals are needed to make reasonable diagnostic, prognostic, and treatment recommendations for this deformity. In addition to the pediatrician, the professions of nursing, dentistry, speech pathology, plastic surgery, and psychology are represented. Also, a single, coordinating physician who will be the central decision-maker in the long series of surgery and rehabilitative services needed for the child is identified.

In the same way, families involved in child abuse and neglect are so complex and so draining on the emotional life of the social worker that the sharing of diagnosis, prognosis, and the development of a treatment plan by the social worker has become broadly accepted for the good of all. When the social worker is asked to carry this load alone, staff turnover rates are enormous and professional satisfactions are minimal. On the other hand, both professional satisfaction and the quality of care are improved when a team has an adequate data base for family diagnosis; can formulate a reasonable treatment plan which makes sense to the community; and has drawn up guidelines for following the family to insure the child's safety or, conversely, to assess failure of treatment. It is, therefore, absolutely essential that the county welfare departments include the hospital-based teams in their professional network of diagnosis by sending, not a spear-carrier, but a decision-maker to the team's meeting. This avoids fragmentation of decision making and insures better care for the family.

Child abuse teams require about six months or 20 cases before they become comfortable and effective. Initially, there is a good deal of suspicion and defense of territorial imperatives. But as time goes on and the team members make reasonable efforts at family diagnosis and the joint development of treatment plans, sharing some successes and, invariably, some failures together, the team becomes cohesive, and its members become respectful of each other. Without losing one's professional identity, each member finds a way to contribute to a general consensus. When a consensus cannot be found, it is reasonable for separate recommendations to go forward to the court, properly leaving final decisions to the juvenile court judge. However, in our experience, this situation has been rare. Rather, as long as the welfare department is adequately represented and participates, hospital-based teams supplemented by community-based teams on which physicians and nurses serve do equally well in providing an accurate estimate of the entire family's capacity.

This book is designed to acquaint members and potential members of child protection teams with the practical guidelines required to develop an adequate data base for family diagnosis, assess risk of repeated abuse, and clarify treatment choices. Such guidelines are also necessary to begin moving from random information, random collection, and random decisions to a fairly logical approach to all the steps in child abuse diagnosis, treatment, and follow-up.

Meeting all of these objectives requires utilization of the problem-oriented record, which assures that no important problem is overlooked in subsequent evaluation. This manual also emphasizes the efficiency of role clarification as opposed to role diffusion. Overall, it describes a practical model which has worked effectively in one setting, and, from the authors' experience, one which should be applicable elsewhere.

It is fortunate that child protection teams are now in a position to introduce methodologies which are likely to result in much improved diagnosis and treatment. It is the hope of the contributors that this practical approach to the operation of multidisciplinary child protection teams will aid teams in the optimal fulfillment of their responsibilities.

C. HENRY KEMPE, M.D.
*Professor of Pediatrics
and Microbiology* •
*Director, National Center for
Prevention and Treatment of
Child Abuse and Neglect*

Preface

The purpose of this book is to provide a practical, down-to-earth handbook for multidisciplinary child protection teams. The book contains a clear description of each team member's role in the evaluation and treatment phases. How to make team meetings efficient and effective is covered. The overall format utilizes the problem-oriented record as it applies to initial evaluation, team conference reports, and follow-up reports. The book is designed primarily for professionals already involved in child abuse and neglect management; and, therefore, it assumes a certain core knowledge regarding the incidence, etiology, legal aspects, and community resources for child abuse and neglect. The reader who is new to the field should first review the Introduction, "Basic information and assumptions regarding child abuse and neglect."

The book is divided into the following four parts:

PART 1: ORGANIZING A CHILD PROTECTION TEAM

This section contains general information regarding team formation. It proceeds from the basics of selecting team members to writing the policies and procedures essential to a well-functioning team. Once a team has developed an effective mechanism for handling cases, chapter 4 describes ways in which the team can increase case finding and reporting in their community. Chapter 5 describes how a team can assess and upgrade the community's diagnostic and treatment services for child abuse and neglect so that cases reviewed by the team are optimally managed at all levels.

PART 2: DIAGNOSTIC TASKS

This section contains a clear description of the evaluative role of each team member during the team's diagnostic process. Each chapter contains a specific task check-list, or data base, for that profession. A sample evaluation for each discipline is also included at the end of each chapter. A professional involved in the child abuse and neglect field should be able to audit his current performance by reviewing the appropriate chapter. Chapter 13 on the coordinator's role describes how one person oversees the data collection to guarantee that it is complete and available for the team conference on time.

PART 3: CHILD PROTECTION TEAM CONFERENCES

The ground rules for making meetings more effective and efficient are discussed in this section. Chapter 15 reviews the problem-oriented record as a logical mechanism for recording the team's deliberations and outlines how to list an abusive family's problems and the team's recommendations for each problem. (The sample evaluations in Part 2 are also summarized in a problem-oriented format.) Chapter 16 then describes some guidelines for common case management decisions that every child protection team has to make—such as when foster placement is needed and when return to the natural home is safe. Chapter 17 acknowledges and discusses the human factors that interfere with optimal team functioning. Chapters 24 and 25 contain additional examples of full utilization of the problem-oriented record at team meetings.

PART 4: TREATMENT TASKS

The rehabilitation of abusive families is examined here. Optimal treatment is a group effort, and no professional should attempt to manage such a family alone. Chapter 18 reviews the special roles of the court, county attorney, parent's attorney, and child's attorney. Chapters 19, 21, and 22 review the specific intervention techniques of the three professionals most commonly involved in the treatment of abusive families—namely, the social worker, physician, and public health nurse. Chapter 20 reviews the key role of the experienced supervisor in protective services. Chapter 23 looks at the full range of current treatment modalities. Chapter 24 discusses treatment review or staffing as it might take place in any therapeutic setting where abusive families are seen. Chapter 25 returns to the child protection team coordinator and her critical role in long-term case management and follow-up.

Acknowledgment

The editor is most grateful to the many professionals who have attended training workshops at the National Center for the Prevention and Treatment of Child Abuse and Neglect over the past four years. By direct workshop participation and later correspondence, these people have stimulated the authors to improve their approaches to the many facets of child abuse and neglect and team functioning. The editor also appreciates the help of those National Center staff members who, although not listed among the contributors to this book, have nonetheless influenced its content in numerous ways. Included are Helen Alexander, Donald Bross, Christy Cutler, Janet Dean, Lloyd Eckhardt, Ruth Kempe, Richard Krugman, Harold Martin, Martha Rodeheffer, Robert Schrant, Brandt Steele and our long-standing friend and consultant, Ray Helfer. I am also indebted to the Robert Wood Johnson Foundation, the Commonwealth Fund, and the Grant Foundation for funding the National Center and many of its research and educational programs. It is hoped that this book will underscore the practical application of such pilot studies. Needless to say, this book stems largely from the day-to-day achievements and disappointments of the Child Protection Team at Colorado General Hospital, an operation long funded by the state of Colorado. And last, but not least, our special thanks to Lois Robinson, Marion Rex, Margaret Anderson, and Lou Frey for typing and retyping this manuscript.

Introduction

Barton D. Schmitt

Basic Information and Assumptions Regarding Child Abuse and Neglect

A. GENERAL STATISTICS

1. The incidence of child abuse is approximately 500 new cases per million population per year (Colorado 1975). The inclusion of child neglect in mandatory reporting may double this figure.
2. Types of child abuse are 85 percent physical abuse, 10 percent sexual abuse, and 5 percent failure to thrive secondary to nutritional deprivation. The incidence of nutritional deprivation in hospitalized cases is approximately 10 percent. Emotional abuse is not found in this analysis, because the types of cases that are severe enough to prove in court are almost always associated with physical abuse or serious neglect.
3. There are approximately 2,000 deaths per year from physical abuse in the United States. This represents a major cause of death in children. The overall mortality rate is approximately 3 percent nationally. In areas where there is early detection and intervention, the death rate is less than 1 percent. In areas where the case finding is inadequate, the death rate may climb to 10 percent.
4. The ages of the victim vary according to the type of abuse and neglect. In physical abuse, approximately one-third of the cases occur under six months of age, one-third between six months and three years of age, and the remaining one-third over three years of age. In communities with a good case finding system there is a larger incidence in school age children. Sexual abuse occurs almost totally in girls, and

1

half the cases are in children under age 12. Failure to thrive occurs predominantly in the first 12 months of life.

5. The risk of physical abuse occurring in siblings of an abused child is that in 20 percent of cases, there is concurrent abuse; and in 50 percent of cases, there is previous or future abuse.

6. The abuser is a related caretaker in 90 percent of cases, a boyfriend in 5 percent of cases, an unrelated babysitter in 4 percent of cases, and a sibling in 1 percent of cases. Overall, adult females and males are equally involved. However, the most important factor is access, the mother being more commonly involved if she is totally responsible for child rearing, and the father being more commonly involved if he is out of work.

B. DIAGNOSIS

1. The most important type of child abuse and neglect to diagnose is physical abuse of a child under the age of two. Every one of these cases is a potentially fatal one.

2. The most difficult diagnostic question is when does physical discipline become physical abuse. The most practical answer is when the punishment leads to bruises. Bruising implies hitting without restraint. Although discipline is necessary to prevent spoiled children, harsh discipline is unacceptable. A few bruises in the name of discipline can easily spill over into a more serious injury the next time. Detection is too late if permanent inflicted injuries have already occurred.

3. Confirmation of the diagnosis of child abuse and neglect is predominantly a medical task. The presence of psychosocial data that demonstrates a family at high risk for abuse is supportive of the diagnosis, but not diagnostic in itself, since the children of these families can also have true accidents. The absence of positive psychosocial data, however, should cause the evaluator to consider that the injury was more likely inflicted by a babysitter or other party.

4. Nonaccidental trauma is currently vastly underreported. A common cause for underreporting is past reporting that was frustrating in terms of inadequate or overzealous intervention by the police, child protective service unit, or courts.

C. ETIOLOGY

1. These parents are usually lonely, unhappy, depressed adults under tremendous stress. They often have childhood experiences in common, mainly in the area of harsh discipline and no model of construc-

tive parenting. These parents are 80 percent to 85 percent treatable. Less than 10 percent of them are psychotic or criminals.
2. Some of these children are special in terms of being difficult, or even provocative. However, most of these parents love their children, even if the child is irritating at times.
3. Inflicted injury usually happens in a moment of anger. It is not a premeditated event. Often the anger is misplaced to the child from some other stress in the parents' day.

D. TREATMENT

1. The highest priority of treatment is to protect the child. If in doubt, the issue should be resolved in favor of the child. The second priority of treatment is to help the parents; and the third priority is to restore the family if possible.
2. Initial hospitalization is often necessary to protect the child while a treatment plan is established for the parents. The utilization of emergency receiving homes, when available, is a more economical approach to this aspect.
3. Unless these cases are reported to child protective services, treatment probably won't occur, and abuse will probably recur. Reporting is the first step toward adequate evaluation, treatment, follow-up, and proper use of the Court when necessary.
4. Modern treatment plans must include more options than traditional case work. Parents Anonymous groups, parenting aides, child rearing counselling, and crisis nurseries should be provided. Special treatment for the child such as therapeutic preschools and play therapy should also be available if he is quite disturbed.
5. The duration of follow-up must be a minimum of six months in most cases, if permanent changes in the family are to be realized.
6. Failure to treat child abuse can lead to reinjury or death. Also, abused children grow up and some of them become violent members of our society. Child abuse has been correlated with playground violence, street violence, juvenile delinquency, marital violence, and criminal violence.

E. LEGAL ASPECTS

1. Initial police involvement can jeopardize therapy. It is unnecessary except in emergencies or when the parents are resistant to child protective services intervention.
2. Jail and criminal prosecution are rarely indicated for the abusive parent. The parents have usually already experienced too much violence

in their lives. They need a nonpunitive, helpful therapeutic approach, not jail.
3. Temporary foster care is necessary in 10 percent to 20 percent of cases. In a hospital setting, where more severe cases are seen, foster care may be indicated in 50 percent of cases. This fulfills the first priority of treatment, namely, the protection of the child from serious reinjury.
4. Termination of parental rights is required in 1 percent to 2 percent of cases. In a hospital setting approximately 5 percent of cases require termination of parental rights. Voluntary relinquishment is preferable if the parents can accept this alternative.

F. CHILD PROTECTION TEAMS

1. Multidisciplinary teams are needed to coordinate the efforts of the multiple agencies involved in child abuse cases and, thereby, to lessen the competition and misunderstanding between these agencies.
2. Since many child abuse decisions have life or death consequences they should be shared, rather than unilateral decisions.
3. Teams need criteria and guidelines for the decisions they must make to decrease the chance of error and increase the likelihood of team consistency.

G. PREVENTION

1. Early identification of families under stress and families at risk for inadequate parenting is possible.
2. Prevention of child abuse and other symptoms of family breakdown is possible by providing these families with added support services and lifelines, such as, parent aides, crisis nurseries, and adequate medical care.
3. A progressive community will be into prevention, as well as the diagnosis and treatment of child abuse and neglect.

PART I

Organizing a Child
Protection Team

1

Team Purpose and Structure

Barton D. Schmitt

A multidisciplinary child protection team is organized to review all cases of child abuse and neglect that are referred to it. A team can have one of several bases, and the most common determinant of a team's origin is an identified geographical base (i.e., county or city). Many teams are linked to child protective service units and county juvenile court systems in a particular county. Another determinant is an identified institutional base, the most common being a hospital-affiliated team in an institution with more than 50 pediatric beds. Since the majority of severe child abuse cases are initially hospitalized, it is not surprising that such teams are necessary. Some mental health clinics have also developed teams.

A team can usually evaluate and review a maximum of 100 new cases each year. The population base that generates this number of cases is about 300,000 people. Therefore, several teams are necessary in large metropolitan areas. At this time, the country needs a great many more child protection teams. Before such teams can function effectively, however, they must acknowledge their purposes and goals.

Team Purposes

The overriding goals are to effectively diagnose and treat child abuse, and to coordinate the efforts of the many agencies involved. Team members must agree on team purposes and goals if they are to avoid working at cross purposes. Once team purposes are agreed on, role definition, task assignment, case reevaluation techniques, and team policies easily follow. Specific team purposes can be divided into diagnostic and treatment aspects.

TEAM DIAGNOSTIC PURPOSES

The following team purposes apply to the diagnostic phase:

1. Insure a comprehensive evaluation and data base. Group pressure promotes this.

2. Establish the team as the community's investigatory and accusatory body. The parents should be able to blame the team for any actions they consider to be "heavy handed," which permits the child protective service (CPS) unit to become a helping agency in the eyes of the parent and allows the assigned social worker to become the therapist that she was trained to be.

3. Review cases for errors. It is always easier to see another's flaws. The team also protects each member from being destroyed by a single serious mistake which can easily happen to people working in this complex field.

4. Review cases to evaluate the safety of the home. Child abuse involves life and death issues, and such decisions should be shared. No major decision should be made unilaterally at staff meetings of one discipline.

5. Review cases to reach a consensus on diagnosis and treatment. It is impossible for any one person or discipline to collect or assimilate all the data necessary in these cases.

6. Formulate the final recommendations for initial treatment.

7. Formulate the tentative recommendations for long-term treatment.

8. Provide telephone consultation services regarding diagnostic questions for physicians and other professionals in the community.

9. Provide a referral mechanism for primary practitioners. In suspected cases of child abuse and neglect, the practitioner may not wish to report the case directly because of his relationship with the family.

10. Improve communication between disciplines and agencies. The team conferences bring the various disciplines together in the same room, making talking with each other and gaining a better understanding of each other's position unavoidable.

TEAM TREATMENT PURPOSES

The following statements refer to the treatment phase:

1. Periodically review and evaluate cases for therapeutic progress and setbacks.

2. Revise treatment programs to suit the changing needs of the case. Case management must be flexible. Approaches that do not work must be discontinued, and new recommendations considered.

3. Utilize all community resources effectively and appropriately. No available resources should be overlooked.

4. Prevent premature return of the child to an unsafe home. All major decisions should stay with the team.

5. Attempt to prevent repeated abuse with its concomitant high risk of death and disability.

6. Focus on family rehabilitation. Consider termination of parental rights only when treatment fails.

7. Provide telephone consultation services regarding treatment questions.

8. Coordinate and improve the emergency services for child abuse within the community. One way to do this is to bring people from these agencies to the meeting for clarification of their roles (e.g., police involvement).

9. Reduce interagency power struggles. Time and continual contact between the disciplines is the most likely catalyst for such change.

10. Insure a day in court for any child who needs it. The team's decision on this matter should be final, and their consensus should automatically overrule the objection of any individual physician, lawyer, or social worker.

Team Members

Team size will vary according to the availability of professionals in a given community. The minimum team size is two professionals who are willing to collaborate around the evaluation and treatment of a family. In most situations, this usually involves a social worker and a physician. The maximum permanent size is about ten, since a larger team will often become inefficient. The minimum time a professional should be assigned to team membership is six months. Preferably, team members will remain involved for many years, because good teamwork requires that duration of continuous involvement.

The following is a list of prospective team members described by priority. The first three members can be described as the "nuclear team." In hospital-based teams, these people see most cases directly. In community-based teams, the nuclear team members may not always see the cases directly, but they should have a background of direct experience in the field that qualifies them to serve as consultants. Members four through eight can be considered as the "consultative team." By definition, they do not see most of the families, but they have broad experience in this field. The professionals described under nine through 15 are not part of the permanent team, but vary from case to case. They are the primary workers involved with a family. It is best for the team to remain small until it is functioning adequately, usually for the first three to six months. After that time, if the team is in doubt about including a new member, they should err on the side of including people for the educational benefits they may bring.

1. *Social worker.* The team's permanent social worker is the consultant for evaluating the safety of the home and recommending treatment strategies for families. A psychiatric social worker is an excellent candidate for this position. The social worker assigned to the team may be the CPS unit supervisor; the CPS worker assigned to the hospital; or a full-time, hospital-based social worker. The latter is essential if the hospital serves multiple counties.

2. *Physician.* The physician is the team's main diagnostician. Ideally, the physician is a pediatrician, but a family practitioner would also be suitable. Even in a large teaching hospital, this will usually be a part-time role.

3. *Coordinator.* The team coordinator is the case manager. He or she functions as a communication center for all the agencies and professionals involved in a case. A team based in a large city or a regional hospital requires a full-time coordinator. On smaller teams, the role may only need a part-time person.

4. *Psychiatrist or psychologist.* The team psychiatrist or psychologist mainly serves a diagnostic role. The team's social worker requires psychiatric back-up to evaluate the 10–20 percent of cases where he or she is concerned about the treatability. This person mainly needs to be qualified in evaluating adults. The psychiatrist or psychologist can play a much expanded role by supporting workers through long-term therapy with these families. Although the psychiatrist can be based either in a hospital or private practice, it is preferable to have a mental health clinic representative on the team if it is community based.

5. *Attorney.* It is helpful to have a lawyer present at team conferences to clarify the many legal questions that arise. Preferably, the lawyer will be assigned from the juvenile court or county attorney's office. In hospital-based teams, the hospital lawyer may attend or, if such a person is not available, the hospital administrator may be able to answer some of the questions.

6. *Developmental specialist.* The developmental specialist is an expert in the development and behavior of young children. Such a person may come from backgrounds of child psychiatry, pediatric psychology, or pediatrics. This professional is extremely valuable in emotional abuse cases.

7. *Law enforcement representative.* Since the police are involved initially on many cases and must work closely with the CPS unit, it is optimal to have them represented on the team. In a large metropolitan area, a representative may be assigned from the juvenile division of the police department.

8. *Public health nurse representative.* Some hospitals have a public health nurse-coordinator, and he or she should be involved in team meetings.

Some county-based teams will have a public health nurse-coordinator in their county who can be requested to attend. This person can help to provide expeditious public health nursing services.

9. *Involved social worker.* Obviously, the CPS intake worker on the case under discussion should be present at the meetings. It is his or her responsibility to bring complete psychosocial data to the team meeting.

10. *Involved physician.* The private physician or house staff physicians taking care of the family under discussion should be invited to meetings to present relevant medical data.

11. *Involved police.* The police intially involved with bringing a child to the hospital should be invited to the team meeting. In most states, only the police can pick up a suspicious case for investigation; therefore, they may be an important source of information regarding the family's initial reactions.

12. *Involved lawyer.* The guardian *ad litem* can be a critical participant in a team session that reviews the standing of a serious case. In some situations, especially when the parents are resistant to intervention, the parents' attorney should also be invited.

13. *Involved nurse.* In a hospital setting, the ward nurse who provides most of the care for the hospitalized child should be invited to the meeting to present his or her observations and facts on the frequency of parental visiting. In newborns of high-risk families, the maternity unit nurse may have valuable information. A community nurse who has contact with the family should obviously attend.

14. *Involved educator.* In some cases the school principal, the child's teacher, or coordinator of a local day care unit or Head Start class can be invited to a meeting that involves one of his or her students. This person does not usually need to become a permanent member of the team, unless the team is based in one school catchment area, such as a military base.

15. *Other involved agencies.* Any other agencies previously involved in working with the family under discussion should be notified of the team dispositional conference and invited to attend (e.g., an ADC worker). Some community teams have found that by including parent participants or minority representatives, the team's appreciation of the reality factors facing these families has improved.

Questions often arise regarding funding of a multidisciplinary team. Usually, the team members are already salaried by county or state funding. A physician can often be found at a neighborhood health center, and a psychiatrist or psychologist at a local mental health clinic. If the team requires a private physician or private psychiatrist, funds must be found to pay these professionals on a fee-for-service basis. Sometimes the psychiatrist will need to be placed on a retainer in order for him to block out two hours a week on his schedule for evaluating new families. If the physician is evaluating less than ten cases a year, he may do so gratis. The only team member that requires special funding is the team coordinator. This must eventually become a budgeted, salaried position. In the meantime, the team may find funds from private foundations; Title XX money; or local assistance, such as from the Lions or Kiwanis clubs.

Special Types of Teams

The following teams have distinctive differences from the multidisciplinary consultative teams described in the last section:

1. *Hospital-based teams.* These have one unique feature. The primary workers on each case are usually extremely experienced and of consultant status. The team pediatrician and social worker have actually seen the case first-hand. This arrangement leads to a unique meeting called a "mini-conference." The mini-conference is an unscheduled meeting between the involved social worker and physician during which some preliminary decisions about diagnosis and tentative treatment are reached. This system promotes multidisciplinary decision making before the official team conference.

2. *State consultative teams.* Some urban teams can provide consultation for less sophisticated counties within their state. Often this consultative unit will be based within a state institution (for example, a state medical center). Consultation can be provided on several levels. The primary team can visit the consultative team, present their problem cases and ask specific questions. In some situations, a traveling consultative team will be in operation. The most efficient mechanism for providing consultative services at a great distance is to use telephone linkage. A full description of the speaker-phone arrangement is found in chapter 13.

3. *Rural teams.* Over 65 percent of the American population live in nonmetropolitan areas where the availability of child abuse teams is, naturally, very limited. The basic nucleus for a rural child abuse team includes the county social worker, public health nurse, and law enforcement officer. This team can adequately handle most minor cases of child abuse. The severe cases can be referred to the nearest metropolitan area for a diagnostic team consultation. Expert witness testimony can then be provided by the more experienced metropolitan team. This may be the only way to convince a small town court that child abuse can actually happen in its community. After the hearing, treatment services must be provided by the local community. The metropolitan team, however, can remain available for consultation. Some have recommended that smaller towns join together and form child abuse teams that cover particular judicial districts, including anywhere from five to ten counties each. The limiting factor in

such an arrangement is the distance involved and the amount of traveling that such a team would have to do. This can be overcome with creative utilization of the speaker-phone (see chapter 13).

4. *Treatment teams.* A treatment team strictly reviews cases that are already in treatment. The need for such a specialized team is debatable. Some advocate its formation when a community consultation team has too many cases to handle, as evidenced by team meetings lasting over two hours a week; a team spending over one-third of its time on the review of treatment cases; or a team repeatedly postponing the review of treatment progress in serious abuse cases. Although these findings point to a need for decreasing the team's work load, it would be more logical to form two multidisciplinary consultative teams. New cases could be assigned to each team alternately or by some other, more selective means. Each team, however, would carry cases from start to finish. Diagnostic and treatment decisions regarding a specific family would always be reviewed by the same team. This would provide the same continuity of care from a team that most disciplines find important within their fields.

2

Getting Started

Barton D. Schmitt

Initial Steps

Designate Team Members

Team members may have indicated an interest in participating on a team or they may need to be recruited. If possible each team should have a strong community member, such as a physician or court appointee, to give it some political clout. Each team also needs at least one member with the extra energy necessary for keeping it going. Although the ideal team size may be five or six, two or more people should be considered a team. If there are just two members, one of them needs to be the child protective worker and the other a medical person, such as a physician or registered nurse. If a team has a choice of members, it should look for the personality characteristics mentioned in chapter 17.

Define Roles

If roles are initially ill-defined, members will become disillusioned and may quit the team. It is unfair to expect anyone to adequately learn their role under fire (for example, being berated by angry parents). Therefore, before undertaking responsibilities, new team members should read some general background information regarding child abuse and neglect. Although it is not essential that new members attend a symposium on child abuse and neglect, it is helpful because it allows them to ask experts specific questions that may not be covered in their reading. As a team develops, the work of each member becomes more clarified.

15

Stop Talking About Starting a Team

Starting a team does not require too much planning; and numerous committee meetings on the subject are usually either a waste of time or a stalling tactic. Basic purposes can be outlined by the group in one or two meetings.

Start Meeting Regularly

A common time should be found that is suitable for all team members. Thereafter, the team should meet weekly or biweekly and discuss cases that have occurred in its community. The meeting should be regularly scheduled so that it becomes a part of each member's schedule. It is much easier to cancel an occasional meeting that is not needed than to schedule each conference separately.

Review All Cases

The developing team should hold conferences on all of its cases. As a bare minimum, each case, including physical neglect and abandonment cases, should be fully evaluated by a social worker and a medical person. If there seem to be too many cases, the less difficult or complex ones can be allotted only five minutes. Major cases usually require 30 minutes each. Only after a system has several years of experience and continuous good supervision should limiting review to major cases be considered. However, guidelines should be in effect that mandate which cases require review so that important cases are not overlooked because of an individual's preferences. Most of the team's eventual expertise will come from reviewing a wide spectrum of child abuse and neglect cases as well as the many variations found in cases of authentic accidents. A detailed description of ground rules for effective team conferences is found in chapter 14.

Utilize All Available Treatment Services

The team should become an expert on community resources, relying on agencies beyond those represented by the team members for comprehensive case management. A community directory of human services may be available; if not, the master treatment list in chapter 15 can be reviewed to determine alternative resources.

Pitfalls

Many teams are delayed in starting and reviewing cases because they get bogged down in side issues. The following subjects can be considered "smoke screens." It must be kept in mind that professionals are not immune to them.

Ideal Team Size

Some teams feel that they cannot start until they have a team psychiatrist and pediatric traumatologist. A team should start with the members it has and grow from that point. As previously stated, team members may be as few as two professionals. The encouraging side of small teams is that they are very efficient.

Team Location

By and large, where the team is based does not matter. There are many possible affiliations and meeting places that a team can select. Hospital-based, CPS-based, and mental health-based teams can all function admirably. The more important decision regarding location is that the team attempt to stay in one judicial district and treatment resource boundary if possible.

Power Struggles

Unnecessary time may be spent trying to decide who the team leader will be before the team even begins to meet. It is much better if this position is filled when a leader evolves from the team spontaneously.

Confidentiality

Professionals sometimes become very reserved about what data they can share with colleagues in child abuse and neglect cases. This often represents an inability of professionals to trust each other. In all states, physician-patient confidentiality is waived in child abuse cases. All professional data (verbal or written) can be shared, including psychiatric data, as long as it is not highly speculative. Law suits regarding a breach of confidentiality are not successful unless malicious intent is proven. If a team does not communicate, a team does not exist. Information can be legally shared with all child protection team members—not only permanent team members, but also temporary team members who attend a specific team conference because they are professionals involved with that case.

Child Abuse and Neglect Definitions

Teams can become enmeshed in the fine points of defining a difficult diagnosis, such as child neglect. They can ponder endlessly which cases are their responsibility. It is important that the team get on with discussing actual cases, rather than trying to decide in advance the cases in which they will become involved.

Policies

Team policies can be written after the team is active. Fine points of state laws and regulations should not keep the team from reviewing cases. In addition, shortcomings in state laws should not lead to attempts to change these laws rather than meeting around ongoing cases.

Trying to Change the Community

The community system, in terms of police involvement and limited availability of treatment resources, should not interfere with initiation of the diagnostic team effort. The diagnostic team should fulfill their responsibility appropriately and avoid getting involved with trying to upgrade the community until a later point in time (see chapter 5).

3

Writing Essential Policies and Procedures

Barton D. Schmitt

Once a team has been reviewing cases and interacting with the community for several months, it should set aside time to develop and write team policies and procedures. Standing policies have several benefits: (1) as standards of care are developed, the quality of care is improved, and the normal forgetfulness and confusion that usually occur with complex cases will diminish; (2) as team functioning is simplified, personnel with less training can do some of the tasks; (3) emergency procedures and phone numbers allow the team to weather unpredictable crises with more finesse; (4) team membership becomes a more satisfying experience, and despite the frequent personnel turnover in the child abuse field, the team is able to continue functioning at a high quality level; and (5) dependency on any single team member is diminished, as the experienced member's knowhow becomes transferred to the inexperienced team member through written protocols.

The writing of these policies and protocols will require some extra team meetings. Usually, specific team members will be assigned to writing the first draft of certain protocols. The following policies and procedures are used by our team and might be a good starting point for the team that has not yet developed its own. State laws may necessitate some specific differences. Generally, the policies are listed in order of priority for efficient team functioning.

Policies and Procedures

CHARTER OR PURPOSE

The statement of purpose records the short-term and long-term objectives of an organization. The team should periodically check its present functioning against its original list of purposes. The statement of purposes is found in chapter 1.

INTAKE DATA CHECKLIST

The data base is the information that is collected by the team during its evaluation. Our team has found that it is very helpful to standardize the collection responsibilities. Such role clarification helps to prevent duplication of efforts. It also brings about family satisfaction because assigned tasks seem to get done and the parents are less confused as to who is doing what for them. Appendix A1 contains the intake data checklist used by our team. The responsibilities of the pediatrician, social worker, and coordinator are listed separately. Dates are recorded when specific tasks are completed.

EMERGENCY PROCEDURES AND TELEPHONE NUMBERS

The most critical time at which to have standard protocols available is during emergencies and crises. It is very hard to improvise at these times or to locate the person who has the correct information. The following four protocols were written to meet this need. They are posted at several key locations in the hospital and distributed to anyone who might require them (for example, telephone operators or head nurses). They should be updated at intervals of six months to one year.

EMERGENCY CONSULTATION

During evenings and weekends, various professionals may need consultation regarding a suspected child abuse case. The pediatricians, social workers, and psychiatrists who have expertise in this field are listed on this sheet (Appendix A2) with both office and home phone numbers. The coordinator is also listed to provide help in clarifying policy or locating someone. If consultations are required frequently, various team members must remain on call using a page-boy system. In these cases, a monthly on-call schedule will need to be typed and posted.

POLICE HOLD

Police holds are needed when parents refuse to allow their child to be hospitalized or attempt to remove him from the hospital before it is safe. A police hold allows the child to temporarily become a ward of the state, and for the police to legally arrest the parents if they attempt to interfere with management. Police holds grant the physician and hospital 48 hours to complete their evaluation. At that point, a temporary custody hearing must be held at the juvenile court. The police hold sheet (Appendix A3) lists the phone numbers of the appropriate judicial or law enforcement agency to call in each county for such purposes. A sample form for the police officer to sign is found in Appendix A4.

COURT ORDER TO TREAT

Court order to treat is indicated when the parents refuse to permit the physician to diagnose or treat a life-threatening illness or one with risk to public safety. An example of the former is when parents refuse to allow their child to have a blood transfusion to save his life because they are followers of Jehovah's Witnesses. An example of the latter is when parents refuse treatment and isolation of their child with diptheria. Prior to taking any legal action in either case, it is important to try to clarify any misunderstandings the parents may have and to use the powers of persuasion to bring them around to the physician's point of view. Even at this point, it is worth warning the parents that the physician will have to obtain a court order to treat their child before actually doing so. The court order for medical intervention when the parents refuse to sign a consent form can be obtained during the day by calling the local juvenile court and getting a verbal order from the judge to carry out treatment (Appendix A5). This verbal order should later be confirmed in writing. At night, the police will usually be able to provide the home phone number of the judge on call in the child's county for similar purposes.

In a hospital setting, the physician can ask the administrator on call to carry out these steps. After the court order is carried out, it is a good policy not to bill the parent for such procedures or transfusions. It is also helpful to send the parents a letter of clarification regarding the hospital's good intentions in the case. An example of such a letter sent to parents who refused a spinal tap on their child is found at the end of this chapter (Appendix A6).

EMERGENCY FOSTER PLACEMENT

The CPS unit should be able to place children in a receiving home on short notice. In this way, abused children who are identified in an outpatient setting can forego a costly and unnecessary hospitalization. An example of a sheet containing the information necessary to reach the CPS worker on call in each county is found in Appendix A7.

CASE MANAGEMENT PROCEDURES

DECISION MAKING CRITERIA

Every team has to make certain decisions on a repetitive basis. These decisions should conform to criteria that have been set down as team policy, thus limiting the possibility of serious error—such as, not placing a child in a foster home when he is in great danger in his natural home. These decision-making guidelines represent the standards of team care. Suggestions for guidelines are found in chapter 16.

INITIAL INTERVENTION PROCEDURES

The steps involved in acute intervention with a child abuse case can be outlined in detail. Separate protocols can be written for different categories of abuse and neglect. Our team has protocols for the management of physical abuse for the hospitalized patient, physical abuse on an outpatient basis, failure to thrive (due to nutritional deprivation) on an inpatient basis, and incest and other family-related sexual abuse. These protocols can be written from the viewpoint of different disciplines. The four protocols mentioned above written for the pediatrician involved with such a case are found in Appendixes A8 to A11.

FOLLOW-UP PROCEDURES

Most teams try to pursue follow-up on all cases as time permits. Selective follow-up by the case's priority is more realistic. The follow-up procedures and guidelines to which our team subscribes are found in chapter 25.

RECORD KEEPING POLICIES

Each team member usually keeps records in a manner traditional for his discipline, but communication is better if the team agrees upon a single record keeping system. A system that has worked well for our team is the *Problem-Oriented Record*. Examples of the master problem list and master treatment list for this system are fully outlined in chapter 15.

4

Improving Case Finding

Barton D. Schmitt

Case finding can be defined as the detection and reporting of suspected cases of child abuse and neglect. Once the team has an effective mechanism for handling cases, the referral of additional cases should be generated. Serious cases of physical abuse are usually brought to the attention of the hospital emergency room or the police. The parent, in these circumstances, often does not attempt to hide the diagnosis if the perpetrator is not present. The cause of less serious injuries, however, is often concealed by the child's parents. It is, therefore, critical that the professionals who have contact with children in our society be able to recognize the findings of child abuse and neglect. The main way to increase case finding is for the experienced team members to become involved with the education of professionals in contact with children. Education must not only point out how to detect child abuse, but also why identification of the problem is essential. The damage of untreated child abuse is done not only to the child, but also to society, leading to juvenile delinquency and violent crime. In addition, professionals and laymen need to be reassured many times that anyone reporting suspected child abuse is immune from any criminal or civil liability in all states.

Health Care System Case Finding

The most likely place for detecting physical abuse is the hospital emergency room. Studies in Denver, Colorado, and Rochester, New York, have demonstrated that at least 10 percent of children under age five who are brought to the emergency room with alleged accidents have nonaccidental trauma. Children's hospitals may have child protection teams to coordinate the management of these cases. However, every hospital that sees children and every large, ambulatory pediatric clinic, for example, a neighborhood health center, needs a standing policy on how to manage these cases. The policy should carefully outline the physician's responsibilities in these cases as well as provide the telephone number of the person or agency to which the case should be reported. Without such a policy, cases go unreported or are reported in an inefficient and, sometimes, inadequate way. The best policy designates one person in the hospital to serve as coordinator for these cases so that they are handled consistently.

Physicians have the poorest record for adequate reporting of child abuse and neglect cases. The best way to approach this problem is through physician-educational programs on child abuse and neglect. The content of these programs should be limited, in most cases, to the physician's role in detection, confirmation, and reporting. Initially, most physicians have inadequate time or little interest in the psychosocial aspects of these cases. The meeting time should be one that is convenient for physicians, such as, early morning or evening meetings. The meeting can often be set up through the local medical society or hospital medical staff. It should be directed mainly towards pediatricians, family practitioners, osteopaths, and surgeons. When house staff physicians are concerned, meetings must be held several times a year, on a continuing basis in all departments of the medical center.

The best case finders of physical abuse are often nurses. In addition to being sensitive to this area of health care, they are the most constant factors in our health care system. Emergency room nurses are in the most strategic position for detecting such cases and should be at the top of the list for educational programs. Sometimes, physicians in emergency rooms are too busy to spend much time interviewing parents regarding the cause of an injury. It is important that the nurse gather this information on all injuries. In many medical settings that do not have a child protection team, a full-time registered nurse is probably the best person to serve as coordinator, interpreter, and implementer of that medical setting's child abuse policy.

School Case Finding

The school is the best setting for early recognition of abuse and neglect in children over age five. Optimal management of these cases requires that the school have a standard operating policy on child abuse. It is best for all the schools in a district or county to have the same policy in operation. This policy should contain clear information on what to report and to whom to report it. One person in each school (often a school nurse) should be designated the coordinator of the child abuse and neglect cases in that school so that essential liaisons with other agencies in the community concerned with this problem are developed. It is also very helpful for all day care centers and preschools to have a standing policy regarding child abuse reporting.

Unfortunately, less than 25 percent of schools have an official policy on child abuse. When a school principal or other person in power refuses to report a case of child abuse that a teacher has uncovered, the teacher can inform the superior that they could be civilly liable. If this strategy fails, the teacher should call the child protective agency and report the case anonymously, if necessary, within 24 hours of detection so that the child protective agency can become involved before bruises or other injuries have disappeared. This approach is in the best interest of the child. Teachers themselves can become better case-finders if a staff development program on this subject is held in each of the schools.

Hospital-Based Team Case Finding

The organization of a hospital-based child protection team automatically increases case finding in that hospital. Hospital employees refer cases because they realize that a simplified mechanism exists for doing so. In addition, the team can actively review suspicious cases seen within the hospital, even without the invitation of the staff using that hospital. The following specific areas are ones in which a team can become involved to increase case finding.

CLINIC

The charts on all patients seen in a pediatric clinic or emergency room should be reviewed by an attending physician. This can be the pediatric consultant to the child protection team or someone to whom he delegates reviewing responsibility. Charts should be reviewed for suspicious findings, such as, unexplained bruises. Review should take place daily and be especially circumspect regarding late night visits to the hospital.

WARD

It is beneficial for a key pediatrician to review all charts of hospitalized patients with unexplained bruises and fractures, failure to thrive, burns, and subdural hematomas. The most efficient way to put this review into operation is to have a contact person on each of the pediatric wards who notifies the child protection team coordinator about cases falling into these categories. The most reliable contact person on the ward is the charge nurse. She should be encouraged to report any suspicious case within 24 hours after admission so that findings don't disappear. If the chart review turns up a child who is suspected of having been abused, the team pediatrician should contact the private attending physician to report the case. If the private physician is reluctant, he can be given a day to read and reflect upon some pertinent references that the team pediatrician supplies. Usually, the attending physician will report the case at this point; but if he continues to be opposed to reporting an obvious case of child abuse, the team pediatrician is legally mandated to do so.

RADIOLOGY

Another source of case finding is to review the charts of all children under age four who have been seen for fractures or had total trauma surveys that were found to be abnormal. The radiology department has this information and it can be released to the hospital-based child protection team with the approval of the chief of radiology. These charts should be reviewed weekly, and any suspicious case should be reviewed with the private physician. When additional information is needed, it can be obtained by a phone call to the parents or a visit by a public health nurse.

TELEPHONE CONSULTATION

Physicians in the community become more willing to consider child abuse when they have a traumatology consultant to whom they can refer cases. The team pediatrician should remain available for medical consultation regarding questionable or proven cases. His or her telephone number should be made known to the practicing medical community.

TELEPHONE REPORTING

Hospitals are one of the few helping resources that have 24-hour telephone coverage. When families that seem to be involved in child abuse call in, they should be encouraged to bring their child to the hospital. If the parents refuse but wish to talk to someone, the inquiry should be transferred to the physician on call in the emergency room; or if the parents seem quite disturbed, the inquiry should be transferred to the psychologist or psychiatrist on call. If these calls are handled properly, case finding will increase even without the availability of a community hot line.

Community Case Finding

The final stage in the development of an excellent case finding system is the implementation of a community hot line. This mechanism for reporting must be staffed 24 hours a day, 365 days a year. In some cases, the hot line can be state-wide and toll free. To be successful, the hot line has two prerequisites: (1) there must be a good intake system behind it, including a social worker and plain-clothes policeman on call for each county and responsive to emergency reports within one hour; and (2) a helpful, non-punitive treatment system must be available. Hot lines can result in tripling the reporting rate. Neglect cases are reported in abundance. The community can experience considerable frustration if a hot line is opened prematurely.

Once the hot line is functional, its utilization can be increased by a public awareness campaign. The phone number can be given in radio and television public service announcements, listed on posters in public buildings, and provided in descriptive brochures in medical settings.

Summary

All case-finding resources will report more readily after they feel it leads to some constructive intervention. Helpful, nonpunitive, immediate intervention leads to even earlier reporting, eventually before any serious injuries have occurred.

References

Broadhurst, D. D., Howard, and Maxwell, C. H. (1975): More About Project Protection. *Child Ed*, 52:67.

Drews, K. (1972): The Child and His School. In: *Helping the Battered Child and His Family*. Edited by C. H. Kempe, and R. E. Helfer, p. 115. J. B. Lippincott, Philadelphia.

Helfer, R. E. (1975): Why Most Physicians Don't Get Involved in Child Abuse Cases and What to Do About It. *Child Today*, 4.

Holter, J. C. and Friedman, S. B. (1968): Child Abuse: Early Case Finding in the Emergency Department. *Pediatrics*, 42(1).

Murdock, G. G. (1970): The Abused Child and the School System. *Public Health*, 60:105.

Plank, E. L. (1975): Violations of Children's Rights in the Classroom. *Child Ed*.

Schmitt, B. D. (1975): What Teachers Need to Know About Child Abuse and Neglect. *Child Ed*, 52:58–62.

5

Improving Community Treatment Services

Claudia A. Carroll and Barton D. Schmitt

Child abuse is a far reaching problem and, as such, it must be viewed as a community problem. It is not the sole responsibility of the Department of Social Service, the Court, or any single agency. One agency cannot meet all the needs of even one family; therefore, it is necessary to think of services and treatment to the family as coming from many agencies that are working together to treat the problem. This requires breaking through the traditional "turfism" which is, unfortunately, a characteristic of many communities across the United States.

To effectively deal with child abuse, an "open systems" approach to the problem must be considered. This approach includes viewing all agencies within a community (public and private, professional and lay) as buttressing and supporting each other in providing services to the needy family. This systems approach and community commitment to provision of treatment services must be based on a foundation of trust and commonality of perspective among agencies. In addition, development of services should be viewed as an evolving process. Moving a community and its services from one level of development to a more sophisticated one takes considerable time.

The purpose of this chapter is to suggest a variety of means to improve community treatment services. We are not advocating one way or the other as being "the answer." Instead, many ideas for developing treatment services are offered so the reader can select the approaches that would be most feasible for his community.

Techniques for Assessment of Community Treatment Services

Improvement of treatment services requires that an analysis be made of the strengths and weaknesses within the present system. The system should be examined for unmet needs, deficits, areas of friction, inadequacies, overlaps, and obstacles to good services. The present system should be compared to an optimal community treatment system which would have available many alternative treatment modalities. These should include emergency homemakers, homemakers for extended periods of time, foster care for child and whole family, residential treatment facilities for the child, specialized day care, lay therapy (parent aides), crisis nursery, individual treatment, marital counseling, group therapy, parenting classes, Parents Anonymous groups, visiting nurses, and treatment for the child (see chapter 23).

Once content is agreed upon, the next step is assessment and listing of all the professionals and agencies currently involved in treatment in a given community. This would include child protection services, courts, county attorneys, district attorney, juvenile police, mental health clinic, public health nurse, foster homes, private agencies, and treatment subcontract units. Each professional agency can be contacted and requested to critically rate all the other agencies and themselves in terms of services provided. This can initially be done at the individual agency level; the information obtained can then be brought to an interagency meeting by one or more agency representatives. Brainstorming for problems can then be carried out with a large group of mixed agencies from the beginning to save time. On the other hand, sensitive data is more likely to be uncovered if small groups are interviewed. Such interviewing could be done by a community leader, program coordinator for treatment development, or an outside expert. Another technique is a self-assessment system, developed by Dr. Ray Helfer, which requires two hours a week for eight weeks and utilizes three or four child protective service workers. It is a comprehensive assessment and it looks very promising.[a] Also, charts or case records of actual patients coming to intake during a given month can be audited six months later (Appendix B). This requires that standards of care for abusive families have been agreed upon in advance. Because this auditing technique is time consuming, it is recommended only in situations where a particular agency is resistant to an important recommended change.

All of the above assessment techniques should lead to the development of a problem list regarding treatment services within the community. The initial assessment should have included a request for tentative recommendations for solving the submitted problems. The agency, committee, or council involved with upgrading treatment services should meet and discuss the data they have received, setting priorities and time schedules for solving individual problems.

How to Improve Community Treatment Services

In every community the development of treatment services requires the concerted effort of many agencies. The county Social Service Department, which is characterized by an "open systems" approach and multiple agency involvement, is well on its way to improving treatment services. As a primary protective service provider in the community, the Social Service Department should take a major leadership role in beginning to organize the community and tap all available resources. In most communities, it is logical for the Social Service Department to be in the position of community organizer. However, if they have not done so, and another agency is able and willing to take on this responsibility, they should certainly be permitted to do so. It is imperative, however, that the agency taking the responsibility for community organizing have a strong link with the Department of Social Services which carries the legal mandate for treatment of the family and protection of the child.

Improving community treatment services can be looked at from two dimensions. First, inadequate utilization of existing resources may be due to a lack of relationship and trust between agencies, turfism, or poor communication. Second, certain resources may be totally lacking and need to be developed. The following 15 ideas are ways to address both of these aspects:

1. The Department of Social Services can develop liaison representatives with each school district, police department, and mental health team. It is extremely important to develop working relationships with each of the other agencies within a community, and often what it boils down to is the need to get to know someone on a one-to-one, first-name basis. The trust that develops through a one-to-one relationship will usually spread to other levels within the agency. The liaison effort also provides a vehicle for discussing problems, sharing ideas, and having opportunities for ongoing dialogue and better working relationships. Two issues which always need to be worked out to improve agency relationships are those of prompt feedback when referrals are made and the most efficient way to accomplish that goal.

2. The Department of Social Services can have monthly meetings with agencies with whom they work closely (for example, the mental health center and the Court). Again, this improves information giving, understanding, and mutual problem solving. For example, joint discussions help the police to see the harmful effects of arrest on long-term therapy, and the social workers to see the value of criminal prosecution in selected cases.

3. Multidisciplinary child protection review teams in their deliberations on optimal short-range and long-range treatment planning are constantly confronted with the reality of shortcomings in treatment services. An im-

portant spin-off of such meetings is applying pressure on the community for better treatment services for abusive and neglectful families. Also, someone sitting on the multidisciplinary review team from the mental health center, for example, can serve as a facilitator to make sure the parents get hooked into the mental health system expeditiously. He can personally arrange first appointments or special types of therapy. All the members on the multidisciplinary team, as representatives of their agencies, can improve the communication and treatment resources within that community from their respective agencies.

4. Reciprocal agreements between agencies can be developed and written out. For example, if one agency develops a hot line, it is extremely important to have in written form the degree to which each of the county agencies will be available to respond to hot line calls regarding their specialized services. Another valuable interagency policy between the child protective services unit and the mental health clinic would be that whenever an abusive parent misses an appointment at the mental health clinic, that agency would notify the child protective service unit within 24 hours, since the missed appointment may signify family crisis.

5. The Department of Social Services should become involved in contracting out with other agencies for some services. Social services should certainly be responsible for much of the treatment to families. However, because of the varying needs and volume of services needed by these families, it is important that the Department of Social Services take on a coordinating role with some families and contract out with other agencies for certain treatment services. For this to be possible, the administration within other agencies must see such services to abusive and neglecting families as a priority in their agency, as well as to sanction the provision of treatment services to the family by their personnel. Another aspect of contracting which has been largely untapped is that of the private sector agencies. There are extensive resources and treatment services available through private agencies (that is, Family and Children's services, Catholic Social Services, Lutheran Social Services, and Volunteers of America). We believe that many of these agencies could be providing a variety of services to the abused, neglected children and their families. Some of the services provided through private agencies could be treatment, both individual and group; marital counseling; parenting classes; and specialized training for day care and foster parents.

6. A listing of private practitioners (that is, social workers, psychiatrists, and psychologists) who would be willing to work with the child or family or both can be compiled. Many practitioners will accept Medicaid for financial payment, and overall services can be expanded by tapping the private practitioner for treatment services.

7. Community agencies should apply for grants collaboratively if possible. It is destructive for local agencies to be in competition with other local

agencies for grant monies. Also, it is far more productive to write the grants for improved community treatment services together.

8. One of the most obvious ways of improving community treatment services is for protective service workers in county departments to have a manageable caseload. At this time, caseloads are skyrocketing to the point where workers are often unable to provide treatment to families because of the enormous pressures the workers are under. It will be necessary for every state to establish a workload standard so that treatment will be available to every family. A workload standard of 22 families is a suggested, manageable protective service caseload at any one point in time.[b]

9. A means of dialogue with legislators can be developed. Since legislators ultimately determine what services are funded, it is important to have an effective means of presenting the statistics to the legislators to back up requests for services and social workers. Whenever a presentation is made to the legislature, it is important to include facts and hard data. It is also important to present long-range plans rather than going in piecemeal year by year with no visible overall plan. For example, it may be important to look at a three-year plan for child protective services of the state and to succinctly and clearly present the points which need to be accomplished each year. In that way, the legislators can view the plan in an organized and anticipatory manner, rather than as yearly, vague, fragmented parts of something they never can quite understand.

10. A child protection council, not attached to any agency but composed of concerned people, can be developed to bring together both lay and professional communities. General meetings can be held to serve as a forum for discussing important issues (for example, child abuse legislation, new treatment programs, problems in the system), but not cases. The child protection council is different from the multidisciplinary child protection team. Although some of the same people may participate in several types of groups and their meetings, the purpose of each group is separate. For this discussion, a multidisciplinary child protection review team (point 3) reviews diagnosis, case management and treatment planning. A child protection council (point 10) is a vehicle for community involvement, and an interagency committee (point 14) concerns itself solely with treatment program development. A community can make use of all three groups if all work in cooperation with each other.

A child protection council brings a wide-base approach to the problem and, in many respects, is able to transcend turfism. People participate because their investment is a genuine one. The types of representation for such a council may include the court, the district and county attorneys' offices, social service departments, and mental health, hospitals, and professional organizations, such as the medical society, Junior League, interested citizens, League of Women Voters, Council of Jewish Women, Parents Anonymous, state Social Service Departments, and many others.

It is important to form working committees from this large group to tap and direct people's interests and energies. The type of committees to consider developing include: (1) an educational and speaker's bureau to sponsor educational workshops and foster community awareness; (2) a legislation committee to work for improved legislation and to interpret current legislation to the public; (3) a task force on standards for each component of a comprehensive protective service system; (4) a task force with the State Department of Social Services to help in presenting pertinent data to the legislature; (5) a public relations committee, and (6) a membership committee to generate more participation.

11. Agencies involved in service delivery should consider a coordinator of volunteers. This person would be a paid staff member and the job would be to coordinate and develop an effective volunteer program. This person can be invaluable in developing the resources of interested people who are willing to give their time and skills. The sign of the times is that many people want to become involved and are needing direction and support. One coordinator of volunteers can multiply services available within an agency if given the opportunity. The coordinator can organize parent aide (lay therapy) programs, parenting education classes, and transportation resources.

12. There are numerous nonprofessional community groups (for example, Kiwanis, PTA, Jaycees, and Junior League) which may be interested in working with the problem of child abuse and neglect. They may be willing to initiate fund raising to start a crisis nursery or other programs. Another cost-effective treatment modality that can be started with minimal funding is a parent aide (lay therapist) program. Often these organizations are looking for opportunities to be visible and helpful within their communities. They are sometimes able to apply for small grants for community services with specific needs through their national organizations.

13. The media can be cultivated as an ally. It can increase community awareness of the extent and severity of the child abuse and neglect problem and draw attention to the existing needs of the community. The media can do much to bring about community pressure for improved treatment services. However, it is best to avoid using case examples and true situations, because such action usually results in increased anger among the community's citizens and a lack of understanding for the parents.

14. Dr. Ray E. Helfer has a different approach to upgrading treatment services. He suggests that the community form a separate *interagency committee* that concerns itself with treatment program development. Dr. Helfer speaks of an interagency committee as a formalized group of professionals who need political clout and influence. A legislator is a helpful member of the committee when changing laws and obtaining public funding is necessary. This committee needs a program coordinator, usually salaried, whose

role is not to provide treatment services, but to find and encourage other professionals to carry out these tasks.

15. An educational approach should be taken with any professional or agency involved with child abuse who is doing an inadequate job. Poor decisions are often made because of a lack of knowledge and understanding of the various aspects of child abuse. Most professionals take pride in their work and wish to do a good job. They appreciate constructive criticism regarding any blind spot they may have. In addition, they may welcome a workshop that would upgrade their expertise. For example, most judges have little training in the behavioral sciences and would be willing to read a good paper or attend a meeting on the psychosocial aspects of child abuse and neglect. A difficult agency representative might be asked to participate on a panel at an open meeting in order to stimulate new thinking on his behalf. Rarely does the educational approach fail; but when it does, more aggressive, disciplinary action must be taken with the professional in the child abuse field who is truly, incurably incompetent.

Preventive Services

A wide range of treatment services for cases of proven child abuse and neglect should be available before prevention can be strongly emphasized. High risk families can be identified by various interview techniques, observations, self-referral, or all three. The community agencies should refer these families to the child protective services unit for additional support or services. Efforts should be made to avoid reporting potential child abuse situations formally as abuse, nor should there be police involvement or a report sent to the state child abuse registry. If the services are presented to the family in a positive way, it should be rare for the family to refuse them. Preventive services require a very sophisticated child abuse and neglect diagnostic and treatment system. A community addressing preventive services has fully developed its therapeutic program.

Notes

[a]Dr. Helfer's Community Self-Assessment form can be obtained through Ray E. Helfer, M.D., Department of Human Development, College of Human Medicine, Michigan State University, East Lansing, Michigan 48823.
[b]Kawamura, G. and Carroll, C. (1976): Managerial and Financial Aspects of Social

Service Programs. In: *Child Abuse and Neglect. The Family and the Community,* edited by R. E. Helfer and C. H. Kempe. Ballinger Publishing Co., Cambridge, Mass.

References

Cohn, A. H., Ridge, S. S., and Collignon, F. C. (1975): Evaluating innovative treatment programs in child abuse and neglect. *Child Today,* 4:10–12.

Helfer, R. E.: Self instruction program in child abuse and neglect. Six units. Prepared in cooperation with the American Academy of Pediatrics and the National Center for the Prevention and Treatment of Child Abuse and Neglect (Denver).

Helfer, R. E. and Schmidt, R. (1976): The community-based child abuse and neglect program. In: *Child Abuse and Neglect. The Family and the Community,* edited by R. E. Helfer, and C. H. Kempe. Ballinger Press, Cambridge, Mass.

Nagi, S. Z. (1975): Child abuse and neglect programs: A national overview. *Child Today,* 4:13–17.

Newberger, E. H., Hagenbuch, J. J., Ebeling, N. B., Colligan, E. P., Sheehan, J. S., and McVeigh, S. H. (1973): Reducing the literal and human cost of child abuse: Impact of a new hospital management system. *Pediatrics,* 51(5):840.

Schmidt, R., Sibrack, C., and Helfer, R.: Community programs for child abuse and neglect: A self-assessment approach. *(to be published).*

PART II

Diagnostic Tasks

6

The Physician's Evaluation

Barton D. Schmitt

The Physician's Role

The physician's main role in child abuse is to be an accurate diagnostician. His main skills should be in detection and confirmation. He must be suspicious enough to find hidden cases, knowledgeable enough of the ten types of child abuse and neglect (see chapter 16) to confirm diagnoses, and able to accomplish both detection and confirmation as expeditiously as possible. His second role is to report these cases to the local CPS unit, so the children will receive comprehensive evaluation, intervention, and follow-up. His third role is to hospitalize the child in need of protection. His fourth role is to fully evaluate or arrange the evaluation of the abused child's medical and psychological needs. His fifth role is to be a preventive force by being supportive and available to high-risk families who cannot formally be reported. This chapter will attempt to outline the knowledge, skills, and perspective a pediatrician needs to effectively participate on a multidisciplinary team.

PHYSICAL ABUSE—DETECTION AND CONFIRMATION

Physical abuse is the most common type of child abuse and neglect. It can be suspected on the basis of the following types of injury histories and physical findings. Many of the physical findings are pathognomonic (distinctive of a specific condition—in this case, child abuse) and speak for the child who is too young to speak for himself. Some histories are so implausible or blatantly phoney that they are diagnostic of child abuse. In contrast, some histories are only suspicious; but in combination with several non-descript bruises, these histories can confirm physical abuse.

The Diagnostic History

When a child readily indicates that a particular adult hurt him, it is almost always true. A confession by either parent or the report of an eyewitness are also diagnostically important, but rarely available.

An Unexplained Injury

Some parents will be reluctant to elaborate on the possible cause of the injury. They may state, "We just found him that way" and claim there are no witnesses. When pressed, they may even become evasive. Some will give a vague explanation, such as "He might have fallen down" or "His brother may have hit him." These explanations are self-incriminating. Normal parents know to the minute where and when their child was hurt. They also show complete willingness to discuss it in detail.

A Discrepant History

Sometimes there is a discrepancy between the histories offered by the two parents, or the history changes in regard to dates, times, and causes. Another common contradiction occurs between the history offered and the physical findings, such as a history of a minor accident with physical findings of a major injury. Examples of this are: a child who fell against a coffee table, yet he is covered with bruises; or a child who allegedly fell on a thick carpet, but who looks like he has been hit by a car. Sometimes the parents' dating of the injuries may be at variance with the clinical dating; or bruises may be of several different ages. Sometimes a discrepancy exists between the history and the child's developmental age. Examples of this are: a one-year-old child allegedly turned on scalding water in the bathtub, or a six-month-old climbed out of his crib. Another contradiction occurs in children who allegedly "bruise so easily." This history is usually misleading, and no new, ongoing bruises appear in the hospital.

Alleged Self-inflicted Injury

The child who is under six months of age is unlikely to be able to induce any accident. Absurd stories, such as, the baby rolled over on his arm and broke it, or he got his head caught in the crib and fractured it, are pure nonsense. Histories implying that the child is masochistic are also uniformly false, such as the child who hurts himself badly during a temper tantrum, gets subdural hematomas by hitting himself with a bottle, climbs up onto a hot radiator, or burns himself up to the elbow by immersing his arm in hot water. Children rarely injure themselves deliberately.

Alleged Third-party-inflicted Injury

When the parents blame their child's injuries on a babysitter, neighbor, or sibling, the physician must remain skeptical. Although such a story could be true, the accused abuser must be interviewed in private as early as possible for confirmation. Often the parent will be unable to remember the name of the accused. Sometimes the blame has been projected onto a nonexistent person.

A Delay in Seeking Medical Care

Normal parents come in immediately when their child is injured. Some abused children are not brought in for a considerable period of time despite a major injury. In extreme situations, children are brought in nearly dead. One study[1] showed that 40 percent of children weren't brought in until the morning after the injury. Another 40 percent came in one to four days after the injury. The parents are usually merely hoping that the event never occurred, or that the injury will not require medical care. In addition, the time of occurrence may be significant. Accidents occurring between midnight and 6:00 A.M. are open to question.

History of Repeated Suspicious Injuries

A suspicious injury is one which is unexplained or seems excessive for the described accident. If a child has suspicious bruises on more than one occasion, or a sibling exhibits similar findings, the injury probably represents inflicted trauma. Many of these children are simply dismissed as "accident prone," which is a serious mistake. Certainly no magic number of accidents per year is indicative of child abuse; and recurrent accidents (even three in one week) can occasionally occur in normal families. However, the authentic nature of the accidents is documented by the complete and plausible accounts which are spontaneously offered. Even in these cases, one should be certain that the sudden upsurge in accidents does not stem from a major family crisis.

Diagnostic Bruises, Welts, Lacerations, and Scars

Inflicted bruises are so common at certain sites that their presence is pathognomonic. Bruises which predominate on the buttocks and lower back are almost always related to punishment (that is, paddling). Likewise, genital area or inner thigh bruises are usually inflicted for toileting mishaps. Bruises on the cheek or numerous petechiae (pinpoint bruises) on the ear lobe are usually secondary to being slapped or cuffed. If one looks closely, there are often associated fading yellow bruises, which mean this area has been hit on other occasions. Accidental falls rarely cause bruises in the soft tissues but instead involve bony prominences, such as the forehead or zygoma (or cheekbone). Bruises of the upper lip and labial frenulum (a membranous fold connecting the lip with the gums) are usually caused by impatient, forced feedings, or by jamming a pacifier into the mouth of a screaming baby as a desperate attempt to silence him. This bruising may remain hidden, unless the inside of the lips is carefully examined. The floor of the mouth may also be torn by similar actions. Bruises in this area cannot be self-inflicted until the baby is old enough to sit up by himself and inadvertently fall over.

Human hand marks are pressure bruises resembling finger tips, fingers, or the entire hand. Grab marks are oval-shaped, finger tip-sized bruises. Several grab marks are often found on the arms or legs where the child was vigorously held during a beating. Encircling bruises occur when the child is grabbed about the chest or abdomen. This results in eight finger bruises on one side and two thumb bruises on the other side. The examiner's fingers can easily be placed into this pattern. Linear grab marks are caused by pressure from the entire finger. An outline of the entire hand is sometimes seen on the back or other sites. Such bruises are outlined because only the capillaries at the edges of the injury are stretched enough to rupture. Often, in slap marks to the cheek, two or three finger-width lines will be seen to run through the bruise. Pinch marks are two small, crescent-shaped bruises facing each other. Human bite marks are distinctive paired, crescent-shaped bruises, usually containing individual tooth marks. Sometimes the two crescents meet to form a complete ring of bruising. The size of the arch can distinguish adults' from children's bites.[2]

Strap marks are one to two inch-wide, rectangular-shaped bruises of various lengths, sometimes covering a curved body surface. These are almost always caused by a belt. Sometimes the eyelets or buckle of the belt can be discerned. Lash marks are narrow, straight-edged bruises and scratches are most often caused by beating with a tree branch or switch. Loop marks on the skin are secondary to being struck with a doubled-over lamp cord or rope.

Bizarre-shaped bruises are always inflicted. When a blunt instrument (for example, a toy or shoe) is used in punishment, a bruise or welt will often resemble it in shape.[3] Children have exhibited tattoos inflicted with a sharp instrument, such as a pin or razor. Numerous puncture wounds may be caused by a fork. Choke marks may be seen on the neck, and circumferential tie marks on the ankles or wrist are caused by rope, cord, or dog leashes. Gag marks may be seen at mouth corners.

Bruises and scars found at multiple stages of healing are extremely important diagnostically and imply repeated beatings. Most falls give bruises on just one body surface. Bruises on multiple body planes are usually inflicted, unless there is a history of a tumbling accident. It is true that tumbling accidents often cause minimal bruises and abrasions, but if there are many, they will predominate on the elbows, knees, and shoulders (E. F. Lenoski, *personal communication*). "Falling down a stairway" is commonly offered as a last minute explanation for unexplained bruises on a child. However, the lack of bruises in the above locations makes this explanation doubtful.

Diagnostic Burns

Approximately ten percent of cases of physical abuse involve burns.[4] The most common inflicted burn seen in an outpatient setting is from a cigarette. These are circular, punched-out burns of similar size which are often found on the palms, soles, or abdomen. A hot cigarette is sometimes applied to the hand to stop the child from sucking his thumb, or to the genital area to discourage masturbation. Bumping into a cigarette only causes a single burn, unless the ash catches in the clothing. Smaller but similar burns have been inflicted with incense or match tips. Burns have also been inflicted with lighters in an aberrant attempt to teach children not to play with fire. The only differential diagnosis to be made is for bullous impetigo. In such a case, the lesions are of various sizes, occur in groups, have purulent crusts, and increase in number while the patient is in the hospital.

Dry contact burns can occur secondary to forcible holding of the child against a heating device (for example, a radiator). These are usually second-degree burns without any blister formation. They usually involve only one surface of the body (for example, the back or both palms). The shape of the burn is pathognomonic if the child is held against a heating grate, touched with a hot iron, or forced to sit on an electric hot plate. Unexplained linear burns are usually caused by running a heated piece of metal across the child's skin for punishment. Occasionally, an adult actually brands a child with his initials using the heated cover of a cigarette lighter, or a hot comb.

Hot water burns, or scalds, are of several types. The most common is a dunking burn—the offender holds the child's thighs against the abdomen in a jackknife position and dunks the buttocks and perineum into a bucket of scalding water. Often, this results in a circular burn which is restricted to the buttocks. With deeper, forced immersion, the scald extends to a clear-cut water level on the thighs and waist. The hands and feet are spared, which is incompatible with falling into a tub of hot water or turning the hot water on while in the bathtub. Sometimes the child is forced to sit in scalding water. This gives the dunking burn and scalds to the back of the thighs and legs. Depending on exposure time, the soles may be relatively spared owing to their thicker skin. The bottom of the toes, however, is not spared. Interestingly, 45 percent of inflicted burns involve the perineum or buttocks[5]—sites which are almost always chosen as punishment for enuresis or toilet-training resistance. Occasionally, the perianal skin will be spared, because it was protected by fecal material at the time of the burn.

Forcible immersion of a hand or foot as punishment can be diagnosed by the finding of a burn which goes above the wrist or ankle without splash marks. Children are not foolish enough to place an extremity into hot water to this depth. Whenever a scald of the hands or feet is full thickness and requires grafting, it points to prolonged hot water exposure and, hence, forced immersion.[6] Burns caused by throwing scalding water at a child are harder to diagnose. A scald limited to the back may mean that the child was trying to run away from an angry parent.

The only differential diagnosis to be made in hot water burns is for scalded skin syndrome, or toxic epidermal necrolysis, caused by Staphylococcus aureus. Unexplained blebs are seen; but they occur at such scattered sites that it would be nearly impossible to have inflicted them with hot water. Also, they continue to appear after hospitalization.

Eye Injuries

Ocular damage in the battered child syndrome includes acute hyphema, dislocated lens, and detached retina.[7] Over half of these result in permanent vision impairment of one or both eyes. Retinal hemorrhage is a clue to subdural hematoma in children with unexplained central nervous system findings. Retinal hemorrhage can also occur, without clinically important intracranial hemorrhage in children with sudden compression of their chests.[8] This finding is called Purtscher retinopathy, or Purtcher's disease.

Brain Injuries

The worst injury in terms of serious sequelae or death is a subdural hematoma. Infants with subdural hematoma often have convulsions, increased intracranial pressure, and may be in a coma.[9] Classically, subdural hematomas are associated with skull fractures secondary to a direct blow by the parent's hand, or from being hit against a wall or door. Numerous other bruises are usually present.

Inflicted subdural hematomas can also occur without skull fractures, scalp bruises, or scalp swelling. In fact, over half of the cases have no fracture.[10] These used to be called "spontaneous subdural hematomas," but recent evidence points to violent, whiplash-type shaking injuries as the causative mechanism.[11] Rapid acceleration and deceleration of the head as it bobs about leads to tearing of the bridging cerebral veins with bleeding into the subdural space, usually bilaterally. Retinal hemorrhage is nearly always present, which helps to establish this diagnosis. In over half the cases, trauma survey reveals bony injury where the child was grasped during shaking.[12] It is important that the physician discard the concept of "spontaneous subdural" in young infants to prevent sending a child home to be reinjured or killed. Likewise, the physician should remain skeptical of the diagnosis "chronic subdurals" secondary to birth trauma. Subdural hematomas due to birth injury will almost always have acute signs and symptoms within 24 to 48 hours postdelivery.

Cephalohematomas are sometimes seen. Occasionally a subgaleal hematoma will be seen as a result of vigorous hair pulling by an angry adult. This diagnosis is most likely if the child has braids at the site.[13] A toxicology screen should be done on unusually sleepy babies who have no signs of trauma.

Abdominal Visceral Injuries

Intra-abdominal injuries are the second most common cause of death in battered children.[14] These children have recurrent vomiting, abdominal distention, absent bowel sounds, localized tenderness, or shock. The most common finding is a ruptured liver or spleen. The most unique findings are tears or other injuries of the small intestine at sites of ligamental support, such as the duodenum and proximal jejunum.[15] Intramural hematomas can occur at these sites and lead to temporary obstruction. These injuries are produced by the whipping force of a punch or blow. They are different from the ruptured spleen, kidney, or viscera that commonly results from the crushing or compressing forces present in traffic accidents or falls. Inflicted chylous ascites and pseudocyst of the pancreas have also been reported.[16,17] Trauma to the abdomen is routinely denied in these cases;[18] therefore, the physician must consider child abuse in any abdominal crisis of undetermined etiology.

Diagnostic Bone Injuries

This subject is fully discussed later in this chapter under *Trauma X-ray Survey*.

FAILURE TO THRIVE SECONDARY TO NUTRITIONAL DEPRIVATION—DETECTION AND CONFIRMATION

Failure to thrive can be defined as an underweight, malnourished condition. A failure-to-thrive baby usually has a weight below the third percentile on the growth curves, and a height and head circumference above the third percentile. Physical examination reveals a gaunt face, prominent ribs, wasted buttocks, and spindly extremities. Failure to thrive is mainly seen in the first two years of life, because this is the time of rapid growth and dependency on adults for feeding. This disorder is detected in most babies before they reach eight months of age. The causes of failure to thrive are estimated as 30 percent organic, 20 percent underfeeding owing to understandable error, and 50 percent caloric deprivation resulting from maternal neglect. The latter type of failure to thrive is a main concern here.[19]

A common error is the misdiagnosis of short stature as failure to thrive. Of the 3 percent of children who are under the third percentile in height, the majority are short but well nourished. In most cases, they have constitutional understature as evidenced by a positive family history for short stature heights and weights that are equally below the third percentile, and serial heights that are following a certain growth trajectory. The few who have organic short stature usually fall away from their growth curves.

Hospitalization

Although some cases of failure to thrive because of feeding errors can be reversed with home management, those children in which nutritional deprivation is suspected must be hospitalized for diagnostic confirmation and treatment. Nutritional deprivation should be suspected if the child has not received any medical attention despite failure to thrive, the parents are not concerned about the child's weight, the mother is depressed or psychotic, the mother overtly rejects the baby, or associated hygiene neglect is present (for example, rampant diaper rash or long, dirty fingernails). An emaciated child who is over two months old and still near his birth weight, or between three and six months old but showing minimal gain in the last two months, should also be admitted immediately. A child with a history of recurrent vomiting, diarrhea, or lack of weight gain despite the alleged intake of abundant calories also requires hospitalization for clarification of the problem. All of these organic-sounding histories are commonly given in babies suffering from nutritional deprivation, but not verified in the hospital.

A Nutritional Rehabilitation Program

This is the starting point for reaching a definitive diagnosis in failure-to-thrive children. The infant should be placed on unlimited feedings of a regular diet for his age. The formula should be identical to the one used at home. Rapid weight gain on a special formula, free of cow's milk protein or lactose, would prove little in terms of previous underfeeding. Supplemental vitamins should be provided; and a nutritionist should be consulted to calculate the daily caloric intake, which should approach 150–200 cal/kg/day (ideal weight). This diagnostic trial of feeding should be carried out for a minimum of one week and often two. A few severely malnourished babies may need formulas containing sucrose (Pregestimil®) or dextrose (Cho-Free®), because of an acquired lactase deficiency.

A child with failure to thrive, but an otherwise normal physical exam, requires very few baseline laboratory tests. A complete blood count; erythrocyte sedimentation rate; serum electrolytes; BUN; urine analysis and culture; stool pH, hematest, and culture; and tuberculin test are adequate. Elaborate endocrine tests, malabsorption studies, gastrointestinal X-rays, and other expensive laboratory tests should be reserved for those who fail to respond to nutritional rehabilitation.

Documenting a Rapid Weight Gain

The underweight infant who gains rapidly and easily in the hospital is a victim of underfeeding at home. A rapid weight gain can be defined as greater than 1.5 oz/day sustained for two weeks. A gain of over 2.0 oz/day in a one-week period (that is, one pound per week) also confirms the diagnosis. Sometimes the hospital weight gain is less than this; but, if it is two or three times greater than a similar period at home, the diagnosis is confirmed. Average weight gains for normal children vary according to age: 0.9 oz/day in the first three months, 0.8 oz/day from three to six months, 0.6 oz/day from six to nine months, and 0.4 oz/day from nine to twelve months. Additional confirmation comes from the observation that underfed babies are ravenous, demanding feeders in the hospital.[20]

The rapid weight gain of the failure-to-thrive child with nutritional neglect can be compared to weight gains in other conditions. Many normal children don't gain much weight in the hospital because of the tests they receive and the endemic viral infections that they frequently encounter. Children with organic failure to thrive demonstrate almost no weight gain in the hospital. The ones with malabsorption problems will often gain no weight despite good caloric intake. Poor feeders may gain one ounce per day in the hospital with great effort on the part of the nursing staff, but the weight gain will level off after the initial few days.

The approximately 30 percent of patients who do not respond to nutritional rehabilitation usually have an organic cause for their failure to thrive. Several articles[21,22,23] review a step-by-step approach to these patients, many of which can be suspected on the basis of a simple physical examination.

SEXUAL ABUSE—DETECTION AND CONFIRMATION

Sexual abuse of children by parents or caretakers includes incest (sexual intercourse), sodomy (anal intercourse), oral-genital contact, and molestation (fondling, masturbation, and exposure). Many of these incidents occur without force. In contrast, rape is usually defined as sexual intercourse forced upon a victim by a stranger using violence or threats of harm. Some studies find sexual abuse to account for ten percent of child abuse and neglect.[24] In most cases, the victimized child is a girl; over half the children are under age twelve at the time of the first offense. A stepfather or a mother's boyfriend living in the home is more likely to be involved in sexual abuse than the natural father.

In some cases, the patient will complain to the physician or some other professional of sexual abuse. More often, neither the girl nor the mother mentions it; and the physician must take a detailed and sensitive history to uncover it. Sexual abuse should be suspected in cases of unexplained pregnancy or genital symptoms. Venereal disease or vaginal bleeding in the prepubertal child should also be carefully screened for sexual exploitation. The diagnosis becomes more probable if the child also has a history of running away from home, or if she is accompanied by her father when she comes to the physician's office. Once sexual abuse is suspected, the physician should carry out the following evaluation:

History of the Incident

In sexual abuse cases, a woman physician should be assigned to the case if possible. Documentation of sexual abuse is usually totally dependent on the history. Therefore, the interview needs to be long, relaxed, and tactful. The patient should be encouraged to reveal all details concerning the incident(s). No other professional should have to repeat this interview. If the patient describes symptoms that could be related to sexual abuse, the story must sometimes be drawn out by a question, such as, "I have a feeling that maybe someone has done something to your body that has frightened you. Why don't you tell me about it?"[25] In addition to facts regarding date, time, place, and person, the physician must document sites of sexual abuse (for example, mouth, breasts, genitals, and anus). Also, information on menstrual history, whether or not force was involved, the patient's concept of intercourse, and whether or not ejaculation took place should be sought and recorded. In children under age four, this information will usually have to come from the mother. Older children should be encouraged to tell their own story in a private setting. After the interview, all of this information should be recorded precisely, since sexual abuse is one of the most difficult diagnoses to prove in court.

General Physical Examination

The patient needs a general physical exam to look for any signs of body injury or infection. The mouth, anus, and external genitals should receive special scrutiny for signs of trauma. The hymen (a membranous fold, partially occluding the vaginal opening) should be inspected for intactness. In some cases there will be redness, abrasion or purpura at these sites. In most cases there are no confirmatory physical findings. If the throat is inflamed, a throat culture for gonococcus should be plated on Thayer-

Martin media, since this has been reported with forced oral-genital contact.[26]

Forensic Vaginal Examination

Suspected cases of sexual abuse usually need to be referred to an emergency room gynecologist with the expertise to perform a forensic vaginal exam that can stand up in court. Evidence (for example, hair specimens, fingernail scrapings, acid phosphatase, and sperm tests) is collected, transported, and analyzed, utilizing a patient identification system that fulfills legal requirements. All rape cases (postpubertal and prepubertal) should be referred to a gynecologist for this procedure. Incest cases should be referred only if intercourse has taken place in the last forty-eight hours, because evidence for sperm rarely persists beyond this time period. Often these cases can be confirmed only by the history. Obviously, molestation cases not involving intercourse do not need a gynecology referral. However, a vaginal discharge in anyone under age eighteen should be examined for sperm regardless of the history. The first pelvic exam in a girl should be preceded by careful explanation and preparation by the clinic nurse. Cases at risk for pregnancy or venereal disease should receive prophylactic stilbesterol, 25 mg, twice a day for five days, or 4.8 million units of procaine penicillin intramuscularly, respectively. The gynecologist will usually attend to this.

DETECTION OF HIGH-RISK BABIES

Inadequate mothering is the inability of the mother to love and care for her offspring. The delayed recognition of this problem in the emergency room when a child appears with evidence of physical abuse or starvation is unacceptable. The high-risk group must be identified early and an attempt made to help such people. The logical person to detect this problem is the pediatrician. He has traditionally made judgments about the mother-child interaction. Nurses are also trained to focus on this dimension. Deficits in mothering are usually first detected in the physician's office. It would be much better if alienation problems were recognized in the delivery room and newborn nursery before the mother went home, so her hospital discharge could be delayed until some form of intervention was initiated.

Even when detection concentrates only on the overt signs of inadequate parenting, casefinding is prolific. These high-risk factors can be uncovered without special interviews or questionnaires (Table 1). Common sense and observation will do. The potential for neglect and abuse correlates best with the finding of a cluster of these signs rather than the presence of an isolated factor. Most of these behaviors increase the risk for neglect; however, child abuse and neglect can be a continuum.[27] Although the majority of cases of neglect will not evolve into physical abuse, some of them will. Factors which make physical abuse more likely are: (1) removal of a previous child for physical abuse, (2) presence of violent behavior in either parent, or (3) harsh discipline.

Prenatal Observation and Data

Some high-risk factors are apparent before the baby is even born. First, a mother may try to conceal the pregnancy. She may avoid prenatal care until late in the third trimester or when labor begins. She may claim that she didn't know she was pregnant, when obviously she didn't want to be pregnant. Second, a pregnant woman who has sought or attempted abortion unsuccessfully is obviously carrying an unwanted baby. Third, some mothers agree to relinquish their baby for adoption but then change their minds after the child is born. Such a child is more than unplanned; he is unwanted. Fourth, the absence of "nesting" behavior, or home preparation, for the forthcoming baby is ominous. Fifth, a new mother needs some degree of family support. The risk of child abuse or neglect is increased if the mother is unwed or has recently been abandoned by her family or her husband. Sixth, the history of serious mental illness in either parent is worrisome (for example, previous institutionalization or current depression). Seventh, drug addicted or alcoholic mothers are obviously unable to take care of themselves, let alone take care of their children. Eighth, if the father has a known criminal record for assault, or a previous psychiatric diagnosis of sociopath, his children may be harmed by him. Ninth, a parent who has injured a previous child or has had a child temporarily removed because of neglect has added potential for repeating the pattern.

Delivery Room Observations

The delivery room affords a very direct impression of mother-baby interaction. Immediately after birth, the nursing staff should be asked to record the following observations: (1) How does the mother look? (2) What does the mother say? (3) What does the mother do? (C. H. Kempe, *unpublished data*). Smiling, elation, eye-to-eye contact, acceptance of the baby's sex and appearance, and a positive response to his vigorous cry are all early signs of attachment.

Nursery Observations

The following information can be noted in the newborn nursery by the physician or the nurses. First, claiming behavior should be observed before the mother is discharged. It can be normal for a mother to feel that the baby is really not hers for a few hours or days; but, if she does not accept the baby as "hers" as evidenced by naming him, wanting to hold him, and wanting to feed him by the time the baby is three days old, a serious delay in maternal attachment has occurred and requires evaluation. Second, the mother may consider the child a disappointment as evidenced by her disparaging comments that he is "ugly," "diseased," or "defective." This situation is especially dangerous if, in truth, the child does not have any of these disorders. Most mothers consider their normal newborn to be beautiful. Third, the high-risk mother may be revolted by the child's odor, drooling, regurgitation, urine, or stools. Fourth, the inability of the mother to properly feed her baby in the maternity ward makes it unlikely that she will be more capable at home. Fifth, a postpartum depression occurring on approximately the second or third day after delivery, and manifested by crying, anxiety, and confusion, may be a serious sign.[28] In some cases, it is due to a rapid decrease in maternal estrogens. However, more commonly it is due to the fact that the mother is overwhelmed by the demands placed on her by the new baby, whom, she has discovered, she doesn't really want. Sixth, if the mother goes home before the baby and then reduces her visiting time, this may indicate that she has not experienced maternal attachment. This is especially likely to happen with premature babies who have a long stay in the hospital. A recent study revealed that visits of fewer than three times in a two-week period meant that problems were forthcoming.[29] A reluctance on the part of the mother to take the baby home once he is ready is another reason for concern. Seventh, the mother who demonstrates her lack of impulse control by spanking the baby or becoming furious at him while he is barely three days old is extremely dangerous (J. D. Gray, *unpublished data*).

Pediatric Office Observations

The pediatrician has been measuring the following risk factors in the office for many decades. First, some mothers don't hold their babies while receiving medical care. They leave their infant almost unnoticed lying on top of the examining table. Second, some mothers hold their babies, but the action is mechanical. They do not relate to their children. They do not smile or make eye contact with them, talk or sing to them, or cuddle them. They avoid body contact by holding the baby far out on their knee. Third, some mothers pick up their babies, but they handle them roughly. They let their heads dangle without support or handle them like packages. Fourth, some mothers return repeatedly to the physician for minor complaints that cannot be verified. Often they will go to the local emergency room, rather than to the office. Although the mother is complaining about the child's symptoms, she may be worrying about her ability to cope with him. Fifth, certain physical findings reveal the value of the child to his mother. Hygiene neglect is manifested by a smelly baby with long, dirty fingernails, and caked dirt and feces on the skin. An uncontrolled diaper rash may indicate infrequent diaper changes. If the hair is worn off the back of the head, the baby is probably lying in one place for extended periods of time. Sixth, the child who is being hit in the waiting room is at increased risk. If he is not even walking, the situation is quite dangerous. Some parents make it very clear that they do not want a spoiled child, and try to teach him things that are beyond his capacity.

COMPREHENSIVE MEDICAL EVALUATION OF CHILD ABUSE AND NEGLECT

The physician must complete the following eleven tasks in order to meaningfully contribute to the dispositional conference (Table 2). These steps go beyond the detection and confirmation of an isolated child abuse or neglect incident. Rather, most of them apply to all types of child abuse and neglect including physical abuse, nutritional deprivation, and sexual abuse. These assignments can be considered the pediatric data base for child abuse and neglect cases.

1. History of Injury

A complete history should be obtained regarding how the injury allegedly happened, and include the informant, date, time, place, sequence of events, people present, and time lag before medical attention was sought. If possible, the parents should be interviewed separately. The parents can be pressed for exact details when necessary. No other professional should have to repeat this detailed, probing interview. The physician must talk with the parents directly, so that his history is not looked upon as hearsay evidence in court. In obvious cases, obtaining the history from the parents on the phone may suffice if they cannot come in. Although the physician commonly forgets to interview the child, such an interview is often helpful if the child is over age three or four. This should be done in a private setting without the parents present. In failure-to-thrive cases, the history is of little value except to rule out errors in formula preparation or feeding. In sexual abuse cases the history is usually the most critical data of all.

2. Physical Examination of Patient

All bruises should be listed by site, and their size, shape, and color recorded. If they resemble strap marks, grab marks, slap marks, bite marks, loop marks, tie marks, choke marks, cigarette burns, a blunt instrument, or any identifiable object, this should be recorded. Special attention should be paid to the retina, eardrums, oral cavity, and the genitals for signs of occult, or not readily observed, trauma. All bones should be palpated for tenderness and the joints tested for full range of motion. In addition, special attention should be paid to the retina, since retinal hemorrhage may indicate subdural hematoma from a shaking injury. The height and weight percentiles should be plotted; and, if the child appears malnourished, he should be given a return appointment for a weight check after two weeks in either a foster home with *ad lib* meals, or in his natural home with specific feeding advice. In sexual abuse cases, the mouth, anus, and external genitals should receive careful inspection for signs of trauma.

3. Trauma X-ray Survey

Every child under five years of age who is suspected of having been abused should receive a radiologic bone survey consisting of skull (AP and lateral), thorax (AP), pelvis (AP, including lumbar spine), spine (lateral, centered at T8 and including ribs), and long bones (AP, including hands and feet (R. L. Wesenberg, *personal communication*). These X-rays are of great diagnostic value, since the clinical findings of fracture often disappear in six or seven days, even without orthopedic care. A child with multiple fractures may still move about and play normally. X-rays need be obtained in children over age five only if there is any bone tenderness or limited range of motion on physical exam. If films of a tender site are initially negative, they should be repeated in two weeks to pick up calcification of any subperiosteal bleeding or nondisplaced epiphyseal separations which may have been present.

The most classic early finding is a chip or corner fracture.[30,31,32] This corner of metaphysis is usually torn off with the periosteum during wrenching injuries to the long bones (for example, during an angry diaper change). From 10 to 14 days later, calcification of the subperiosteal bleeding will become visible, giving the classical double contour lines. By four to six weeks after injury, the subperiosteal calcification will be solid and start to smooth out and remodel. After several months, the only finding will be cortical thickening and metaphyseal squaring. X-ray findings usually last for six months after an injury but rarely 12. The most diagnostically conclusive X-ray is one which includes multiple bone injuries at different stages of healing. Such an X-ray implies repeated assault. Unusual fractures of the ribs, lateral clavicle, scapula, and sternum should be suspicious for nonaccidental trauma.[33] Skull films sometimes reveal several areas of unexpected soft tissue swelling. Rare bone disorders such as osteogenesis imperfecta, infantile cortical hyperostosis, scurvy, syphilis, and neoplasms may resemble nonaccidental bone trauma. However, a skilled radiologist can easily differentiate these entities. Babies with nutritional deprivation need trauma X-rays, because approximately ten percent of them have associated skeletal injuries. Sexual abuse cases rarely require X-ray surveys.

4. Bleeding Disorder Screen

A bleeding panel would include a platelet count, bleeding time, partial thromboplastin time, prothrombin time, and thrombin time (W. E. Hathaway, *personal communication*). A normal bleeding panel strengthens the physician's court testimony that bruising could not have occurred spontaneously or with minor injury. On a practical level, bleeding tests are rarely indicated. Children with subtle bleeding tendencies demonstrate ongoing bruising in the school, office, hospital and foster home. Screening is not needed for bruises confined to the buttocks, bruises resembling weapons, or hand bruises. It is also unnecessary when one parent or the child accuses a specific adult of hitting the child. The main indication for screening is nonspecific bruises where the parent denies inflicting them, or a history of alleged "easy bruisability" is present.

5. Hospitalization of Selected Patients for Their Safety

When a child protection services worker or police officer brings in a child, they usually only want a physician to document the medical evidence for physical abuse. In cases where the home is unsafe, they will take the child to a foster home after the medical evaluation is completed. Over 50 percent of our cases are managed as outpatients. In contrast, when a parent or guardian brings a child with suspected nonaccidental trauma to the emergency room or clinic without any prior agency involvement, the child should be hospitalized, so that he will be in a protective environment until child protection services can become involved and evaluations regarding the safety of the home can be completed.[34] The extent of injuries is not relevant to this requirement. A child with a minor inflicted injury could return home and receive a second, fatal injury on that same day.

The reason given to the parents for hospitalization can be, "His injuries need to be watched," or "Further studies are needed." It is not helpful to mention the possibility of nonaccidental trauma at this particular time. If the parents refuse hospitalization, a police hold can be obtained, but it is rarely required and need not be a routine procedure.

Failure-to-thrive cases, suspected as secondary to nutritional deprivation, must be hospitalized or placed in a foster home for the one to two weeks of nutritional rehabilitation required for confirmation. In addition, these patients are extremely difficult to follow as outpatients. There is a ten percent risk of concomitant physical abuse; and, in some cases, death from starvation has occurred because of inadequate follow-up.[35]

In sexual abuse cases, the first priority is to prevent continued sexual exploitation. Immediate placement of the child in a hospital or foster home, depending on the availability of child protection services intervention, is required.

6. Color Photographs

Color photographs are required by law in some states.[36] In most juvenile court cases, they are not essential to the primary physician's testimony. In cases where an expert witness who has not actually examined the child is to testify, color photographs are mandatory. When criminal court action is anticipated, they will usually be required and are taken by the police photographer. In cases of nutritional deprivation, "before" and "after" photographs may occasionally be helpful. In sexual abuse cases involving physical harm, the police will usually arrange for photographs. Whether or not medical photography is available, the physician should carefully diagram the body-surface findings in the official medical chart and date and sign the entry.

7. Physical Examination of Siblings

There is approximately a twenty percent risk that a sibling of a physically abused child has also been abused at the same point in time.[37] Therefore, all siblings should be brought in for total body surface examinations within 12 hours of uncovering an index case. If the parents say they can't bring them in because of transportation problems, the protective service agency can accomplish this. If the parents refuse to have their other children seen, a court order can be obtained and the police sent out. In failure-to-thrive cases, the examination of siblings is usually unnecessary. In sexual abuse cases, all the patient's sisters should be interviewed within 24 hours, because it is not uncommon for more than one child to be victimized.

8. Official Medical Report in Writing

This report is required by law and should be written by the examining physician. Since it is an official document, it should be typed. And, since the report will be used in court, its accuracy and completeness is extremely important. The report should not be simply a copy of the admission work-up or discharge summary, because the evidence for the diagnosis of child abuse is often lost in these highly technical documents. The report should include:

(a) History
    (1) date and time patient is seen or admitted
    (2) date, time, and place of abuse incident
    (3) informant (parent, child, or both)
    (4) how abuse occurred, and who allegedly caused it
    (5) any history of past abuse
(b) Physical exam (description of the injury or injuries)
    (1) list injuries by site (e.g., head, arms, legs, back, buttocks, chest, abdomen, or genitalia)
    (2) describe each injury by size, shape, color, and other important characteristics

(3) if the injury identifies the object that caused it, always describe it
(e.g., strap mark or cigarette burn)
(4) use nontechnical terms, such as, "cheek" instead of "zygoma,"
"bruise" instead of "ecchymosis"
(Note: A diagram of body surface findings is helpful, but is *not* as
important as the verbal description of the findings.)
(c) Lab tests (X-rays, blood work, and any other diagnostic tests)
(d) Conclusion: concluding statement explaining why nonaccidental
trauma is suspected
(Tables 3, 4, and 5 are sample reports of physical abuse, nutritional
deprivation, and sexual abuse.)

9. Behavioral Assessment

The abused child is likely to have associated behavior problems. Some
may be primary behaviors (for example, negativism and hyperactivity)
making the child difficult to live with and, therefore, prone to abuse. Other
behaviors (for example, fearfulness and depression) may be secondary to
abusive treatment. Often, the abused child's individual need for therapy
will be overlooked, unless these behavioral symptoms are uncovered. Behavior screening questionnaires completed by the parent are excellent detection devices (Appendix C). They are available for four age groups and
are not specific for child abuse.

10. Developmental Assessment

Abuse and neglect of the infant and preschool child can lead to developmental delays. These problems can be recognized by routine use of the
Denver Developmental Screening Test (DDST) or another developmental
exam for this age group. A school report may be helpful in the comprehensive assessment of the abused, school-age child.

11. Preparation for Court Testimony

Good court testimony depends upon solid knowledge of the case. The
physician must have talked with the parents and examined the child first
hand. He must keep precise medical records regarding the dates and content of these exams and interviews. The initial medical report that he sub-
mits must be completed carefully, so it does not become inconsistent with
his later court testimony. Before the hearing, the physician should review
his records and confer with the county attorney about the points he wishes
to stress. On the witness stand, he should offer organized and convincing,
yet fair testimony. In a case of severe child abuse, it is extremely important
for the child's well being that the physician present his findings and expert

opinion in as ironclad a manner as possible. Some 10 percent of cases will require an expert witness rather than the primary physician.

SUMMARY

Some physicians already are pediatric consultants to child abuse teams. Others will soon enter into such roles, because all children's hospitals and major teaching hospitals will probably have such teams within the next five years. The physician can expect to require at least a year of team experience to develop reasonable expertise in this field.

Other physicians will want nothing to do with multidisciplinary child abuse teams. The reasons for this decision are numerous—for example, they do not want to deal with angry parents or to testify in court. These physicians still have two important roles to play in child abuse. First, they should refer their child abuse cases to the medical consultant on their community child abuse team. This should be looked upon as a legitimate consultation for a life-threatening disease. Second, they should continue to refine their skills at casefinding. The role of detection in child abuse will remain the responsibility of all physicians everywhere.

TABLE 1. *High-risk Checklist for Newborns and Babies*[a]

Most of the high-risk factors described below can be detected before a newborn baby is discharged from the nursery. Some factors will be evident even before the baby is born. Most of the factors can be detected by the routine observations of nurses and physicians, a special interview not being required. When one of the serious risk factors (*) or a cluster (2 to 4) of the other risk factors is present, the mother should be referred to the hospital social worker for an in-depth interview regarding the safety of the home and the family's specific needs.

A. Prenatal history and observations.
  1. The mother conceals the pregnancy (e.g., no prenatal care).
  2. Abortion is unsuccessfully sought or attempted.
  3. Relinquishment for adoption is sought, then reversed.
  4. No "nesting" behavior (e.g., preparation of layette).
  5. Unwed mother without emotional support.
  6. History of severe marital discord.
  7. History of serious mental illness, institutionalization, current depression, or repeated foster homes in either parent.
  8. History of drug addiction or alcoholism in either parent (very high risk if the mother is currently addicted).
  9. History of violent behavior or prison sentence in either parent.
  *10. History of previous abuse or neglect of another child.
B. Delivery room observations.
    How does the mother look?
  *1. Negative appearance (sad, depressed, angry, agitated).
  2. Passive, disinterested, apathetic appearance.
    What does she say?
  *1. Negative comments about the baby (expresses disappointment, anger, disparaging remarks).
  2. Negative comments about self.
  3. Negative comments about others (specify relationship).
    What does she do?
  *1. Doesn't want to see or look at baby.
  *2. Doesn't want to touch or hold baby.
C. Maternity ward observations.
  *1. Lack of claiming behavior or maternal attachment by 48 hours of age (e.g., doesn't want to hold, feed, or name her baby; no signs of cuddling, rocking, eye contact, or talking to the baby).
  *2. Disparaging remarks about the baby (e.g., that he is ugly, defective, a disappointment, mean, bad, etc.).
  3. Repulsion at the baby's drooling, regurgitation, urine, stools, etc.
  4. The mother feeds her baby in a mechanical or other inappropriate way.
  *5. A postpartum depression (i.e., may mean the mother is overwhelmed or can't attach).
  6. The mother attempts to sign her sick newborn out of the hospital against medical advice.

continued

TABLE 1. *(continued)*

7. Prolonged separation of the baby from his mother due to neonatal complication, maternal complication, or any severe illness requiring hospitalization in the first six months of life (e.g., prematurity).
*8. Inadequate visiting or telephoning patterns if the mother is discharged before the baby.
*9. Reluctance to come in for the baby when his discharge is approved.
*10. Spanking of the newborn or overt anger directed toward him (e.g., for crying).
D. Pediatric office observations.
   *1. Lack of holding the baby.
   *2. Holding, but no signs of attachment (e.g., no eye contact, talking, cuddling).
   *3. Rough handling.
   *4. Hygiene neglect.
   *5. Spanking of a young infant.

aPrepared by B. D. Schmitt, B. Souza, J. D. Gray, and C. H. Kempe, Denver and Honolulu.
May be utilized in direct service settings without author's permission but not for publication.
(Revised July 1976.)

TABLE 2. *Medical Evaluation Checklist*

1. History of injury.
2. Physical examination of patient.
3. Trauma X-ray survey on selected patients.
4. Bleeding disorder screen on selected patients.
5. Hospitalization of selected patients for their safety.
6. Color photographs of selected patients.
7. Physical examination of siblings.
8. Official medical report in writing.
9. Behavioral assessment.
10. Developmental assessment.
11. Preparation for court testimony.

TABLE 3. *Physical Abuse—Sample Medical Report*

D.F.
BD: 2/26/72
CGH #444555

History. The child and both parents were brought to CGH on April 29, 1973, at 3:00 P.M. by the police. The child was admitted for intensive burn therapy. At 8:00 A.M. on this day, the father reports that he bathed this 14-month-old baby because she had "messy" pants. It is known that the parents are currently trying to toilet train this child. Despite her crying, he admits to holding her in the bathwater continually for 15 to 20 minutes. When he took her out, he noted the burn. Allegedly, she usually cries during the bath so this didn't alarm him. Also, the father states that "he can't tell hot from cold water." He states that the bruise on her cheek is probably from a fall off the sofa yesterday. He states he didn't notice the bruise until we pointed it out. The parents deny easy bruisability in the child.

Physical exam.
1. 70–80 percent body burn up to midchest, involving both forearms. Many blisters present ranging in size from 1–8 inches. No open burns.
2. 2–3 cm., round, fading bruise on left cheek, scattered bruises of left earlobe, less than 0.5 cm. These are yellow-blue and at least 5 days old.

Trauma X-rays: Normal.

Conclusion. This burn is a classic dunking burn, probably inflicted as punishment for resistance around toilet training. The forearm burns are from struggling to get out of the tub. The child is old enough to climb out unless forcibly held. The bruise on the left cheek and ear is the type that usually results from being slapped, and is older than the father's description.

George Zimmerman, M.D.

Medical report condensed into problem-oriented format.

Physical abuse
   —75 percent body scald from forcible immersion.
   —punished by father for toilet training resistance.
   —slap mark bruise on left cheek and ear.
Recommendations
   —officially reported to CPS.
   —Routine pediatric follow-up by Dr. Davis (private pediatrician).
   —Surgery clinic follow-up for burn care postdischarge.
   —Trauma X-rays when condition stable.

TABLE 4. *Nutritional Deprivation—Sample Medical Report*

D. L.
BD: 1/22/73
CGH #333444

History. This 7½-month-old girl was admitted on August 2, 1973, for the second time for severe failure to thrive. The mother states that the child has frequent vomiting and is a picky eater.

Physical exam: Scrawny child with little fat tissue. No other findings.

Hospital course: The child had a ravenous appetite. There was no vomiting. On a regular diet the following weights were recorded:
1. Birth, 6 lb, 13 oz to admission (gained < 1 oz/wk)
2. Admission #1 (May 29), 7 lb, 14 oz
   Discharge (June 11), 9 lb, 3 oz (gained > 2 oz/day)
3. Two months at home, no weight gain
4. Admission #2 (August 2), 9 lb, 3 oz
   Discharge (August 9), 10 lb, 2 oz (gained > 2 oz/day)

Trauma X-rays: Normal.

Conclusion: This child has been seriously underfed at home as documented by rapid weight gain in the hospital on two occasions. Treatment in the home has failed.

Benjamin Taylor, M.D.

Medical report condensed into problem-oriented format.

Nutritional deprivation
   —underweight, scrawny, 7½-month-old.
   —1st admission, gained > 2 oz/day × 13 days at 4 months old.
   —2 months at home, gained 0.
   —2nd admission, gained > 2 oz/day × 7 days.
Recommendations
   —officially reported to CPS.
   —routine pediatric follow-up by PNP (S. Evans).

TABLE 5. *Sexual Abuse—Sample Medical Report*

T. L.
BD: 6/12/67
CGH #222333

History: This seven-year-old child was brought to Colorado General Hospital August 20, 1974 by her mother because of concern about sexual molestation of the girl by her husband (girl's stepfather). The mother is worried this has been going on for six months and quite frequently. The following history is directly from the mother. In the past two weeks, since the mother quit work, Tracy has been coming to her to say such things as, "Daddy tickles my bottom with his tongue, then he potties on me" (interpretation—oral-genital contact and ejaculation). The mother states that she has found the stepfather and daughter lying together on their bed, and both have jumped when she walks in. The mother came in today, because last night Tracy told her that her father "tickled my bottom with his finger," while the mother was at the laundromat. She says she wants her husband or daughter or both to get help; and she has confronted her husband with this. He denies molesting Tracy, but says he will go to get help for himself. The girl is unwilling to talk to the examiner. However, she says yes when questioned about her mother's story. She denies that her father has ever put his penis in her bottom.

Physical exam: No signs of physical abuse. No signs of genital trauma. Hymenal opening intact and virginal.

Conclusion: This seven-year-old girl has been repeatedly sexually abused by her stepfather. This includes oral-genital contact and other forms of molestation. Urgent intervention is needed.

Benjamin Taylor, M.D.

Medical report condensed into problem-oriented format.

Sexual abuse
    —oral-genital contact and other forms of sexual molestation.
    —repeatedly over 6 months by stepfather.
    —no intercourse by history or exam.
Recommendations
    —officially reported to CPS.
    —routine pediatric follow-up by Dr. Driver (NHC pediatrician).

References

1. Smyth, S. M. (1972): Child abuse syndrome. *Br Med J*, 3:113.
2. Levine, L. J. (1973): The solution of a battered-child homicide by dental evidence: Report of case. *J Am Dent Assoc*, 87:1234.
3. Sussman, S. J. (1968): Skin manifestations of the battered child syndrome. *Pediatr*, 72:99.
4. Gillespie, R. W. (1965): The battered child syndrome: Thermal and caustic manifestations. *J Trauma*, 5:523.
5. Keen, J. H., Lendrum, J., and Wolman, B. (1975): Inflicted burns and scalds in children. *Br Med J*, 1:268.
6. Stone, N. H., Rinaldo, L., Humphrey, C. R., and Brown, R. H. (1970): Child abuse by burning. *Surg Clin N Am*, 50:1419.
7. Mushin, A. S. (1971): Ocular damage in the battered child syndrome. *Br Med J*, 3:402.
8. Tomasi, L. G. (1975): Purtscher retinopathy in the battered child syndrome. *Am J Dis Child*, 129:1335.
9. Silber, D. L., and Bell, W. E. (1971): The neurologist and the physically abused child. *Neurology*, 21:991.
10. Guthkelch, A. N. (1971): Infantile subdural hematoma and its relationship to whiplash injuries. *Br Med J*, 2:430.
11. Caffey, J. (1972): On the theory and practice of shaking infants. *Am J Dis Child*, 124:161.
12. Guthkelch, A. N., *op cit.*
13. Hamlin, H. (1968): Subgaleal hematoma caused by hair-pull. *JAMA*, 204:339.
14. Touloukian, R. J. (1968): Abdominal visceral injuries in battered children. *Pediatrics*, 42:642.
15. Gornall, P., Ahmed, S., Jolleys, A., and Cohen, S. J. (1972): Intra-abdominal injuries in the battered baby syndrome. *Arch Dis Child*, 47:211.
16. Boysen, B. E. (1975): Chylous ascites. *Am J Dis Child*, 129:1338.
17. Penna, S. D. J., and Medovy, H. (1973): Child abuse and traumatic pseudocyst of the pancreas. *J Pediatr*, 83:1026.
18. O'Neill, J. A., *et al.* (1973): Patterns of injury in the battered child syndrome. *Trauma*, 13:332.
19. Togut, M. R., Allen, J. E., and Lelchuck, L. (1969): A psychological exploration of the nonorganic failure-to-thrive syndrome. *Dev Med Child Neurol*, 11:601.
20. Whitten, C. F., Pettit, M. G., and Fischhoff, J. (1969): Evidence that growth failure from maternal deprivation is secondary to undereating. *JAMA*, 209:1675.
21. Kohler, E. E., and Good, T. A. (1969): The infant who fails to thrive. *Hosp Pract*, 4:54.
22. Hannaway, P. J. (1970): Failure to thrive: A study of 100 infants and children. *Clin Pediatr*, 9:96.
23. Riley, R. L., Landwirth, J., Kaplan, S. A., and Collipp, P. J. (1968): Failure to thrive: An analysis of 83 cases. *Calif Med*, 108:32.
24. Sgroi, S. M. (1975): Sexual molestation of children. *Child Today*, 4:18.
25. Sarles, R. M. (1975): Incest. *Pediatr Clin N Am*, 22:633.
26. Abbott, S. L. (1973): Gonococcal tonsillitis-pharyngitis in a 5-year-old girl. *Pediatrics*, 52:287.

27. Koel, B. S. (1969): Failure to thrive and fatal injury as a continuum. *Am J Dis Child*, 118:565.

28. Asch, S. S. and Rubin, L. J. (1974): Postpartum reactions: Some unrecognized variations. *Am J Psychiatry*, 131:870.

29. Fanaroff, A. A., Kennell, J. H., and Klaus, M. H. (1972): Follow-up of low birth weight infants—the predictive value of maternal visiting patterns. *Pediatrics*, 49:287.

30. Caffey, J. (1957): Some traumatic lesions in growing bones other than fractures and dislocation: Clinical and radiologic features. *Br J Radiol*, 30:225.

31. Silverman, F. N. (1974): Radiologic aspects of the battered child syndrome. In *The Battered Child* (2nd ed.), edited by R. E. Helfer and C. H. Kempe, p. 41. University of Chicago Press, Chicago.

32. Silverman, F. N. (1972): Unrecognized trauma in infants, the battered child syndrome, and the syndrome of Ambroise Tardieu'. *Radiology*, 104:337.

33. Kogutt, M. S., Swischuk, L. E., and Fagan, C. J. (1974): Patterns of injury and significance of uncommon fractures in the battered child syndrome. *Amer J Roentgenol*, 121:143.

34. Helfer, R. E. (1974): The responsibility and role of the physician. In *The Battered Child* (2nd ed.), edited by R. E. Helfer and C. H. Kempe, p. 25. University of Chicago Press, Chicago.

35. Adelson, L. (1963): Homicide by starvation. *JAMA*, 186:458.

36. Ford, R. J., Smistek, B. S., and Glass, J. T. (1975): Photography of suspected child abuse and maltreatment. *Biomedical Community*, 3:12.

37. Lauer, B., Ten Broeck, E., and Grossman, M. (1974): Battered child syndrome: Review of 130 patients with controls. *Pediatrics*, 54:67.

7

The Nurse's Evaluation

Carole L. Bridges

The nurse's effectiveness on a multidisciplinary child protection team depends on four factors: (1) his or her nursing skills, (2) perception of the role, (3) the body of nursing knowledge and guidelines of nursing practice, and (4) the role expectations held by other team members. The task of this chapter is to more clearly delineate those aspects of nursing knowledge and practice which are required to help abusive families.

When nurses intercede with patients, they are engaging in the practice of nursing. This practice is comprised of two functions: (1) the identification of the patient's needs and (2) the provision of appropriate services. Although the general assessment and treatment tasks are held in common with many other types of health professionals, the specific nursing role differs in the focus and means of providing patient care. While a physician is primarily responsible for the diagnosis and treatment of a patient's pathology, a nurse is primarily concerned with a patient's needs, which are derived from his reaction to a situation, rather than his pathology per se.[1] Nursing intervention begins with assessing the impact of stress (for example, disease, treatments, life events, and developmental changes) on the individual's available pool of physical, social, and emotional resources. She identifies the patient's situation-derived needs and his coping deficits. The nurse provides for those needs the patient cannot provide for himself. She supports adaptive resources that the patient can mobilize to meet his own needs and explores alternatives to maladaptive reactions.

These nursing functions are particularly germane in the assessment and treatment of abusive families because the family members possess a limited reservoir of adaptive coping resources. Abusive parents have learned maladaptive behaviors in reaction to situations which arouse feelings of personal inadequacy. These feelings of inadequacy are easily evoked because their early life experiences did not provide the emotional supplies necessary to develop an adequate array of responses to cope successfully. Nursing efforts which focus upon the special resource needs of abusive parents and their children provide immediate help to these families. Appreciation of the relationship between patient needs and nursing practice in abusive and neglecting families enhances the effectiveness of the nurse's patient care activities and helps clarify her role on a child protection team.

The Nurse's Assessment

The majority of nurses function in health care settings where the diagnostic confirmation of physical abuse is primarily the physician's responsibility. The nurse's assessment with these families involves collection of a comprehensive data base which defines the family's needs. The data base may serve multiple functions: it (1) enables the team to construct appropriate treatment plans, (2) assists in establishing the proper diagnosis when physical evidence is ambiguous, (3) provides a basis for offering therapeutic services to family members for identified needs, and (4) documents suspected abuse and neglect in families under the nurse's jurisdiction, or in instances where other professionals are not inclined to report child abuse or neglect. In settings where nurse practitioners function as primary care providers, they should refer to chapter 6 for assistance with the diagnostic process in suspected child abuse and neglect cases.

In cases of suspected child abuse and neglect, the nurse should focus her assessment in three areas: (1) the child's responses to adults, to procedures, and to objects and how the child utilizes his body to communicate feelings, needs, and abilities; (2) the parents' responses to adults and to history-taking and how they present their concerns and utilize information; and (3) the parent-child interactions with assessment of parental empathy toward the child, the appropriateness of expectations, and how the child utilizes his parents.

THE CHILD'S RESPONSE

Children of all ages who are normal in their growth and development protest intrusive or painful procedures and physical handling by unfamiliar adults. The most dramatic signal alerting one that a child may be abused or neglected is the haunting submissiveness which is displayed in his behavior. Abused or neglected children allow themselves to be carried into strange environments by unknown individuals without protest. While blood samples are drawn or injections given, the child lies quietly without crying, without tears, without speech. Small babies lie motionless on the unsteady weighing scale; healthy babies object strenuously with crying. Following painful procedures, older abused children may thank you or resort to flattery, saying, "Thank you, nurse. You're a nice nurse. I like you nurse."

When injuries are present, older children may respond with accurate descriptions of events if asked how the injuries occurred, but many will respond with solitude. Some, through play or oblique references to a brother or sister, will give clues that they indeed have knowledge of the event, but are unwilling to share this information directly with you. The only comment made by one four-year-old boy during the entire visit for his burnt and infected finger was "My brother cries."

Reenactment of traumatic, abusive events in these children's lives may come at some later point in spontaneous play. Initially, they often cannot use the available toys in constructive play because of parental intolerance and fear of playfulness. This behavior also reflects a deficit in the parents' life experience (and now that of their children) of how one uses toys for play. Even though the children exhibit undue fear of having their clothes become dirty in play, encopresis or enuresis (incontinence of urine or feces) is common.

Abused and neglected children frequently display language delays and deficits in gross motor development. A nurse can assess and grossly esti-mate the severity of these developmental delays by use of routine screen-ing tests, such as the Denver Developmental Screening Test. The nurse also should determine if other deficits in basic health care exist. For exam-ple, growth delays, nutritional and dental needs, immunization status def-icits, and chronic health problems not receiving ongoing medical care will frequently be identified as the nurse assesses the child and explores these health concerns with the parents.

THE PARENTS' RESPONSE

Parents' responses exhibit a variety of behavioral forms, and most characteristic is their inability to view their child in a realistic manner. They also seem to lack the appreciation of how inappropriate their own behavior appears to others. Parents may interpret normal infant or child behavior as willful actions. For example, a parent may interpret a baby's startle reflex as the child's deliberately waking himself up to cry. Parents may repeatedly complain about illnesses that are not supported by evaluation of the child. Another pattern commonly seen in some parents is the use of weekend or evening office hours for seemingly insignificant symptoms.

Many parents come in with a hidden agenda that relates to their abusive tendencies or behavior. Some report illness symptoms to the receptionist, but when the nurse or physician discusses the symptoms, the parent seems to lose interest and begins expressing other complaints about the child. For example, a mother, while her child was being evaluated for undescended testes, seemed to have little investment in discussing this problem with the nurse and physician, but instead described in detail recent episodes of encopresis in the child. A series of three human chorionic gonadatropin injections were ordered for the child's treatment over a two-week period. Noting the behavior of the parent, the nurse requested that she be notified when the patient appeared for each of these treatment visits. With the third and final visit, the nurse found multiple bruises around the child's buttocks, genital area, and thighs.

Parental concern about illnesses in one's children is universal. Abusive parents may also be genuinely concerned, but their behavior conveys more of a "complaint" quality than simply worry about their child's illness. In addition, there is an element of persistence about the complaint, probably because the actual message (of wanting help in dealing with their children) is obliquely communicated in the form of symptoms. This message is often missed by health professionals. For example, a mother complained persistently that her child vomited after every feeding. The nurse's attempts to demonstrate feeding techniques to the mother were met with further resistance and complaints that, in spite of the nurse's suggestions, the infant continued to vomit his feedings. Compliance in following the nurse's recommendations was not gained. As the mother-infant bonding problem continued, without correct identification by the staff, the infant began to fail to thrive.

It should be recognized that many health professionals are quite reluctant to look beyond the presenting symptoms and confront parents directly, yet empathetically, about their underlying parenting problems. Opportune statements which are uncritical and offer help with these problems are not always met with parental hostility. Often, they are met with relief. The mother of the failure-to-thrive infant described above could not, on her own, initiate foster placement of her child to provide temporary relief in a difficult situation. She could respond readily to the nurse's acknowledgment of her general distress with her infant. She permitted the nurse to arrange for temporary foster care and agreed to begin seeing a child protection team social worker to discuss her problems. Hindsight analysis of the behavior of abusive parents frequently uncovers repeated but disguised attempts to get someone to help them.

PARENT-CHILD INTERACTION

In cases of suspected child abuse and neglect, nurses should closely observe the parent-child interaction. Frequently, parents respond to the child as an inanimate object, with apparent lack of appreciation of a child's feelings. A parent, while dressing a child, may bang the child's head against the examining table without a flicker of awareness of such action. Sadly, the child may also show no response to the trauma. Parents may make derogatory or frightening statements about the child in his presence, as though the child either could not hear or would have no feelings about the comments.

Observation and history-taking often reveal the parent's lack of insight into his child's needs. The children may be admonished not to play with available toys, because their parents do not appreciate a child's need to play. In addition, the parents may not be sensitive to a child's needs for predictability of meal and bedtimes and consistency of discipline regarding safety issues. As a result of their parents' inability both to anticipate and to respond to their needs, abused and neglected infants or children often act as though they do not have any needs. In situations which produce anger, fear, and the need for parental comfort in normally-developing children, the abused or neglected child does not seek out or cling to his parents for comfort. Conditioned by experience and the need to survive a parent's poorly-controlled anger, a curious role-reversal takes place—the child may demonstrate more concern and awareness of his parents' needs than parents do for the child's needs. The behavior of both children and parents reflects a particular form of poverty—that is, a very limited repertoire of responses which does not address their needs adequately and a low estimation of their personal worth.

THE THERAPEUTIC COMPONENT

Even during the diagnostic phase of child abuse and neglect, therapeutic considerations should guide the nurse's interactions. Warmth, predictability, and empathy are important qualities for all health practitioners to possess in order to generate trust and credibility in the eyes of their patients. Behaviors conveying these qualities are not those that abusive parents have customarily experienced. Initially, they may be mistrusting and wary of these overtures. Eye-contact will be difficult for them to sustain.

For one to learn to trust after learning to distrust during the developmentally-appropriate time in infancy, a complex, twofold task must be undertaken. Nurses must first meet the parents' early unmet dependency needs (upon which trust is normally developed in infancy); and second, nurses must help the parents confront the additional task of "unlearning mistrust." The nurse's interactions with these parents are therapeutic when they reflect an appreciation of these lifelong, unmet needs. The nurse must be willing to sit and talk openly with these parents and children about their family life experiences. In addition to conveying a message of caring to them, the time the nurse invests helps her to understand and accurately identify the parents' and child's resources, needs, and deficits. This allows her to function more effectively in helping the parent explore alternatives to inadequate or abusive responses; in providing for those needs that the parent cannot provide for himself; and in supporting any adaptive behaviors he may possess. By focusing her attention on helping the parent modify his reaction to his situation, she can help him experience the process of learning to meet life situations with new and more successful responses and to effect desired change in his life. This experience of oneself as effectively engaging life and producing change as needed is probably of greater significance in the long run than the particular change itself.[2]

Several pitfalls can occur which interfere with the therapeutic component of the nurse's role. Nurses who confine their function with abusive families to detection of signs of physical abuse and neglect drastically limit their contribution to meeting the family's needs. Blaming parents for inadequate or abusive parenting has little remedial value and tends to increase their defensiveness, assault what little sense of self-esteem they may possess, and only serves to perpetuate the problem. Nurses may inadvertently model maladaptive behavior by placing the same unrealistic expectations on the children as their parents do. For example, children may be rewarded for not crying or protesting during painful procedures and praised for being "good boys" or "good girls." Children may be *talked about* but not *to* during health visits. In a nonflaunting, nonobtrusive manner, nurses should be models of healthy behaviors for both parents and children and demonstrate empathetic concern for their needs.

The Nurse's Role in Reporting

Mandatory reporting statutes charge health professionals with the responsibility of alerting the designated state agency to investigate all cases of suspected child abuse and neglect. In Colorado, as in other states, nurses are specifically named in the statute as accountable by law for reporting to the social service department their concerns about any child they believe may be in jeopardy owing to both the parents' questionable ability to act in the child's best interest and the child's inability to speak on his own behalf.

Practically, however, in most health care settings, it is the physician who makes the diagnosis of nonaccidental trauma or neglect, documenting and submitting the report. Nurse practitioners who function as primary care providers are responsible for filing reports of suspected abuse and neglect in the families they treat. In obvious cases of abuse and neglect, these reporting roles will usually suffice.

Other situations may occur where the issue of who will report or when to report is not as clear. It is important for the nurse and physician to work out in advance what they will do if the nurse feels that subtle signs of abuse and neglect are present, and if the physician is, at the time, unaware of these dynamics. How they will initiate communication in these situations, approach further evaluation of the family, and arrive at a decision to report or not must be negotiated prior to the acute situation when abuse or neglect is suspected. The nurse can also remind the physician that he can readily refer the case to the nearest child protection team pediatrician for consultation. In those difficult instances when the nurse feels strongly that abuse or neglect or both are present, and persuasion fails to sway the physician who is not inclined to report the situation or seek consultation, the nurse can submit a report with pertinent information anonymously by phone or by letter to the Department of Social Services in the county of the family's residence as soon as possible. Although this represents a method of last resort for the nurse, an analogous situation could exist in some school settings, when the school administration is not inclined to report evidence of physical abuse or neglect in school children.

Any decision to report is difficult; however, one must keep in mind that intervention provides needed services to parents and children caught in destructive family patterns. Reporting does not represent a punitive action. Even with the mandatory reporting statute, empathy for the family's plight, rather than the nurse's liability for failure to report, should be the compelling force guiding the nurse's actions. Assuming accountability is, in addition, part of the development of professional autonomy in nursing.

Early Detection and Prevention

It is far preferable to detect high-risk families, providing supportive and preventive services, than to try later to repair the damage caused by chronic dysparenting and physical abuse. Nurses, by virtue of their wide distribution throughout all types of health care settings, are in a unique position to assume a preventive, early detection, and health advocacy role in child abuse and neglect. To assume this role, nurses must recognize the behavioral characteristics of abusive parents and their children and appreciate the cyclic inheritance pattern of abusive dynamics. Physical trauma is then not a prerequisite to diagnosis of high-risk families. Prevention and early detection are probably nursing's major contribution in addressing the problem of abused and neglected children.

To engage in nursing practice with the goals of prevention and early detection, nurses must acknowledge a number of factors, or characteristics, which are inherent to various health care settings and directly influence nursing functions. Certainly, the types of patients and their particular needs are important components influencing the delivery of health care in each setting. Another factor is the type of health care site—inpatient or outpatient setting, homes, and schools. A third factor is the *time framework* in which "things" are expected to happen. The health care sites with their different time frameworks have a direct impact on the nurse's role in assessment and intervention.

Outpatient settings, health clinics, or private doctors' offices are characterized by short-term exposure to the patient and his family. Over time, each encounter may be added to the previous one, producing a *slide show* quality of viewing patients at successive points in time. Abusive families in outpatient settings must be assessed, diagnosed, and managed (if treatment continues here) within the short-exposure framework. It is imperative that nurses learn to utilize efficiently the relatively short time during which the patient is available to them. For example, the nurse can be assessing the parent-child interaction while the parent is undressing the child to be weighed and during temperature taking.

In contrast, in-patient settings permit constant exposure to parents and their families for more extended periods of time, providing the opportunity to assess daily family functioning. This exposure rapidly multiplies and intensifies the quantity and variety of data available for assessment, producing a *"moving picture show"* quality of viewing the patient. Nurses on hospital wards are able to accumulate data of familial interaction and should identify the internal resources and types of responses utilized by all family members. This data is exceedingly valuable in effective case disposition.

School settings and home visits by the public health nurses are work settings in which the time frameworks are variants of outpatient settings. In a school a nurse has sequential but expanded exposures to the child (up to five days each week, for nine to twelve months each year), but limited contact with the parents. School nurses have a generous time allotment to document their observations of both physical signs and typical behavioral response patterns seen in abused and neglected children. The child's capacity to respond to various types of school activities is a valuable indicator of the adequacy or inadequacy of his reservoir of coping responses. Home visits by public health nurses involve brief but continuous patient encounters and introduce another important variable—the family within its own home setting.

THE SCHOOL NURSE

School nurses who are knowledgeable in the assessment of physical signs and characteristic behavioral patterns of abused and neglected children can: (1) identify both high-risk and actively abused school-age children; (2) help teachers model healthy "parenting behaviors" for children; and (3) help design educational curricula which promote the development of self-esteem and, thereby, interrupt the early stage of the inadequate-parenting cycle.

Teachers are in an optimal situation to be careful observers of a child's behavioral responses. Nurses can help teachers appreciate the behavioral styles that normally developing children enlist to cope with the demands of classroom interaction and learning. They can help teachers identify and understand that some behaviors, while perhaps easier to contend with in the classroom (for example, the solicitous or compliant child), may be detrimental to the child's normal personality development. Such behavior may be a warning that a child is growing up without adequate parenting. Teachers can help identify children who have limited or dysfunctional coping resources and refer them for further evaluation. Physical education teachers have a natural opportunity to detect signs of physical trauma. Nurses can help their school faculty to further develop their knowledge base and assessment skills in identifying abused and neglected children through in-service training. They can help develop guidelines for initiating diagnostic consultation, obtaining referrals to treatment resources, and reporting suspected cases of abuse and neglect. (See Chapter 4.)

Schools provide society with access to every child from ages six to sixteen. Schools give children a daily opportunity to interact with other adults who may respond to them in ways that differ from their experiences at home. If inadequate parenting exists at home, the "adequate parenting" behavior of teachers could enable the child to broaden his scope of coping responses without fear of harsh punishment or criticism for failures. Schools can provide a child with an opportunity to define his self-estimation differently by acknowledging and reinforcing success and the self-image of "good." Those children who provoke abusive responses in their peers and teachers must be actively intervened with to reverse their harmful style of coping. Nurses can play a helpful role in coordinating the intervention plan. School nurses can help teachers to understand when their responses inadvertently reward children for unhealthy behaviors and to encourage and reward a child's healthier responses.

Many events occur naturally in school which have an impact on a child's feelings and awareness. Nurses can act as consultants to educators providing input and knowledge about the developmental issues in children. They can help determine the classroom opportunities which would support the child's developmental accomplishments, enhance his self-esteem, encourage his exploration of alternative ways of coping, and broaden his understanding of life experiences. Structuring classroom activities to provide children with tasks they can master builds feelings of personal competence. If classroom discussion is encouraged, traditional subjects of study can have a dual purpose. Stories about families, places, people, and life events readily provide children with added dimensions of learning about themselves, in addition to the goals of teaching reading skills or manipulating numerical values.

On a junior and senior high school level, nurses should be participating in the development of courses with specific content on parenting skills and family life dynamics with actual experience in caring for small infants and children. Formalized coursework on babysitting with on-the-job training and play schools based in high school facilities are two approaches school nurses might develop to help better prepare future parents.

THE MATERNITY NURSE

Nurses located in prenatal, neonatal and postpartum settings have a vital role to play in the identification of high-risk families and the provision of services that will short circuit the abuse cycle. In prenatal settings, nurses should take family histories which include an emphasis on the expectant parents' early life experiences. (Parenting behavior is primarily learned from one's parents. This will continue to be true until schools assume a role in this educational task.) Appropriate phrasing of questions to elicit this information is very important. For example, when exploring the possibility of high parental expectations, one might say, "Some parents have very high ideals for their children. I'm wondering how your parents felt about this?" Or, "Many parents feel that spoiling children is a serious problem. I'm wondering how your parents felt about this?" Assessment of expectant parents' methods of discipline and punishment and problem-solving styles and resources should be explored in a similar manner. The process parents use in agreeing upon names for their babies, the meaning of the baby's name, the timing of the selection, the mother's response to quickening, and the parents' expressed expectations and fantasies regarding the baby are all useful indices of healthy or unhealthy parenting attitudes and responses. Prenatal nurses should also assess the degree of the parents' isolation or involvement with other significant people.

Families who display multiple high-risk factors should be offered frequent obstetric visits, the opportunity for a group experience with other expectant parents, and pediatric involvement prior to labor and delivery. The basic goal of intervention is to help these parents develop trust in health professionals and other "parent friends" who can continue to serve as "lifelines" following the baby's birth. Early assessment allows a maximum amount of time to provide needed support services prior to delivery.

Nurses in the labor and delivery room and postpartum and newborn nursery settings have multiple opportunities to assess parent-infant bonding behavior. The prenatal family history should alert the nurse to parents who have potential bonding difficulties and unrealistic expectations of their babies. Early opportunities for physical contact in feeding should be offered while anticipating that many of these parents may have difficulty tolerating these moments with their infants due to their fears of closeness.

Additional supportive services should be offered to the high-risk family during postpartum hospitalization with ample provisions included in the discharge plan. The focus of nursing care initially should be on the mother, providing her with food and comfort. The pediatric nurse or physician or both should visit the parents on the ward and provide basic education on care of the newborn. Examination of the newborn in the parents' presence can provide further insights into the parent-child interaction and can be a learning experience for the parents.

Nurses in the newborn nursery should assess the behavioral styles of all infants and help interpret the baby's unique behavior to the parents. Potentially abusive parents have difficulty perceiving their infants as they really are. For example, difficulties may arise when the parents expect and need a certain kind of behavior from their infant, but the baby exhibits a different kind of response. Sensitive infants, who have difficulty quieting themselves, or very placid infants, who require additional efforts to arouse them, place increased demand on parents to understand their special needs. Potentially abusive parents will have great difficulty coping with these added demands, as well as in helping each other take care of the infant and allowing another adult to care for the infant while they spend time away from the home. Identification of parental expectations, accurate assessment of the baby's style of response, and interpretation of the baby's behavior to the parents are all very important functions of the maternity nurse.

At the time of discharge, numerous supportive services should be initiated on behalf of the high-risk family. These services are more fully discussed in chapters 21 and 22. Often, the maternity nurse will be instrumental in initiating these resources.

THE PEDIATRIC NURSE

Since abusive parents have difficulty assessing their children realistically and responding to them appropriately, pediatric nurses must be alert to signs of impaired parent-child interactions. Because these parents tend to have poor communication skills, nurses must listen with a "second ear" to their words and behaviors for messages of distress.

Growth and developmental lags in infants and small children are red flag signals to health professionals that problems exist for the child. Plotting weight, height and head circumference on growth grids can be helpful in detecting early growth problems. Approximately 50 percent will be directly attributed to caloric deprivation of the infant. Periodic developmental screening (such as the DDST) by pediatric nurses can identify delays in a child's ability to perform age-appropriate activities which may indicate parenting problems. Language development should also be assessed; many abused children demonstrate language deficits. The child's reaction to touch, to strangers, to their parents, and to painful procedures should be observed for abnormal responses.

The manner in which parents handle their children, both physically and emotionally, should be assessed for appropriateness to the child's developmental state. Dressing, feeding, holding behaviors, and verbalizations by the parent will demonstrate the degree of parental empathy toward the child, and his capacity to respond to the child's needs. Questions regarding the parents' views on weaning, toilet training, and discipline should be part of every routine health history in infancy and early childhood. Potentially abusive families tend to have rigid, high expectations of their children in these areas. Nurses in pediatric settings must be careful not to focus all their attention on the baby during health visits with potentially abusive parents. The parents may perceive this as deprivation of their own needs which only intensifies their anger toward their infant. Taking a careful early family life history from both parents can be useful in identifying inherited patterns of abuse and neglect as well as demonstrating one's interest in the parent's life experiences and needs. For those families in which there is a high "index of concern," frequent pediatric visits with the same health staff should be provided, and the names and phone numbers to call after office hours given.

Pediatric nurses could lead parent groups as a routine, preventive function in their office and clinic practice. Groups will help isolated parents identify with one another and form adult relationships which can be used in rescuing one another during times of stress. Utilizing other adults tends to provide immediate relief from acute distress, encourages pursuit of healthier alternatives for handling one's feelings of anger and frustration, and improves the self-esteem of both the rescuing parent and the rescued. After the parents have been able to meet some of their own needs, the group can evolve to include educational content on baby care and child development. With parents who feel emotionally malnourished and deprived, serving food and beverages is often useful in facilitating group interaction.

THE EMERGENCY ROOM NURSE

All settings which provide emergency care to children must be alert to encounters with potentially or actively abusive parents. Nurses should listen carefully for messages or pleas for help concealed in frequent night and weekend visits in the disguise of minor illness complaints. Frequent visits for persistent symptoms that cannot be verified by physical exams should alert the emergency room nurse to possible parental distress. Parents may say they are worried about a disease hurting their child when, in reality, it is the parent who is fearful he may inflict injury. Approximately ten percent of children seen in emergency rooms for trauma have been injured by their own parents.

Nurses in emergency rooms should use growth grids to plot weight, height and head circumference on all small infants and children; otherwise, a failure-to-thrive diagnosis will easily be missed in this setting. Failure-to-thrive infants need the protection of health professionals and should not be followed on an outpatient basis for prolonged periods of time without active intervention. The emergency room history must include information regarding the source of the child's routine health care. Followup to health professionals involved with a child's ongoing care is extremely important. The central registry on reported child abuse can be utilized whenever "hospital shopping" is suspected.

Nurses should devise a system for flagging the records of children seen in the emergency room for all accidents and ingestions. Often the nature of the child's injuries and a discrepant history from a parent will make the diagnosis of nonaccidental trauma obvious. However, in other instances, the pattern of too many injuries or ingestions, even with plausible explanations, should alert the nurse to assess whether danger to the child exists in his home environment. Lack of parental surveillance, which leaves the child unprotected at a time when he is developmentally unable to provide for his own safety, requires intervention. Public health and child welfare agencies should be alerted by phone and written report of all children who may be in jeopardy and warrant further investigation.

THE PUBLIC HEALTH NURSE

Public health nurses have unique opportunities to help abused and neglected children and their families. They can provide frequent and predictable home visits to help the parents reduce their sense of isolation and divert their volatile releases toward the child. The public health nurse may also be the first to become aware of new stresses in the parents' lives which may again increase the risk of child abuse.

Often, it is necessary for more than one health professional or agency to provide services to meet the multiple needs of abusive and neglecting families. The more deprived or distressed the parents feel, the more difficulty they will have accepting another person providing for the needs of their child. Frequently, one group of health workers must focus on helping the parents, and another focus on helping the child. The public health nurse is vital in coordinating such care for the family as well as providing direct health care services to either the parents or the child. (See chapter 22 for further development of the public health nurse's role.)

THE ADULT MEDICAL NURSE

Nurses who work in adult settings should give patients an opportunity to express their concerns about the stresses involved in being a parent. For example, the nurse might say while taking a history, "Many parents experience times of stress with their families. I'm wondering what stresses you might be having?" When adults complain of vague physical symptoms, nurses must appreciate that somatization of one's angry and aggressive feelings is a common phenomenon, especially when other coping mechanisms are not available. Confused and persistent complaints of physical symptoms, such as, abdominal pain, headache, backache, and gynecological problems may be signs of mounting tension in the face of unresolved stresses and must be considered along with other physiologic etiologies.

Parents must evolve through their own developmental stages to cope adequately with the "losses" which occur as their children become more independent. Optimally, the child should receive parental permission for continued developmental emotional growth, which in turn gratifies parents capable of adequate parenting. Abusive parents, however, experience crises during developmental transitions when dependence-independence issues are aroused. These parents frequently have difficulty supporting independent behavior in their children. In all routine health care examinations of parents, the nurse should assess the parents' "parental development" and identify any inadequate or inappropriate coping behaviors.

Nurses in adult medicine should be familiar with community resources to which they can refer patients with parenting problems for individual, group, or family treatment. Forms for initiating referrals to public health nurses or social services should also be available. It must be appreciated that for every abused or neglected child detected in maternity or pediatric health care settings, there are parents of these children who are known to adult medical services. Nurses in adult care settings can, therefore, play an important role in early detection of abuse and neglect and in the initiation of preventive services.

Factors Influencing the Nursing Role

The role expectations of nurses held by other child protection team members, the prevailing notions of hierarchy and power, the role overlap created by shared skills and functions with members of other health disciplines, and the services needed by the patient population will all have an impact on the nurse's role. The skills the nurse possesses are additional factors which play on her perception and actual performance of her role. These skills vary with her educational preparation and work experience. The nurse's skills also are affected by her personal life experiences, which may either enhance or inhibit her ability to empathize with the plight of abusive parents and their children.

Role consensus occurs when all team members overtly and covertly concur in the delineation of the nursing role. Disagreements surrounding any of the factors described above will, however, create role conflicts which, then, must be resolved through negotiation by the team members. Otherwise, effective nursing performance will be jeopardized. Nurses must play an active role in the negotiation process and assume responsibility for articulating to other team members the functions that nursing practice can contribute to patient care of abusive and neglectful families.

Conclusion

This chapter focuses on nursing functions with abusive and neglecting families. Some of these functions are shared with other child protection team members; others provide a unique focus for nurses. The situation-derived needs of families who abuse and neglect their children define an area in which nurses can assume responsibility for patient assessment and care. To enhance the effectiveness of treatment plans and prevent nursing role dissatisfaction, nurses must participate in the disposition process when they have provided assessment and intervention services to families being evaluated by the child protection team.

TABLE 1. *The Nurse's Evaluation Checklist*

Focus of assessment on responses, resources, and coping behavior in three areas:
1. the child's *response* to adults, procedures, and objects; how he communicates his feelings, needs, and abilities.
2. the parents' *responses* to adults and history-taking; how they present their concerns and utilize information.
3. the *parent-child interactions* with evaluations of parental empathy toward the child, appropriateness of expectations; how the child utilizes his parents.

Utilization of nursing assessments:
1. identify each family member's needs, deficits, and resources.
2. provide therapeutic services by helping parents and children modify their reactions to their situation.
   a) exploring with family members alternatives to inadequate or abusive responses.
   b) providing for needs they cannot fulfill themselves.
   c) supporting adaptive behaviors.
3. contribute to the CPT treatment plan and participate in the disposition process.
4. assist in establishing the diagnosis when physical evidence is ambiguous.
5. report to Department of Social Services any suspected child abuse and neglect in children under her jurisdiction, or when other professions are not inclined to report.
6. detect high-risk families and provide preventive services in varied health care settings (i.e., school, pediatric, maternity, newborn nursery, emergency room, public health, and adult medicine).

References

1. Woolridge, P., Skipper, J., and Leonard, R., Eds. (1968). Behavioral Science, Social Practice and the Nursing Profession, pp. 5–15. Case Western Reserve University Press, Cleveland.
2. Daniel, J. H., Hide, J. N. Jr. (1975): Working with high-risk families: Family advocacy in the education program. *Child Today*, 4(6):25.

8

The Social Worker's Evaluation

Claudia A. Carroll

The social worker's evaluation in a child abuse or neglect situation is essential to careful assessment of the family. In combination with the data of the other disciplines, the social work evaluation helps to place a particular family's strengths and weaknesses in perspective, so that intervention can be logical. The main purpose of this chapter is to discuss the various aspects of the social worker's initial evaluation, as well as some guidelines which may be used during this phase.

Knowledge and Skills Essential to the Protective Services Evaluation

As a foundation to doing an adequate evaluation, the social worker needs to have a sound background in the following seven areas of knowledge and skills.

Knowledge of Child Development

A good foundation in normal child development and age-appropriate behaviors is required. This is useful in recognizing age-specific incongruities in behavior and appearance. It is important to be familiar with issues surrounding attachment, identification, and separation.

Understanding of Abuse and Neglect Dynamics

Familiarity with the basic characteristics of situations, parents, and children that contribute to child abuse and neglect is essential. Then, the worker must be able to interface these factors with judgment in deciding what constitutes a high-risk situation.

Knowledge of Pertinent Legal Process and Skill in Court Procedure

Knowing the legal definitions of abuse and neglect in state civil and criminal statutes, the procedures for exercising them, and the legal mandates for agencies such as police, courts, and social service departments is critical. Knowing how to file juvenile court petitions, testify, write progress and recommendations reports for the court with specific case plans, and the timetable to implement plans are also essential.

Frequently, the social worker needs to help prepare the parents for the court hearing. The parents should always be fully aware of the worker's recommendations and plans prior to the court hearing; whenever possible, this should be a mutual plan of the parents and the worker in the interest of the children.

Ability to Take Referral Information

Skill in knowing how to glean as much factual information as possible, often from very reluctant parties, explaining what action will follow the referral, giving assurance, and taking action quickly to initiate the actual evaluation are necessary intake skills.

Ability to Communicate through Writing

Knowing how to write succinct, accurate reports regarding intake findings, action taken, treatment plans, treatment progress, and recommendations is very important. Skills include the ability to relate content and style of writing to medical, social, legal, mental health, and educational agencies.

Skill in Interviewing Techniques

The worker must know how to make psychosocial evaluations, give support and information about what will happen to the parents, and begin establishing a treatment plan. This is an area of great importance, since it is the worker's immediate task to begin establishing an alliance with the parents, which serves as the foundation for the treatment plan. Moving beyond the parents' initial feelings of anger, loneliness, and guilt requires perseverance, understanding, and skill. (Simply assessing the family as

nonmotivated and resistant is unacceptable in protective services. The social worker must assertively and sensitively reach out to the families.)

Ability to Integrate Areas of Knowledge and Skill

This area has a twofold implication. First, the worker must be capable of
blending together all of the gathered information in a comprehensive, organized picture of the family. Second, the worker must be able to combine
sometimes disparate areas—for example, maintaining a supportive relationship with a parent, yet testifying in court regarding the family's
shortcomings.

Initial Evaluation Responsibilities of the Social Worker

In a very simplistic sense, the social worker's main tasks are to ask the
parents the right questions, listen carefully to what the parents say, and
make sound judgments with large doses of common sense. It is, of course,
difficult to implement these ideas in practice, yet it is important to keep
them in mind in order to maintain a perspective and not become muddled.

Before discussing the various tasks performed by the social worker during an evaluation, the ability of the worker to come to grips with the
anxiety, and energy required to do intake evaluations in child abuse and
neglect will be described. First, the social worker must be aware of the
following nearly universal feelings: (1) anger at the parents, (2) denial that
the child's injury was, in fact, nonaccidental, and (3) fear that something
critical will be left out of the evaluation or that some blatant danger signals
will be misinterpreted.

A helpful way of handling these types of feelings is to keep in mind some
of the ideas previously discussed by Dr. Brandt F. Steele, Dr. C. Henry
Kempe, and others in the literature on child abuse. For example, to be
angry with the parents will not be productive in any way. In dealing with
the anger, it is helpful to use the organizing principle that the abusive
parent is an abused child grown up. In other words, these parents have
never had the opportunity in their deprived and needy lives to learn or
know other types of child rearing; they themselves, in many respects, are
still very childlike and immature. To avoid the tendency to deny that the
injury was inflicted, one must keep in mind that abusive parents, through
their abusive behavior, are asking for help.[1] They do not want to treat their
children badly. Denying that abusive behavior is occurring in a family is
only setting up the family for further failure and, very likely, more dangerous abuse.

Compounding the feelings the social worker will inevitably experience are the feelings the parents are having, which are often fear and loneliness. These feelings frequently are transformed into anger toward the social worker. The most important thing to keep in mind here is not to take what the parents are saying as personal attacks, but to interpret their behavior as a way of life for them.[2] In most situations, the social worker and the parents can work through this period. It requires considerable resiliency, patience, and understanding by the worker; but, in most cases, the parents will begin to believe that the worker cares about them, and they will take that important step of beginning to trust the social worker.

Perhaps one of the most comforting aspects of the multidisciplinary approach is in relation to the two areas discussed—that is, the feelings of the social worker and the feelings of the parents. For example, there is an inherent check and balance to the amount of denial which can go on, since the other team members will be able to help the primary therapist recognize it. Also, the social worker alone does not have to deal with the many problems (e.g., great dependency, argumentative nature, and frustrations) of the parents, because other disciplines are involved, and there is added opportunity for a variety of people with different expertise and from various agencies to handle these areas constructively.

Once the social worker's need to master certain universal feelings in these types of cases is understood, the five major tasks of the social worker during an evaluation can be discussed. Each of these tasks is closely related to the others; none should be considered in a vacuum, but rather as one of five tasks together comprising the evaluative role of the social worker. The tasks are: (1) evaluation of the safety of the home, (2) intervention with the parents, (3) initiation of legal action, (4) initiation of ongoing treatment services to the family, and (5) collaboration with other agencies.

EVALUATION OF THE SAFETY OF THE HOME

The first decision which must be made regarding the home's safety is sorting out referrals which require a full evaluation from those which do not. A full evaluation is indicated when: (1) the injury is inconsistent with the explanation, (2) the injury is an unusual accident, (3) either parent may be borderline or psychotic, and (4) poor parent-child interaction has been observed. A full evaluation is not indicated in custody matters in divorce cases (custody evaluations require another type of careful evaluation) or in neighborhood squabbles. These circumstances should initially be evaluated by the appropriate agency (for example, the county Department of Social Services or the police). They should not begin by having the extensive evaluation of a child abuse and neglect case.

In order to evaluate the safety of the home, one must keep in mind the three major areas in operation at the time of the abuse, and ask questions addressing those areas: (1) Do the parents have the potential to abuse—

that is, were they abused as children? Did they experience a "motherless," lonely childhood? Do they see severe punishment as warranted to get their child to "shape up"? (2) Is the child in some way difficult (for example, colicky or premature)? Or is the child perceived by the parents to be special or different? and (3) Is there a precipitating crisis which triggers the abuse?[3]

Other specific areas included in the social work evaluation are: (1) a psychosocial evaluation of each parent, (2) an assessment of the total family functioning—what is the need-meeting system of the family? A good organizing principle here is "Who is doing what for whom?" Usually, in the abusive family, the child is taking care of the parent, or so the parents expect (C. Pollock, *personal communication*), (3) a determination of the perception of the child by each parent—Is the child seen as a separate individual? Is he seen as good or bad? and (4) an assessment of the prognosis for future abuse—This last area is the compilation of the first three points, with special emphasis on the strengths and weaknesses of each parent, their coping skills, and adaptability.

During this initial acute phase, it is important to have good psychiatric consultation readily available in those situations where: (1) the safety of the home is unclear, and a further evaluation by another person would be useful, (2) termination of parental rights is strongly considered, or (3) where there is consideration that one parent is psychotic, dangerous to his child or others, severely depressed, or suicidal. In those children who require hospitalization because of inflicted injuries, it can be assumed that there is a serious lack of impulse control, severe psychopathology, or both in the parents which must be evaluated closely.

The social worker has specific responsibility at the multidisciplinary (dispositional) conference to present a succinct, yet sufficiently detailed, evaluation regarding: (1) personal history of each parent, (2) significant information about the child and his role in the family, (3) principal features of the family, (4) diagnostic impressions, (5) safety of the home, and (6) tentative treatment plans or recommendations. (These treatment recommendations may be modified as needed by the team at the meeting.) If the social worker doing the initial evaluation will not be the continuing therapist, the person who will be assuming that responsibility should, if at all possible, be in attendance at the team meeting.

INTERVENTION WITH THE PARENTS

One of the most frequent questions that arise regarding evaluations with abusive parents is, "How do you get your foot in the door?" This action doesn't depend as much on the social worker's background and education as on the way in which the worker comes across to the parent in terms of attitude and sensitivity. If the worker communicates a message of understanding and shows interest in what has been happening to the parents, he or she will find that most parents will respond positively. Furthermore, it is important to relate to the parents' feelings of being scared and alone, letting them know that you think they are good people.

Second, protective service workers must also be aware of their own feelings about being involved in protective service. Anyone who is in this field must do some real soul searching regarding their motivation to do this work, and how comfortable they feel with the responsibilities, power, and authority inherent in the job. Protective service workers must be screened carefully with considerable emphasis given to personal qualities. (Chapter 20 discusses this point in detail.) A protective service worker must feel comfortable identifying him- or herself to the parents as a representative from the Department of Social Services. Clearly, the social worker's feelings about this will, in some part, be communicated to the parents, and will affect how they, in turn, feel about being involved with protective services. If the protective services worker is uncomfortable in a position of power, the parents will assume some of that worker's anxiety.

Third, it is extremely important to be completely honest with the parents about what is happening. Most parents during this initial period of time have many questions, as well as associated anger and fears regarding any agency involvement with them and their child. It is helpful to address both their feelings and questions in a straightforward and candid manner. For example, it is best for the worker to tell the parents from the beginning that he or she is from the Department of Social Services, that a referral was received, and what the specifics of the referral are. (The exception to this is maintaining the confidentiality of the referral source.) It is also necessary to talk with the parents about the filing of a child abuse report as required by law, and the legal steps which may or may not be initiated. In this way, the parents have the opportunity from the beginning to know what is happening to them. The worker is, therefore, setting the stage for the early development of a trusting relationship and precluding an escalation of suspiciousness. Maintaining a firm, yet sensitive attitude conveys the message that the worker is interested in the parents, sees them as good people, and is going to stand by them until their situation improves.

Concomitantly then, a fourth component of approaching the parents becomes apparent—predictability. As implied in the previous paragraph, one of the universal goals in all child abuse situations is to help the parents learn to trust others. It is, therefore, imperative that the social worker be predictable with the parents. The best way to accomplish this is to help the parents anticipate all agency actions by preparing them in advance. Examples of this predictability would include sharing with the parents, ahead of the court hearing, the social worker's report and recommendations; discussing with them the recommendations of the multidisciplinary team meeting; and whether or not the police will be contacting them.

Several good rules to follow when getting started with a family are:

1. Make an appointment with the family. Don't just drop in, since such action would heighten their suspicious inclinations.
2. Visit the parents as soon as possible following your phone call or initial contact with them. Setting an appointment for one or two days in advance is anxiety provoking to the parents.
3. Interview the parents separately and then together. More information will be gleaned in this way.

An extremely important area where the social worker can be of invaluable assistance to the parents is in helping them work out concrete problems such as transportation, child care, financial problems, and hospital bills. Many of our parents move from crisis to crisis, and help in these areas often needs to be provided so that the parents can become less overwhelmed. Helping the parents compartmentalize their problems, so they can begin to feel some relief and sense of control over their lives, must begin before any other type of change in their relationship with their children can be expected.

INITIATION OF LEGAL ACTION

The protective service social worker most often has the responsibility of initiating legal steps to protect the child. The legal considerations during the acute phase of intervention are: (1) whether a police hold is necessary to keep the child in the hospital, (2) the reporting of nonaccidental trauma cases to the local law enforcement agency, and (3) whether a juvenile court petition is indicated for removal of a child from his home or for the court to gain jurisdiction of the matter or both. In discussing all three of these areas, it is important that each county Department of Social Services has written guidelines available to its workers, discussing when each is indicated.

A social worker performing acute intervention in a crisis situation must know the specific steps to take when a child must be removed from his home—for example, Who to contact? What forms need to be filled out? The specific steps, as well as the agency philosophy, should be spelled out. Trying to determine these steps at a time of crisis is nonfunctional, and perhaps even dangerous to the child in question, if action isn't taken quickly and smoothly. The following three documents are examples of guidelines developed for use at the Adams County Department of Social Services in Colorado (Appendix D1-3):

1. Criteria for Filing a Neglect Petition.
2. Guidelines for Placement of a Child in Foster Care.
3. Guidelines for Returning a Child Home and Case Closure.

The specific ideas contained in these guidelines may or may not be applicable to the reader and his setting; however, what is being suggested is a clear agency statement regarding important areas, as well as step-by-step guidelines developed within each agency for the protective service workers.

INITIATION OF ONGOING TREATMENT SERVICES TO THE FAMILY

If the social worker can be a positive, moving force during the crisis stage, it is more likely that the parents will accept services and intervention during the next phase—ongoing treatment. In most situations, the families will be in need of a variety of intensive services from several different agencies, and early referrals should be made to the other agencies. If the social worker doing the evaluation will not be the ongoing therapist, it is important that he or she remain actively involved with the parents until the new therapist can be introduced to the situation. At all times, the parents need someone on whom they can rely for continuous support and understanding. If adequate staff is available to permit sufficient and uninterrupted time to the family's treatment, it is preferable for one social worker to do both the initial evaluation and the ongoing treatment in that: (1) the services and support to the family have continuity, (2) the difficult process of beginning to trust a person does not need to be repeated, and (3) the establishment of rapport with the family is often easier at the initial time of crisis, rather than after the crisis has passed, and the parents have become psychologically well-defended again.

COLLABORATION WITH OTHER AGENCIES

There are a variety of other agencies that the social worker comes in contact with during the course of an evaluation, depending on what action is needed in the situation. For example, if a child needs to be taken into protective custody, it is necessary to involve the police or juvenile court. In working with the police, it is most helpful if there are one or two juvenile officers who have been specifically trained in procedures in the area of child abuse and are sensitive to the problem. This can be accomplished through inservice training with the local police departments on an ongoing basis. It is truly time well spent. Unnecessary punitive legal action (i.e., arresting the parents) can be avoided if there is trust and good communication between the law enforcement agencies and the Department of Social Services. Often the police who make a referral to the department are not advised of the outcome and, therefore, are left with the impression that "nothing happened." However, if they find that prompt follow-up and help is available to the parents, they may consider incarceration and criminal action less necessary. See Chapter 12 for a full discussion of police involvement in child abuse cases.

Other professionals with whom the worker may need to share information and discuss plans are mental health workers, medical personnel, and various attorneys involved in a case. The parent's attorney can be a key person to smooth case-flow. If he is knowledgeable about child abuse, its dynamics and effects on the child, he can be instrumental in gaining cooperation for the worker from his clients. If he is an attorney not familiar with these problems, the child protective service unit should begin to educate him, because, without his sanction, any case-plan can be undermined. Sharing information with the parent's attorney and the guardians appointed for the children is also essential.

Guidelines for Evaluation Content

The following three tools are being included in this chapter to help social workers in actual evaluation and its recording. The three tools to be discussed are:
1. comprehensive social history outline.
2. brief social history outline.
3. high-risk checklist for physical abuse cases.

COMPREHENSIVE SOCIAL HISTORY OUTLINE

With the current heavy demands on protective service workers and their time, it is necessary to see in what way their time can be best utilized. Inevitably, dictation is one of the areas which falls down when a worker is hardpressed for time. Also, in many situations, significant information never gets included in the record while tangential, extraneous material does. For these reasons, we developed a system of recording at Adams County Department of Social Services in Colorado to streamline the material, as well as its location in the record, and to free some of the workers' time.

One general outline can be used for all the services offered by the agency, with specific addenda pertaining to the area of specialization (e.g., adolescent services, employment, services to unmarried parents). The recordings (Appendix D 4–8) are organized in the following manner:
1. Family Social Study—filled out by Intake Social Worker and applicable to all types of cases.
2. Addendum for Neglect/Abuse Cases—filled out by Intake Social Worker.
3. Family Service Recording—an ongoing recording form filled out by the treatment worker at regular intervals and at the time of case closure.

4. Initial Social Study for Child in Foster Care—filled out at time of child placement.
5. Child Placement Service Recording—an ongoing recording regarding a child in placement which is filled out at regular intervals and at the time of case closure.

BRIEF SOCIAL HISTORY OUTLINE

In those settings where such detailed information as contained in the Comprehensive Social History Outline may not be necessary (such as in a hospital, or private agency or practitioner's office), the following outline is one suggestion for recording a child abuse situation:
1. Identifying data (family composition, age, living arrangements, referral source and reason, and dates of interviews).
2. Personal history (elaboration on high-risk checklist or weaknesses of patient; strengths of patient).
3. Summary impressions and recommendations (disposition, awareness of problem by patient, treatability, degree of risk in home to child, prognosis, and motivation).
4. Follow-up (progress notes).

A sample social work evaluation using this format appears at the end of this chapter.

HIGH-RISK CHECKLIST FOR PHYSICAL ABUSE

This is a 10-point list of areas that we have found by experience to be correlated with risk to a child in his home (Table 1). The main purpose of the checklist is to ensure completeness in interviewing and to help in organizing one's impressions about a family. It also helps in arriving at more than "gut level" feelings about a parent's abusive profile.

It should not be used to diagnose or confirm whether or not abuse took place in a home; rather it is a tool for assessing the safety of the home, after the diagnosis has been confirmed by medical findings. The one exception to this is the confirmatory value of a low (healthy) score in situations of a single unexplained injury that could not have occurred in normal play, but was not witnessed (e.g., an unexplained fractured wrist).

A low score on the checklist documents that the parents do not have in operation those three major areas characteristic of abusive parents—the potential to abuse, see the child in a distorted way, and the presence of crisis. The ten factors of the high-risk checklist are geared at getting to those three important areas. This checklist is not applicable to neglect or failure-to-thrive cases; it only pertains to physical abuse situations. The checklist should never be filled out in the presence of the parent(s).

A "concerning" score is probably anything above 30 percent. (Percentage scores are calculated by multiplying raw scores by 2.5.) Both parents do not have to have high scores for the family to be considered high risk. If one parent does, that is sufficient to warrant further investigation. What are particularly differentiating are scores above 70 percent. We are in the process of validating the scores at the University of Colorado Medical Center.

The ten factors on the checklist are weighted differently (Table 2). Again, this was a subjective judgement based on the combined experience of having seen hundreds of abusive parents. We gave the lowest weighting, or importance, to the following areas:

1. Parent repeatedly beaten or deprived as a child.
4. Parent with low self-esteem or socially isolated.
10. Child unwanted or at risk for poor bonding.

These three areas received the lowest weighting, because they are common findings in society, and their presence does not necessarily mean that the parent will abuse. For example, a parent may have hated his childhood when he was abused so much that he has made a conscious decision to treat his children differently.

The following four areas received intermediate weighting:

2. Parent has criminal or mental illness record.
3. Parent suspected of abuse in past.
5. Multiple crises or stresses.
7. Rigid expectations of child's behavior.

Numbers 2 and 3 represent more pathology in the parents' lives than the first grouping. Number 5 could be the precipitating factor to the abuse. Number 7 is setting the stage, so to speak, for the parent to feel it is warranted to abuse the child.

The following three areas received the highest weighting:

6. Violent temper outbursts.
8. Harsh punishment of child.
9. Child difficult or provocative.

Numbers 6 and 8 received the highest rating, because they demonstrate that the parent currently is displaying aggressive behavior towards society and his child. Number 9 is weighted highly, because the child is capable of precipitating the abuse. Also, all of these factors deal with problems in the present, thus placing the child in current danger.

Working with the Juvenile Court

For a community to have an effective protective service system, it is essential that there be a good working relationship between the local county Department of Social Services and the Juvenile Court. One cannot operate without the other. Developing a relationship with the court may take years; but it can begin by having regular meetings with the court personnel, including the judges and referees. These meetings between the two agencies can serve as a forum to identify problems, approaches to the problems, and better communication and trust. The county Department of Social Services and the Juvenile Court may never see eye-to-eye on all matters, nor should they; however, what is more important is that there is an ongoing dialogue and a means to solve problems.

Another extremely important person for bringing about effective relations with the juvenile court is a competent and concerned county attorney. Protective service workers must have access to the county attorney prior to the hearing in order to prepare cases correctly. The county attorney, in many respects, becomes a liaison with the Court. He must, therefore, be respected for his competency by the Court and the social workers.

COURT REPORT OUTLINES

Agencies need protocols and guidelines for social workers regarding all aspects of court (for example, criteria for filing juvenile court petitions and court report outlines for each type of hearing). We cannot expect the Court to make good decisions without an adequate data base from the social worker. The judge needs clear information on which to build the case and base his decisions.

The following outlines were developed for use at the Adams County Department of Social Services in Colorado and were mutually agreed upon by the Department of Social Services and the Court following numerous meetings (Appendix D 9–13 contains these outlines and a sample court report):
1. Juvenile Court Petition Outlines.
2. Adjudicatory Hearing Outline.
3. Dispositional Hearing Outline.
4. Review Hearing Outline.

TESTIFYING IN COURT

Testifying in court need not be a traumatic experience. Much depends on the workers' confidence prior to the hearing and adequate preparation. A protective service worker may be called to testify pertaining to a certain case of which he has first-hand knowledge; or he may be called to testify as an "expert witness." (An expert witness is one who, even if he has not seen the abuse, can testify to such things as probable damage to a child without intervention, normal childhood development, and the abusive profile.)

The following guidelines may be helpful in court testimony:

1. If asked in court what a social worker does, make a clear and concise statement. Some ideas would be that a social worker is a behavioral specialist who, through counseling and assistance, helps the family maintain minimum standards of good care and protection of their children.

2. Be prepared to state your qualifications to be a social worker: education, work experience, and articles written. Furthermore, it is sometimes necessary to be specific with regard to qualifications to be a protective services worker, such as special training, books read related to the area, the number and type of cases for which one is or has been responsible.

3. Questions may be asked regarding what is involved in the evaluation and treatment of an abusive family. A synopsis of these stages in everyday language is sufficient.

4. Document the facts of a case of which you have first-hand knowledge with specific details, such as dates and statements made by the parents to you. It is very useful in your testimony to be able to refer to such specific statements made by them, particularly in relation to the child, their view of him, expectations, and discipline.

5. Remain calm and composed. Try not to become defensive during cross-examination.

6. If you do not understand a question, say so. Ask for it to be repeated. Don't allow the opposing attorney to back you into saying something you don't mean or understand. Listen, and think through the questions carefully.

7. If asked to state your opinion, do so explaining on what you are basing your opinion.

8. Go over your notes and records regarding the family before the hearing. You may refer to your notes when necessary while testifying.

9. When beginning your testimony about the parents, *always* start by saying something positive so that your subsequent testimony, which may be negative, is seen to be in a balanced perspective. This also helps the parents during the hearing, as well as keeps them somewhat receptive to future counseling. For example, "I believe these are good people who have been experiencing the following difficulties..." or "I believe Mrs. S. truly loves her child, but for these reasons she has not been able to protect her..." are helpful introductory statements.

10. It is helpful to the parents to share in their failure. You might say, "I believe Mr. and Mrs. F. have tried to improve their situation; however, there have been few people or services that have been helpful to them in the past with their many responsibilities."

11. In assessing the safety of the home, it is useful to compare the factors in operation in the family which correlate with the abusive profile. This point is often questioned in court.

12. Be prepared to discuss normal developmental milestones for the age of the child in question, particularly if there are delays related to the parents' inability to care for the child.

13. Convey your concern for both the children and the parents in your testimony. Help the Court understand that because of the parents' childhoods, they have not been equipped to raise their children differently. Never accuse the parents of being bad.

14. Share your report and recommendations with the parents prior to the hearing. What is said in the hearing should not be a surprise to them; rather, they should be prepared for it in advance.

15. Avoid the "them-us" camps prior to the hearing. There is a tendency for the parents and their attorney to group outside the courtroom on one side of the hall, and the social worker, county attorney, and witnesses on the other. Avoid this at all costs, since it only creates more distance between the worker and the parents. Go over and talk with the parents; ask if they have any questions. Remember, these are frightened, lonely people and going to court is reinforcing their already poor self-images.

16. Anticipate the questions the opposing attorney is likely to ask. This helps in preparing your testimony.

17. Avoid psychiatric jargon in testifying. Describe the situation regarding what is happening in the family as clearly as possible for the Court.

18. Of those things about which you are confident, testify conveying that confidence. If you are uncertain regarding a particular point or don't know the answer to a question, it is all right to say so.

19. What to present in testimony from your total evaluation will depend largely on the type of hearing (for example, temporary custody, adjudicatory, dispositional, and review), as well as your judge and the information he requires. Minimally, it is necessary to be able to address those areas described in the court report outline specific to each type of hearing. Expectations of the Court will vary, depending on the judge. Therefore, it behooves the worker to have a sense of the local Juvenile Court's unique characteristics. If these expectations are unknown, ask the judge what information he needs, and initiate meetings between the Court and the Child Protective Service Unit so that significant information will be conveyed to the court during the hearings.

20. Don't try to second-guess the Court either in your written report or testimony. Your recommendation should be based on what you, in your best judgement, feel to be in the best interests of the child, not what you think the judge will order.

21. Prior to testifying have the names of the children and parents clear in your mind. Nothing can dilute testimony more than mixing up names on the witness stand.

Special aspects of how to use the Court from the social work standpoint include:

1. Encourage the parents to come to the hearings. Parents can be represented by counsel and not appear at the hearing; however, this encourages denial on their part, and it does not involve them in planning with the

Court and Department of Social Services. Often, the Court can serve as a positive, moving force on a case which has stagnated.

2. Bring a case back into court when it is not moving (for example, parents refusing to see the social worker). It is tragic to lose the time between hearings (three or six months) in a child's life. If the parents refuse to cooperate, set the hearing for an earlier date to expedite planning.

3. Pursue an early adjudication when termination of parental rights is a strong consideration from the beginning of involvement with the family, or when the parents are refusing to participate in the treatment plan (i.e., denying responsibility for the injuries, and are fixated on projecting blame to a third party, thus precluding their involvement in positive planning for the future) and where the child has serious injury(ies). In large part, adjudication can be obtained with well-documented, *currently* available information, and court delays are often legal tactics which should be avoided.

4. Do not let the county attorney "negotiate" with the parents' attorney without your input. "Hammering out" a stipulation, or plea bargaining, can be dangerous to children and should be done only with mutual agreement of the attorneys, social worker, and other involved professionals.

5. Consider court filings judiciously. It is easier to file a case early in the involvement with the family, rather than months after the intake evaluation when no progress has been made with them. In addition, evidence loses its potency and cannot be used the greater the period of time between the incident and the filing.

6. Try to have the same judge hear the case each time it is reviewed by the Court. Familiarity with the family and its problems aids the Court in making a decision.

Pitfalls

Lack of Resources

One of the difficulties characteristic of the social work evaluation which has not yet been discussed is related to the current dearth of adequate resources and staff in community agencies. This situation increases pressure on the social workers and contributes to a high turnover rate. Protective service workers today feel great inner frustration. They want to provide more and better services to families; however, under the current fiscal constraints, they are unable to do so. To execute these evaluations, a special type of energy which allows a person to move quickly, assimilate the information, and make good judgements is required. When a social worker has too many cases to evaluate, the quality of service is often, by necessity, reduced. To maintain the quality of service, as well as reduce worker turnover, a variety of approaches must be considered:

1. Provide workers with other than evaluation responsibilities. Doing "intakes" is particularly draining work, with no sense of completion. It is important for the social worker to have the opportunity to work with one or two families on levels other than the evaluative level and to provide services from evaluation through treatment to case closure. It is also helpful to have protective service workers carry some voluntary service families who are motivated and openly wanting services. Among the other types of experiences which can be used to balance the draining nature of abuse and neglect evaluations are: groups, therapy with a child, and supervision of a lay therapist.

2. Consider difficult case decisions as shared responsibilities utilizing the multidisciplinary review team and involving other agencies in the case.

3. Provide much ongoing support to the social workers from their supervisors, peers, and the administration of the Department of Social Services.

Misleading Evaluations

It is easy to be seduced by some parents who are particularly apt at portraying good impressions, yet are masking more severe pathology. To avoid being caught in this trap, don't make a decision based on just one aspect of a family. Put together the total picture, check all resources where the family might be known, and interview the parents more than once to solidify or amend initial impressions.

Over-identification with the Parent, Child, or Community

Maintaining objectivity in these cases is sometimes difficult, though absolutely necessary to make the best decisions regarding the family. For example, if the parents' rights are considered to the exclusion of the child's rights, the child could be placed in great physical and emotional danger.

Sample Social Worker Evaluation

I. Identifying Data
   Family Composition: Father—Robert Dubin, 19 years old
                          Mother—Janet Dubin, 18 years old
                          Child—Brian Cohen, 16 months old

The Dubins were referred to Colorado General Hospital by a private pediatrician from a small, rural Colorado community where the family resides.

The referral was based on a possible failure-to-thrive diagnosis. Mrs. Dubin felt Brian wasn't gaining adequate weight, and she was having difficulty getting him to eat. In general, Mrs. Dubin thought that there was "something wrong" with Brian; further, she considered him to "bruise easily." Brian had a history of frequent bruises. At the time of being seen at Colorado General Hospital, he had three unexplained facial bruises. Over the previous six weeks he had almost continuous bruises of the face. On one occasion, he had grab marks on the arm from being held too tightly which, the parents agreed, occurred while Mrs. Dubin was holding onto him by the wrist. Due to the concern for frequent, unexplained bruising on this child, a trauma X-ray series was done at the hospital. It revealed a six-to-eight-week-old healing fracture of the right collar bone. Mr. and Mrs. Dubin could offer no explanation for the broken collar bone, other than to say that, in the past, he had climbed out of his crib and fallen accidentally.

In terms of the child's weight and development, there was no indication of underfeeding; rather he was seen by the doctors to be a small child, which is likely genetic to this family. Brian impressed me as a rather sad, depressed child. While being observed in his crib on the nursery ward, he seemed to sit in one place without much movement for extended periods of time.

Mr. and Mrs. Dubin were interviewed on January 22 and 23, 1976, for a total time of approximately two and one-half hours. Earlier in the medical evaluation of Brian, the Dubins were quite cooperative in sharing information. However, later in the evaluation, when there was concern regarding the bruises and the broken collar bone, Mrs. Dubin became very angry and agitated. There had been previous reports of suspected abuse in their community, and Mrs. Dubin wanted to leave the hospital immediately when she realized this was part of the evaluation.

II. Personal History

Mother: Janet is an attractive, neat 18-year-old woman whose affect was one mainly of anger and suspicion. She refused to share any information regarding herself initially. However, interestingly enough, she did speak freely following the decision to hospitalize Brian. She impressed me as being a girl of above-average intelligence, who was extremely angry with the world in general, and distances herself from others through her temper.

Janet described an emotionally-impoverished childhood, receiving little positive nurturing from either parent. Janet felt she was somewhat closer to her father than her mother, and she described him in terms of "respect." There was a markedly distant relationship with her mother, and Janet said that she "never felt loved by her." Janet grew up in Colorado, where her father is a rancher and her mother is a housewife. She is the oldest of two children, and she perceived that her younger brother was the preferred child by both parents. Janet was severely disciplined as a child ("blistered on the rear"), and she values discipline as a means for a child to respect his parents. At age sixteen, she ran away from home with her boyfriend by whom she was pregnant. She described a difficult pregnancy with Brian, being sick most of the time. She returned home alone to have the baby. Janet considered legal relinquishment of this baby twice—once following his birth and, more recently, at the time she married Robert.

Brian has had no consistent parenting from birth, having been moved from relative to relative most of his life. He has only been with Janet and Robert for the past five months. Janet perceives Brian to be "spoiled" from having been taken care of by various people. Little warmth was noted when Janet either talked of or held Brian. Janet is currently pregnant and due to have her second baby in a month. Her fears over this baby and of wanting to be a "good mother" to the infant appear to be the precipitating crisis in the situation. Janet claims to have no friends in the community and is extremely isolated.

Father: Robert is a young, 19-year-old man with a pleasant, friendly manner. He was soft-spoken and sincere when answering questions presented to him. He impressed me as having a calming effect on his wife; when seen together, he repeatedly would rescue Janet, answering questions for her.

Robert was born and raised in North Dakota, the oldest of four children. His father works as a mailman; his mother is a secretary at a local grade school. He describes both parents as "giving to their children" and feels he had a happy childhood. There appeared to be no abuse present in his childhood. Following graduation from high school, where he received average grades, Robert moved to Colorado to work for his uncle on a ranch. It was in this community that he met Janet; they dated six months before marrying and have now been married ten months.

Strengths: I see two major strengths in this situation. First, the marriage appears to be stable at this point, with each indicating they are happy. Janet, in particular, indicated that her relationship with Robert is much different than others she has had. She says she has "never been happier." Second, Robert impresses me as being a reasonably healthy individual who seems very much concerned about his wife and step-son.

III. Summary Impressions and Recommendations

This situation is a difficult one because Janet Dubin is experiencing extreme ambivalence regarding her son, and this has been evident over an extended period of time. I question whether she has ever bonded with this baby, considering that she almost relinquished him twice and has only taken care of him a few months of his total life. This indicates her ambivalence and need for intensive therapy. Without treatment regarding her feelings for Brian, I feel the prognosis for Janet to ever mother this child is very poor. She may need help and permission to, in fact, relinquish him for adoption.

Janet Dubin is a parent who presents several characteristics consistent with the profile of an abusing parent. For example, she was abused as a child and describes severe punishment that she felt was warranted to learn respect for her parents. I see Janet to be a needy, lonely individual with a very poor self-image as a result of her own impoverished childhood. The current situation is exacerbated by Janet's vehemence in refusing any type of counseling.

At this time, I see Brian to be at high risk for future abuse. There has been no explanation for either the fracture or the numerous bruises to this small child. (The experience of the Colorado General Hospital Child Protection Team has been that in true accidents, parents know where and when their child was hurt.) Janet Dubin currently is refusing to recognize any problems and is defending herself through her extreme anger.

A police hold was obtained on Brian Cohen on January 22, 1976. A temporary custody hearing was held at the local juvenile court on January 25, 1976. At that time the Department of Social Services was awarded temporary custody of Brian Cohen for foster placement.

I recommend that Brian Cohen remain in foster care for the present time, and that his return to his parents' custody be contingent on the following:

1. the establishment of a therapeutic relationship with the parents and, particularly, with Mrs. Dubin. The one person she seems to trust at this time is the local pediatrician. It is, therefore, my recommendation that this pediatrician help in arranging therapy for Janet and talk with her about the need for help.
2. a period of at least three to six months of intensive counseling and therapy.
3. frequent visits between the parents and Brian to begin the emotional attachment by the mother to this child, as well as to provide the opportunity to assess the quality of the parent-child relationship.
4. a period of success with the new baby in which Janet Dubin receives considerable supportive services (i.e., the public health nurse).

   If, in the next six months, the mother's therapy has shown no progress, and the relationship between Brian and herself has not indicated marked improvement, I would strongly recommend that the Court terminate parental rights.

Claudia Carroll, M.S.W.
Clinical Social Worker
Child Protection Team
University of Colorado Medical Center

Social Worker Evaluation—Condensed into
Problem-Oriented Format

1. Physical Abuse
   —frequent bruises observed by family pediatrician, once grab marks of arm to which mother admits.
   —admission on 1-22-76 with three unexplained facial bruises and unexplained fracture of right clavicle.
   —bleeding test normal.
   —two previous reports of suspected child neglect and abuse.
   Recommendations:
   —report on central registry form.
   —follow-up call to family pediatrician.
2. Patient's Emotional Status
   —developmental testing indicates lags in personal, social, and language areas.
   —sad, depressed affect.
   Recommendations:
   —stimulation program carried out in foster home by public health nurse.
3. Mother's Emotional Problems (age—18 years)
   —frightened, angry, distrusting, denial of problems.
   —isolated.
   —emotionally impoverished childhood.
   —severe discipline as child, values this as effective.
   —perception of Brian as "spoiled."
   —now pregnant and due in one month, seen to be precipitating crisis.
   —difficult pregnancy with Brian.
   —considered relinquishment of Brian twice, ambivalence continues regarding child.
   —check list score—65 percent.
   Recommendations:
   —individual therapy for mother.
4. Step-father's Emotional Status (age—18 years)
   —candid, sincere, soft-spoken.
   —appears attached to Brian.
   —rescues mother; has calming effect on her.
   —checklist score—7 percent.
   Recommendations:
   —involve step-father in periodic joint therapy sessions to give mother additional support and relief.
5. Safety of the Home
   —young couple with 18-month-old baby with unexplained fracture and bruises.
   —high-risk for future abuse.

—mother resistant at this point to any intervention.

—child has had a series of caretakers since birth; returned to mother's care four or five months ago.

Recommendations:

—temporary custody to Department of Social Services for foster placement.

—long-term planning needed via Juvenile Court to establish consistent environment and parenting.

—appoint counsel (guardian *ad litem*) for child.

—full evaluation of parental home before considering returning Brian.

—urge voluntary relinquishment or termination of parental rights and adoptive placement if intensive therapy not successful during six months.

Additional Information:

—mother and child not accepted in small community.

—married ten months, considered good marriage by both.

Claudia Carroll, MSW
Child Protection Team
University of Colorado Medical Center

Social Worker's Evaluation Checklist

Evaluation of the Safety of the Home

—assess each parent, perception of child and prognosis for reabuse.

—refer selected families for psychiatric consultation.

—present evaluation and tentative treatment recommendations at dispositional conference.

Intervention with Parents

—convey attitude of understanding to the parents.

—interpret information on behalf of the parents to others having contact with them.

—be predictable with the parents by helping them anticipate all agency or hospital actions in advance.

—help the parents understand what is happening regarding the child(ren) and their family.

—encourage parental involvement with child's hospital care.

—help the parents with concrete needs.

Initiation of Legal Action

—request police hold or court action or both when indicated.

—share assessment of family with county attorney, parent's attorney, and guardian *ad litem*.

Initiation of Ongoing Treatment Services to the Family
—remain actively involved with family until ongoing treatment worker becomes available.
—allow or encourage parents to direct anger toward initial social worker so they may have positive relationship with second social worker.
Collaboration with Other Agencies
—share information and discuss case plans with other professionals involved with the family.
—provide inservice training to other agencies on regular basis to improve communication and trust.

TABLE 1. *Checklist for physical abuse high-risk factors*[a]

This checklist should only be completed *after* a careful psychosocial history has been elicited. It is not intended as the content for a rapid interrogation. At this time, the significance of a specific score is in the process of being validated. Its main purpose is to help the interviewer with completeness.

Grade the boxes for the mother and father as follows: not present, mild, or severe, and circle the appropriate number. Notice that some categories have more importance than others. The highest number in each category means severe, and the middle number means mild. The maximum high-risk raw score a parent can receive is 40. Only one high-risk parent is required to put a family at high-risk.

Mother Normal Mild Severe	Father Normal Mild Severe	
0–1–2	0–1–2	1. Parent was repeatedly beaten or deprived as a child (e.g., repeated foster homes, no helpful parent model during childhood).
0–2–4	0–2–4	2. Parent has criminal or mental illness record (e.g., record of assault and battery, prison, drug abuse, alcoholism, mental hospitalization, or any current indication of psychosis).
0–2–4	0–2–4	3. Parent suspected of physical abuse in the past (e.g., official reports, mysterious death of a sibling, child abuse reported or suspected in previous marriage).
0–1–2	0–1–2	4. Parent with low self-esteem, social isolation, or depression (e.g., feelings of worthlessness, no lifelines, no close friends, unable to ask for help, no enjoyment even at home, unlisted telephone, lack of transportation, poor coping skills, suicide threats/attempt[s]).
0–2–4	0–2–4	5. Multiple crises or stresses (e.g., generally chaotic life, marital discord, multiple separations, threats of divorce, recent significant loss[es], poor work stability, debts, recent or frequent moves, overcrowded living conditions).
0–3–6	0–3–6	6. Violent temper outbursts in either parent toward child or others (e.g., impulsive acting out, doesn't care if someone gets hurt, physical abuse of spouse, puts fist through walls, throws furniture, breaks up the house, one parent spontaneously states she/he suspects the other because of his/her temper).

continued

TABLE 1. *(continued)*

Mother			Father			
Normal	Mild	Severe	Normal	Mild	Severe	
0–2–4			0–2–4			7. Rigid and unrealistic expectations of child's behavior (e.g., expects child to perform beyond his capacity in obedience, respect for his parents and developmental milestones; afraid of spoiling the child or sees child as spoiled; intolerance of normal annoying behavior, and expects child to gratify and love them; sees child as extension of self, rather than as separate individual).
0–3–6			0–3–6			8. Harsh punishment of child (e.g., physical punishment in the early months of life; child seen to be deserving of punishment; current frequent spanking, in its extreme—sadistic punishment).
0–3–6			0–3–6			9. Child is difficult or provocative or both, or is perceived to be by parents (e.g., any frequent misbehavior that causes anger in the parent such as excessive crying, temper tantrums, hyperactivity, aggressiveness, destructiveness, negativism, and defiance).
0–1–2			0–1–2			10. Child is unwanted or at risk for poor bonding (e.g., premature baby, Caesarian-section baby, out-of-wedlock baby, baby almost therapeutically aborted or relinquished for adoption, baby with hospitalization in first six months of life causing prolonged separation, step-child or adopted child).
/40%			/40%			TOTAL Note: This % can be calculated by multiplying the raw score by 2.5.

[a]Developed by B.D. Schmitt, C.A. Carroll, J.D. Gray—Child Protection Team at the University of Colorado Medical Center, 4200 East Ninth Avenue, Denver, Colorado 80262. May be utilized in direct service settings without authors' permission, but not for publication. Comments will be appreciated and may be sent to the Child Protection Team. (6th Revision, June 1976.)

TABLE 2. *Rating the high-risk checklist*[a]

	Normal (not present)	Mild	Severe
1. Parent beaten or deprived as child	Infrequent spankings, consistent mothering as child	Frequent spankings, some bruises, received intermittent mothering	Severe beatings; repeated foster homes; no helpful parent model in childhood
2. Parent has criminal or mental illness record	Not present	Present but demonstrates rehabilitation	Current psychosis; chronic pattern of psychiatric problems
3. Parent suspected of abuse in the past	Not present	Official report of mild abuse; children not placed in foster care	Official report of serious abuse; children placed in foster care or died
4. Parent with low self-esteem, social isolation or depression	Not present	Intermittent coping skills; no current lifelines or unreliable ones.	Severely depressed; no lifelines in past or present
5. Multiple crises or stresses	Not present	Moderate environmental or marital problems, or both	Chaotic lifestyle; severe environmental or marital problems, or both
6. Violent temper outbursts	Not present	Damages property	Attacks people
7. Rigid and unrealistic expectations of child's behavior	Not present	Afraid of spoiling child; unrealistic expectations	Intolerant of normal behavior; very strict parent
8. Harsh punishment of child	Not present	Current frequent spankings or use of belt, not in head area	Physical punishment of baby prior to crawling; sadistic or dangerous punishment or both
9. Child difficult or provocative or both or perceived to be by parents	Not present	Child triggers abuse by intermittent provocative behavior	Child triggers abuse by constant provocative behavior (i.e., seen as having no good points)

continued

TABLE 2. *(continued)*

	Normal (Not present)	Mild	Severe
10. Child unwanted or at risk for poor bonding	Not present	Risk factors present but bonding adequate	Risk factors present and bonding poor

^aDeveloped by C.A. Carroll and B.D. Schmitt—Child Protection Team at The University of Colorado Medical Center, 4200 East Ninth Avenue, Denver, Colorado 80262. May be utilized in direct service settings without authors' permission, but not for publication. Comments will be appreciated and may be sent to the Child Protection Team. (Revised June 1976.)

References

1. Steele, B. F.: *Working with Abusive Parents from a Psychiatric Point of View.* DHEW Publication No. (O.H.D.) 75-70, p. 4.
2. *Ibid.,* p. 22.
3. Schneider, C., Pollock, C., and Helfer, R. E. (1972): Interviewing the Parents. In *Helping the Battered Child and his Family,* edited by C. H. Kempe and R. E. Helfer, pp. 55–56. J. B. Lippincott Company, Philadelphia.

9

The Psychiatrist's Evaluation of the Parents

Harriet C. Stern

This chapter describes my personal approach to evaluating parents of abused children, which has evolved during several years of working with a child protection team. It has been modified by my own assessments and has been influenced by valuable feedback from my colleagues. I encourage the reader to be similarly flexible in developing his or her own approach, basing it on personal style and experience, and to be prepared to adapt to the unique circumstances encountered.

Introduction

Although an optimal social work evaluation may have been done, the psychiatrist necessarily repeats a basic evaluation, for several reasons. First, the social worker's evaluation may not be available to the psychiatrist at the time he or she must do an evaluation. Second, by doing his own evaluation the psychiatrist may pick up inconsistencies in the histories obtained. Third, the psychiatrist may have to testify about his evaluation, and therefore he needs to obtain the information first-hand. Finally, and most important, his need to establish rapport with the parents requires that the psychiatrist start from scratch, without prejudgment.

My evaluation begins with at least a three- to five-minute telephone briefing by the team coordinator, outlining the data already obtained and the reasons the parent is referred for psychiatric evaluation. As in all consultations, the psychiatrist who knows what is asked of him is the most likely to be able to provide it. If written information is available—agency reports and pediatric, social work, or developmental evaluations—I skim it and set it aside. It may help me in focusing my interview to know that a child has had multiple previous injuries or is mentally retarded as a result of birth trauma or previous injury. However, I am careful to avoid following slavishly anyone else's material or impressions.

Before meeting with parents, I consider the reasons for referral and the information requested. If either has not been spelled out, it may be worthwhile to make a phone call to clarify the situation. This may determine the way in which I allot my time, and what I will include in the interview. For example, if the referring professional is concerned that a parent might be psychotic, I would include a formal mental status examination, which I do not administer routinely.

Reasons for Psychiatric Referral

Generally, there are three reasons for psychiatric referral. The first, and most general, is to help in assessing the degree of risk of child abuse by the parent in question. There may be a need for another opinion to establish this risk. Or, the referral may be prompted by the expectation that the case will go to court, where the testimony of the psychiatrist will carry more weight than that of other involved professionals. The second reason is to diagnose psychopathology other than the risk of child abuse. For example, the psychiatrist may be asked to determine the presence and degree of depression, and whether or not there is a risk of suicide. The psychiatrist may also be asked to diagnose psychosis or character disorder. In addition to these standard psychiatric diagnoses, he may make a developmental diagnosis of the parent, or determine if a crisis has arisen in the parent-child relationship. For example, the parent's development may be arrested at the oral level, making adaptation to the marriage and to parenthood difficult. Or, the parent who enjoyed the "lap baby" may be hurt and angry when his toddler starts to explore the rest of the world or provokes irritation in various ways.

The third reason for psychiatric referral is to assess treatability and to recommend treatment priorities. These might include immediate hospitalization because of the danger of suicide, murder, or psychotic decompensation. Or, the psychiatrist might recommend medication to control psychosis or to alleviate overwhelming anxiety. However, these are unusual recommendations. The psychiatrist will more often address himself to an assessment of the parent's ability to make use of existing resources for therapy in order to predict the likelihood of success, and determine the possible pitfalls.

The ability to "use" therapy can be determined by the parent's past history of receiving and using help and also by his use of the interview. If he has been helped when he needed it in the past, the parent is likely to trust a therapist to provide appropriate help. But, if the people to whom he looked for help in the past abused him, trust in a therapist will be hard-won at best. These factors can be assessed by attention to how the parent relates to the interviewer: Does he see him as a potential source of help? If so, what does he do with this perception? Does he wait passively for "the help to come"? Or, is he able to be more active in defining the help he needs? The ratio between the parent's capacity for insight and his need for support may help to determine what kind of therapy, and therapist, makes sense.

Within the possibilities of the community, the psychiatrist may recommend whether a lay therapist, individual psychotherapy (supportive or insight-oriented), marital therapy, group therapy (for example, Parents Anonymous), or a special residential treatment program for abusive parents is most likely to succeed.

The psychiatrist should also try to determine whether or not the parent usually is able to control his impulses. Child abuse necessarily involves a failure in impulse control, but it may be atypical. If, on the other hand, the parent is generally impulsive, and has a history of acting out, the success of therapy is doubtful. If this is the case, the child protection team may decide to recommend termination of parental rights. Whether or not termination can be obtained, it will be wise for the community to refrain from investing money, time, and effort in therapy which is unlikely to succeed.

Method of Evaluation

For the past several months, I have interviewed parents at my private office, which is located away from the medical center. I began to do this for my own comfort and convenience. It saves me travel time, and guarantees that, if a parent fails to keep an appointment, I will have other work at hand. Also, I feel more relaxed in my own office than when "uprooted" to the medical center. This arrangement also works well for parents. So far, none has failed an appointment. It may be that a parent under multidisciplinary scrutiny is glad to get away from the scrubbed and shiny medical center to an office furnished like a living room.

I allow two hours for an evaluation of one parent. I prefer to evaluate parents individually, since I feel I have the most to offer in assessing individual psychopathology. However, the team's assessment of the family should include an interview with the parents together. If I am asked to interview both parents, I usually see them together for an hour and separately for one or two hours.

A friendly, empathic, nonjudgmental attitude is essential. No matter how horrified the interviewer is by abuse of the child, he must be able to empathize with the distress of the parent—usually an abused child himself—to conduct a successful interview and evaluation. If empathy is lacking or impaired, permanently or temporarily, the psychiatrist or other professional should consider whether he is suited to such work. If he is not, he should change to an area offering more personal satisfaction.

I begin the interview by asking if the parent understands—and thereby inform him—that I will report my findings to the child protection team, the Child Welfare Department, and the court. This information has never changed the amount or quality of information given to me. By informing parents in this manner, I avoid contaminating their relationships with other psychiatrists or mental health professionals with a betrayal. Then, adopting a naive posture, I ask how it is that they have come to see me, and allow the parent to tell his story in his own way.

I ask for details and clarification as the parent talks, occasionally being mildly confrontive. For example, I may ask, "What do you make of your child having so many injuries?" "Do you really think rolling off the sofa would cause a skull fracture?" My purpose in raising these questions is to evaluate the parent's reality testing and defensive style. I don't accuse or continue to push in the face of a steadfast denial. I have never obtained a "confession"; this is not my goal. If I have advance information, it may prompt a certain line of questioning; and I may later compare the details told to me with those obtained by other interviewers.

Next, I ask how life was going for the family before the injuries occurred. Details of the family situation are important, because frequently a family crisis precedes episodes of child abuse. However, I am also interested in the congruence, or lack of it, between events and expected feelings. For example, a man who had been out of work for two months, but who claimed he was not distressed by this situation, might be (1) lying, (2) strongly defended against intolerable feelings of impotence, or (3) truly infantile and actually gratified to be out of work. I would need more data to choose the most likely possibility.

At some point in the interview, I ask the parent to tell me about the injured child, from conception to the present. I am particularly interested in the parent's feelings toward and perceptions of the child. Was the pregnancy consciously desired? Was this desire confirmed by reasonable self-care and adequate prenatal medical care? Was the pregnancy attended by unusual anxiety? Did the parents-to-be have support systems available during the pregnancy, labor and delivery, and were they able to make use of them?

The parents' attitudes toward "helping" figures and their ability to make use of this help may determine a prognosis for therapy. If the parent was not satisfied with the help available, what were his complaints? Do they seem to be realistic? Do they represent a transference problem? Or, was the helper addressing the parent as an adult, when he was feeling like a child? What clues does this offer about whether and how therapy can be successful?

What was the parents' initial reaction to the child? Statements, such as "Bloody!" "Beautiful" or "Something was wrong with him," all give clues to the emotional climate in which the child was received.

The postpartum period is particularly crucial for a woman. Her labored body is undergoing rapid physiological changes. At the same time, her psyche faces monumental tasks: seeing herself in a new role of mother and attaching to an infant, who, in reality, may be nothing like the fantasies she maintained during the pregnancy.

The father also must attach to the infant. His attachment is complicated by the stress of separation from his wife and the threat of sharing her love with the infant.

Are there factors present that make attachment more than normally stressful? Is the baby physically intact, the hoped-for sex, placid or lively enough to suit the parents, and easy to satisfy?

When the family leaves the hospital, who is available to help and support the parents? How confident is the mother of her ability to nurture and satisfy the child? Is the father helpful, removed, competitive with his wife, competitive with the baby? How does feeding go? Do the parents see the child in realistic terms, as a helpless, totally dependent creature; or are they attributing to the child unrealistically precocious accomplishments ("The baby turned over both ways in the hospital.") and motivations? How does the parent feel when the baby cries? (See the sample evaluation at the end of the chapter.)

Obviously, these are too many questions to be asked in an interview. If they were asked, the interview would seem like an interrogation. Instead, I encourage the parents to tell me "how it went," and I *listen* with these considerations in mind. I ask the specific questions which seem relevant, but I find the parent's spontaneous associations the most valuable.

During the parent's account of the child's development, I try to assess the degree and accuracy of the parent's empathy with the child's needs at various developmental stages. I listen for rough spots the parents have in dealing with the child's total dependency during the early oral stage; the vicissitudes in that dependency during separation and individuation; control battles during the anal stage, and oedipal conflicts. I inquire about the parents' philosophy of discipline, or "teaching a child right from wrong." This question I ask naively, even if the child is four months old. I pursue details of the parent's approach. If it seems to entail an unusually precocious view of the child, I may ask the parent to reflect on what he said: "Do you think a nine-month-old understands (remembers) . . . ?"

I ask about the parent's own life. What were his parents like? How was discipline handled in his home? Was he expected to be responsible beyond his years? How much gratification was he offered? These considerations reflect a belief that parenting is learned primarily through first-hand experience, regardless of conscious determination to the contrary. Beside his parents, who were the important adults in his life? Who gave him help when he needed it? What significant losses did he endure through death, separation, abandonment, or divorce?

At some point in the interview, I ask about the relationship to the spouse—how the couple met, what attracted the parent to his spouse, and the length and nature of the courtship. I find a short courtship (two to four months) characteristic of the marriages of abusive parents. I also ask about the marriage—the punctuating events and the ups and downs. Parents vary as historians, and some are willing to reveal much more than others. I am equally interested in *how* I am told as in *what* I am told. By this, I mean that I am assessing the ability to relate, the defensive style, the degree of anxiety and conflict, the capacity for insight, and ultimately the treatability of the person I interview. I may ask the parent if he feels there are problems in the home, what he feels the problems are, and what kind of help he would like or could tolerate. These are questions I will ask myself, at any rate; sometimes the parent can help with the answers.

I do not administer a formal mental status examination routinely. However, it is important if it has occurred to me, or to any other professional, that the parent might be psychotic. I was once embarrassed when I evaluated a mother whom I found to be "grossly deprived, extremely mistrustful, distant, anxious, and demonstrating inappropriate affect," and, two weeks later, she was admitted to the state hospital with a diagnosis of paranoid schizophrenia. In retrospect, a mental status examination would have helped me to reach a more precise diagnosis.

In preparing my report, I try to think and write in a manner which will be understood by nonpsychiatrists. I describe the course of the interview and the history obtained, emphasizing those elements relevant to questions of child abuse and treatability. I "diagnose" a degree of risk to a given child, either by the individual parent or the total home setting or both. Then I enumerate the factors which have led me to that diagnosis. I try to make some prediction about whether treatment is likely to be successful, and what the treatment priorities should be. In the course of writing many reports, I have developed a personal style which seems effective to me and my colleagues. I rely on feedback from other involved professionals for criticism of how well I have gotten my point across. My style is still evolving.

Other Roles for Psychiatrists

Although, in some settings, psychiatric evaluations are a routine part of all child protection team evaluations, such frequent evaluations often become impossible because of the volume of cases and the expense. Therefore, it is necessary to plan psychiatric consultation that will be useful within practical limits. Consultations may include direct evaluations of difficult cases, but they should also emphasize supervision and teaching so that the skills of the team's social worker, the welfare case worker, and others will improve, making fewer direct evaluations by psychiatrists necessary.

Similarly, courts must be more receptive to the expertise of team social workers and caseworkers, who may have accumulated many hours of experience with the family under consideration and may have a background of work with many similar families. To rule out such expert testimony, accepting testimony only from a physician, shortchanges the court and requires the psychiatrist to personally evaluate more parents than otherwise would be necessary. Perhaps a psychiatric expert in court could interpret data obtained and presented by other professionals in selected cases.

When a psychiatrist testifies about a parent he has evaluated, it is important to make statements which are as definite as possible and to back up the statements with relevant data that one has at hand, either in a written report or notes. Having informed the parent that I may be required to testify, I do so in a clear, firm manner. I keep in mind, and try to convey, that the parent listening to my testimony is not a criminal, but is himself an unfortunate, abused child, who could not help treating his child as he was treated. When I discuss treatment recommendations in court, I look at the parent and try to let him know, nonverbally, that I am concerned about him.

A final role for the child protection team psychiatrist is that of a treatment consultant. A consultant may provide ongoing supervision of an individual therapy case or a number of cases. Alternately, the psychiatrist may be available to review difficulties arising in therapy, either in individual supervision or in a case conference. Another form of treatment consultation may be to reevaluate a parent some time after treatment is undertaken to determine whether it is safe for a child in foster placement to return home.

When reevaluating abusive parents, it is important to distinguish a superficially compliant attitude from genuine change in parenting attitudes. It may be helpful to see the parent(s) with the child or gather information from others who have seen them together. Reports of the outcome of unsupervised visits are also important data. When a preponderance of evidence suggests that a parental crisis has been resolved, and the parent has improved self-esteem and a more realistic attitude toward the child, the psychiatrist may recommend that the child be returned to the parents' home. In so doing, the psychiatrist must thoughtfully assess, and make specific recommendations concerning, the continuation of therapy or welfare supervision. Even parents who have made good use of therapy and apparently have improved their lives may be stressed by the termination of therapy or the loss of external support. Too many children have been reinjured or killed in the face of such stress.

Sample Psychiatric Evaluation

Mrs. Y. is the 20-year-old mother of nine-month-old Peter, who had been in protective custody for six months. The placement was arranged by the Welfare Department following an episode in which Mrs. Y. had allowed Peter to slip under the water during a bath. He had stopped breathing and subsequently was found to have brain damage. He also had shown poor weight gain, which improved after placement. The evaluation was requested to assess the prognosis for residential treatment for Mrs. Y. and her husband, who had been evaluated by another psychiatrist.

Mrs. Y. was an overweight woman, about four and one-half months pregnant, of dull-normal intelligence. She was cooperative during the interview and generally unguarded in her statements. For example, she bragged about physically bullying her husband; she claimed that she had knocked him unconscious on more than one occasion and had once split his lip, so that it required fourteen stitches. Furthermore, when I asked her if there was anything she thought I should know about her, she answered, "I have a high temper." She related the episode of dropping Peter in the water, emphasizing that she was afraid to hit him on the back (to clear his airway), for fear she would "break his back." Before Peter was placed, she felt "nervous" with him. She said, "Every time he'd cry, I'd feel I'd done something wrong to him." Since the accident, Peter had been "slow," as was she.

The pregnancy with Peter had been difficult. Mrs. Y. had gained 95 pounds, apparently by acting on her "cravings" for banana splits. She became toxemic, with high blood pressure and visual disturbance. To treat the toxemia, her doctors induced labor. Mrs. Y's first impression of Peter was that he was "bloody." She was told that "something was wrong with him." He was kept in the hospital beyond her discharge, because of jaundice. When Peter did come home, Mrs. Y. had little help with him. She said she had no acquaintances in the apartment building and remarked, "I keep to myself."

Mr. and Mrs. Y. were married when Mrs. Y. was 18, after a three-month courtship. Mr. Y. was the first man Mrs. Y. had dated, since her parents had not allowed her to date until she became 18. She wanted to marry to get away from home. Her mother was an alcoholic; her father was "high tempered." They argued continually. Mrs. Y. also felt harassed by the next-door neighbors, who blamed her for some alleged homosexual activity with their daughter.

As a child, Mrs. Y. had been beaten with a belt by both parents. Typically, the beatings followed her failing to do the housework to the satisfaction of her parents. She also had "too many" accidents as a child. For example, when she was five, she straddled the window ledge of a car driven by her father. Although he advised her to get down, he kept on driving. She fell on her head when he drove over a bump. She was said to have brain damage as a result.

In school, Mrs. Y. was a failure. She repeated several grades, was in special education classes, and finally dropped out in seventh grade. She got into physical fights with boys and had no friends.

Conclusions

Mrs. Y. was an extremely high-risk parent for child abuse. She herself had been a neglected and abused child, who had several preventable accidents and was beaten severely by both parents when she failed to live up to their excessive expectations. She was basically an isolated individual involved in an early, highly dependent marriage, indicated by the short courtship and the explosive nature of the relationship. The pregnancy with Peter was complicated by toxemia, which was exacerbated by her poor impulse control in eating. Her initial reaction to the baby was negative. After the accident, she identified Peter with the damaged part of herself. Peter's poor weight gain and Mrs. Y.'s "nervous" and guilty response to his crying suggested a lack of empathic parenting. I saw Mrs. Y. as a classic example of a parent highly at risk for child abuse.

Furthermore, her limited intellect, generally poor impulse control, and lack of conflict about her explosive outbursts made it unlikely that Mrs. Y. would benefit from therapy. At the time of my evaluation, a one-month residential evaluation of Mr. and Mrs. Y. had begun. This would be an opportunity to gather more data about the parenting behavior and the accessibility to treatment of both Mr. and Mrs. Y. My own prediction was that these parents would prove unlikely to change. If this were substantiated, foster care for Peter would need to be continued and an effort made to obtain termination of parental rights. Also, the Welfare Department would need to be alert to the possibility of harm to the next baby.

Psychiatric Evaluation Condensed into Problem-oriented Format

1. Physical abuse and nutritional deprivation (six-month-old)
   —near drowning.
   —failure to thrive, but responding to routine feeding.

2. Patient's physical problem
   —possible brain damage secondary to hypoxia of near drowning.
3. Mother's emotional problems (20-year-old)
   —abused by both parents.
   —dull-normal intelligence.
   —violent temper outbursts toward people, with minimal motivation for restraint.
   Recommendations:
   —Attempt residential treatment.
   —Prognosis—unlikely to change.
   —Consider petition to terminate parental rights.
4. Marital problem
   —serious discord with physical violence.
5. New crisis
   —Mrs. Y. is four months pregnant.

TABLE 1. *The Psychiatric Evaluation Checklist*

1. Contact referral source for briefing.
   A. Summary of data already obtained.
   B. Reason for referral; specific questions to be answered.
2. Inform parents that interview material will be shared with child protection team, Child Welfare Department, and the Court.
3. History of injury.
4. Recent history of family life.
5. History of injured child.
   A. Development.
   B. Feelings.
6. History of parents' life.
   A. Object relations.
   B. Losses.
   C. Discipline.
7. History of the marriage.
8. Assess parent's impulse control, ability to relate, and ability to use help.
9. Write report.
   A. Diagnose parents' degree of risk for child abuse.
   B. Diagnose other psychopathology if relevant.
   C. Detail treatment recommendations.

Reference

Steele, B. F. and Pollock, C. B. (1968): A psychiatric study of parents who abuse infants and small children. In: *The Battered Child,* edited by R. E. Helfer and C. H. Kempe, pp. 103–152. The University of Chicago Press, Chicago.

10

The Psychologist's Evaluation

John R. Bond

Because the recognition and assessment of psychological aspects in abuse and neglect cases may often be far less specific and distinct than the medical findings, the utilization of both psychologic and psychiatric skills on the multidisciplinary team lends considerable strength to the reliability and validity of the team's decisions and recommendations. The importance of this is emphasized if and when a case is brought to court.

Clinical psychologists and psychiatrists typically share certain common emphases and expertise in the role of psychodynamics of diagnosis and treatment, just as the pediatrician and radiologist share a similar medical orientation. The psychiatrist may bring specific abilities to bear on a case in dealing with psychosomatic or psychopharmacological problems. The psychologist, in turn, can bring to the team particular skills in differential diagnosis and modification of behavioral patterns. The focus of this discussion, however, will be limited to the psychologist's contribution to the team diagnostic process.

The Psychological Evaluation

There is nothing magical about any tests or measures. They are simply "structured interviews" which offer certain distinct advantages over the generally less structured, traditional interview technique. For one thing, they usually get more information in less time. While it is true that any good, experienced psychologist should be able to estimate a patient's intellectual functioning within five points, determining that estimate may require a minimum of four or more hours of contact with the patient. A well administered intelligence test can offer the same information in an hour or less. In addition, well-standardized tests and measures offer a degree of verifiable reliability and validity which would be difficult to duplicate via traditional interviews.

Although there is quite clearly no universal format utilized by all psychologists in their evaluations, a comprehensive assessment generally utilizes several different types of input and includes at least the following three major components:

1. History

Both the social worker's case history and the medical history are extremely helpful. In addition, the psychologist usually conducts his or her own interview in order to obtain specific information pertinent to his needs, as a means of establishing rapport, and also because it provides him with an opportunity for clinical observations of the individual's mental abilities, social interactions, and general demeanor.

Some clinicians prefer to review all the background information available prior to evaluating an individual. They feel that this increases the usefulness of their findings by helping them to focus upon specific areas of concern. Others choose not to read the social history or other pertinent records until after they have completed their evaluation. They argue that whatever information may be lost by not emphasizing predetermined areas of inquiry is more than compensated for by avoiding the diagnostic contamination and "me too-ism" which is always a danger in such an approach. Psychologists in the second group usually review the case records prior to reporting their findings and, of necessity, they utilize a more comprehensive repertoire of assessment procedures.

2. Tests and Measures

Intelligence tests. The term tests is used here to indicate standardized instruments which offer quantifiable indications of individual differences within well-defined parameters of reliability and validity. Thus, we have intelligence tests which allow for the reasonably consistent appraisal of an individual's intellectual abilities (as operationally defined in this culture) relative to those of other individuals of the same age.

The intellectual assessment of abusing or neglectful parents may be pertinent not only in the determination of their basic competence as the caretakers of their children, but also in the selection of appropriate treatment programs. For example, it may be determined that a particular mother is capable of providing an acceptably safe home for her child if she is able to increase and improve her child-rearing skills and expectations. If she has normal or higher intelligence, she might be referred to a "parent effectiveness" type of group training program. This would likely be an inappropriate recommendation, however, if her measured intelligence was found to be borderline retarded. With borderline intellectual abilities, she would likely gain little from group learning experiences and would require the kind of personal, individual tutoring and modeling which might best be provided by a paraprofessional in her home.

Other tests and measures.   Other psychological instruments helpful in diagnostic and treatment procedures include some which approach the relative preciseness of the standardized intelligence tests and others which are more appropriately perceived as quasi-quantifiable measures. These are useful in the assessment of a number of areas including the following:
1. preschool or prelanguage developmental levels.
2. psychosocial skills.
3. visual-perceptual functioning.
4. language abilities.
5. scholastic achievement.
6. interests and attitudes.
7. vocational skills.
8. personality dynamics.

This list is far from exhaustive, but it does serve to provide an indication of the variety of specifically oriented tests and measures available to the psychological diagnostician.

3. Personality Assessment

The third portion of the psychological evaluation utilizes data from both the history and the various tests and measures administered. The psychologist has at his disposal both objectively scored personality measures such as the Minnesota Multiphasic Personality Inventory (MMPI) and certain instruments frequently referred to as "projective techniques." The latter have established a niche for themselves in the psychodiagnostician's armamentarium, more because of their usefulness in providing clinical insights than as a result of their established validity coefficients. There are many "projectives" with the Thematic Apperception Test (TAT) and Rorschach perhaps the best known. The Rorschach has been widely used since its development 55 years ago, and, while controversy still continues regarding both its reliability and validity, the fact that it has been administered tens of thousands of times during the past half century provides a rich accumulation of Rorschach protocols for clinical comparison.

Although the projectives may not fully satisfy the demanding requirements of the research statistician, they do provide a stated and consistent theoretical basis for clinical assessment which is certainly more reliable, and, very possibly, as valid as the internalized standards relied upon by psychologists and psychiatrists in arriving at their individual "clinical impressions." When utilized as a part of the total evaluation procedure, projectives offer a valuable means of gaining an additional perspective into the psychological dynamics which may lie at the core of the abusive or neglectful behavior being evaluated.

After obtaining some or all of the data noted above, the psychologist's responsibility is to integrate the information in a meaningful way in order to both offer a diagnostic statement and, whenever possible, provide information pertinent to specific questions raised by the social worker or other team member. In addition, the psychologist should be able to utilize the information and insights gained through his evaluation to generate practical and effective treatment recommendations.

SPECIFIC AGE-APPROPRIATE TESTS AND MEASURES

The various measures and techniques selected by the psychologist in the evaluation battery will usually be determined by four variables: (1) his personal and professional bias, which is an amalgam of his training, theoretical background and basic personality, (2) the age of the individual being examined, (3) the presenting problems or reasons for evaluating this particular individual, and (4) the amount of time available for the evaluation.

It is obviously not possible to indicate here the specific psychological instrument most appropriate for every evaluation contingency. The following is a suggested battery which has proven to be useful in abuse and neglect examinations for each of three age ranges: (1) infants and preschool children, (2) school-age children, and (3) older adolescents and adults.

SPECIFIC INDICATIONS FOR PSYCHOLOGICAL EVALUATION

Most children with inflicted head injuries need psychological evaluation of their level of functioning both to assess their current abilities and to serve as a baseline to check future progress against. For example, careful psycho-developmental examination of a battered eight-month-old infant, who was born full-term and reported to be developing normally at pre-trauma check-ups, would not only indicate the probable amount of damage done to the child's current functioning, but also the degree of deficit he or she may suffer in the future. Such information is critical to decisions relating to the future acceptability of the child to the parents and the possible need for special nursing or custodial care.

The psychological evaluation of the older, verbal, and mobile child should provide information about any of the child's characteristics which might have contributed to his being abused. These include considerations, such as, hyperactivity, excessive negativism or stubbornness, academic disappointment, slowness in a bright family, or, conversely, precociousness with dull parents. In addition, the older child may be able to indicate fears and anxieties indirectly through the projective instruments that he cannot articulate directly in an interview. This is particularly true in cases involving emotional or sexual abuse and incest.

A psychological evaluation is also useful when the individual being examined is the alleged or known perpetrator of abusive or neglectful acts against a child in his or her care. With neglect cases, in particular, the intellectual adequacy of the caretaker may be the critical factor, and, in these instances, valid intelligence testing is far more likely to stand up in court than clinical judgement alone. Indications of judgement impairment owing to either organic brain dysfunction or significant psychopathology may be uncovered by the psychologist. Again, the relatively nonthreatening avenue of projective techniques (e.g., the Rorschach) may reveal deep-seated, negative feelings the perpetrators have toward the abused child—feelings they are not consciously aware of.

Summary

In the field of child abuse and neglect, all the pertinent information needed or desired is seldom available to those charged with the responsibility of formulating diagnoses and treatment plans. Because delays may result in additional trauma, the situation is, in many ways, analogous to an attempt to accurately describe the picture on a jigsaw puzzle when only a few of the pieces are in place. The psychologist on the multidisciplinary team can help to recognize, identify, assess, and place in appropriate context, a number of the pieces of the puzzle. Finally, as a student of human behavior the psychologist can serve as an integral part of the team in arriving at the difficult, operational treatment or placement decisions which may literally mean life or death in child abuse and neglect cases.

Sample Psychological Evaluation

Re: G. J.
BD: 11-13-60
Eval: 3-29-77
CA: 16-4

BACKGROUND AND OBSERVATIONS

Mr. and Mrs. J. are the teenage parents of six-month-old Jeannie, who was admitted to Children's Hospital on March 31 of this year for multiple bruises about her neck and chest, left knee trauma, and multiple fractures of the ribs, showing various stages of healing. Mr. J., age 19, a Lance Corporal with the United States Marines, acknowledged that he had injured his daughter, claiming that the injuries were inadvertent and caused by his handling and playing with her too roughly.

The case is currently being handled by the Child Protective Services Unit at Children's Hospital and Mrs. J., age 16, was referred to a psychological evaluation by the CPS case worker, Mr. H. K., primarily for assessment of her intellectual capabilities.

Mr. J. accompanied his wife to the evaluation and willingly agreed to talk briefly with me before she was seen. While he was obviously and, understandably, anxious in the situation, he responded in a generally positive manner. Mr. J. indicated that his daughter was currently in a foster home and that the reason for this was entirely his fault, since he was "... not paying attention and playing too rough" with her. While he appeared to have somewhat mixed feelings regarding the appropriateness of Jeannie's removal from the family, his general attitude was positive, or perhaps even optimistic. He stated that he and his wife currently live with another couple, of whom the husband is a Corpsman in his unit, and that this older couple has been extremely helpful to him and his wife. Mr. J. appeared to be trying to impress me with the significant changes which had occurred between himself and his wife following Jeannie's removal. He stated, "My wife and I don't argue any more."

However, as it turns out, the two main reasons for their arguments, as far as Mr. J. was concerned, were: (1) his wife's negative attitudes regarding sex and (2) her inability to recognize or assume responsibilities on her own. Regarding the latter, Mr. J. indicated that she "... needs to be told what to do, how to do it, and when to do it. She always says, 'I don't know,' when I ask her anything." When I asked Mr. J. how these major problems had been so quickly resolved following Jeannie's removal, he acknowledged that they had not actually been resolved. Rather, he implied that, with the help of the couple with whom they are living, they are learning to handle these problems better.

Mrs. J. appeared to be an attractive, young woman who looks closer to 18 than 16 years of age. She was well-groomed and mild-mannered with a generally pleasant personality but little in the way of self-confidence. She also expressed some ambiguous feelings regarding the removal of her daughter although she admitted that, in large part, she was relieved, since she had been unable to get her husband to stop handling Jeannie so roughly. Her complaint was that her husband insists upon unquestioned authority at home and refuses to listen to her whenever she attempts to interfere with his handling of Jeannie. She perceived their marital problems to be related to their sexual difficulties as well as the lack of two-way communication and the rigidities already mentioned, and acknowledged feelings of impotence in dealing with her husband because of this. As a result, she experienced considerable frustration, since he often refused to allow her to pick up the crying baby on the grounds that it would spoil the child. She acknowledged that she "... can't stand to hear the baby cry" and experienced, therefore, many frustrating and conflicting times because of her husband's prohibitions against picking Jeannie up.

TESTS ADMINISTERED AND RESULTS

1. Wechsler Adult Intelligence Scale
      Verbal I.Q.   84
      Performance I.Q.   79
      Full Scale I.Q.   81

Verbal Tests	Scaled Score	Performance Tests	Scaled Score
Information	6	Digit symbol	8
Comprehension	6	Picture completion	8
Arithmetic	6	Block design	4
Digit span	7	Object assembly	6

2. Graham-Kendall Memory-For-Designs Test
      Difference Score   5.5
3. Wide Range Achievement Test

	Grade level	Percentile
Reading	7.7	25
Spelling	6.3	13
Arithmetic	5.7	9

4. Incomplete Sentences Blank
5. Draw-A-Person
6. Rorschach

Mrs. J.'s answers to most of the Wechsler items were characterized by extremely slow response times. This may be partly due to generalized depression related to the traumatic events of recent months and the current placement of her daughter in a foster home. But, I suspect it is primarily indicative of her limited abilities and minimal self-confidence. Mrs. J.'s fund of knowledge, as well as her reasoning capabilities, is spotty and irregular. Areas or moments of adequate comprehension and judgement are followed by indications of grossly inadequate, or rather inappropriate, capability. Throughout it all, there was a strong feeling of uncertainty, lack of confidence and concreteness, and a generalized impression of impotence. The subtest scores covered a relatively narrow range. They appeared quite consistently indicative of a limited overall intellectual capability which is in the low, dull-normal range.

Mrs. J.'s reproductions of the Graham-Kendall figures strongly suggest that, during her school years, she was probably carrying the burden of at least a mild to moderate degree of visual-perceptual problems which tended to further degrade her academic skills. Her difference score of 5.5 on this scale placed her at the high-risk end of the borderline range. There are indications that these problems were far more significant some five or more years ago and have likely ameliorated with age.

Mrs. J. essentially completed the ninth grade in school. Her demonstrated academic achievement levels are essentially appropriate with this information, taken in conjunction with her measured intelligence. Reading skills are roughly in the middle seventh-grade range; spelling and arithmetic abilities are at the mid-fifth- and sixth-grade levels.

The various personality measures reinforced the clinical impression of a generally mild, unobtrusive personality, and a predisposition which fit in comfortably with somewhat limited intellectual abilities. The pieces fit so comfortably, in fact, that the resultant personality is one characterized by placidity, benignness, and impotency as primary ego-defense mechanisms. The resulting attitude of compliant complacency permitted the interrelationship between Mrs. J. and her husband to continue. It allowed him to assert his immature self without serious threat of challenge or reprisal by her. However, following the marriage, with its division of responsibilities, Mr. J. apparently began to be dissatisfied with his wife's primary dependency. And, following the birth of their first child, Mrs. J. discovered parts of her own personality which had been dormant, causing her to shift her primary relationship from her husband to her daughter in a way which later threatened and antagonized Mr. J. Throughout their relationship, Mrs. J.'s conflicting feelings regarding sex served as a constant difficulty and appear to have grown to even more significant proportions with the advent of their current problems.

SUMMARY, CONCLUSIONS, AND RECOMMENDATIONS

Mrs. J. is a 16-year-and-4-months-old married woman. Her 6-month-old daughter is currently in a foster home because of physical abuse by the father. Mrs. J.'s measured intellectual abilities yield a Full Scale I.Q. of 81, which is near the bottom of the dull-normal range of intelligence and places her at approximately the 10th percentile with respect to the population at large. Generally, Mrs. J. has developed a benign personality pattern which serves to complement and, essentially, disguise her limited intelligence. She is physically attractive, socially pleasant, and inoffensive. The combination of these characteristics tends to present an overall image of a somewhat shy, quiet-spoken, and slightly immature young woman.

Beneath this image, however, is the reality of a definite intellectual limitation, pervasive feelings of psychological and social impotence, and a gross lack of self-assurance. In addition, Mrs. J. obviously has a number of unresolved personal and emotional problems, particularly in the area of her sexuality.

It is my impression that Mrs. J.'s limitations and problems have served to make her a relatively ineffective protector for her daughter, despite her recognition that her husband was abusing the child. In addition, her sexual difficulties and close identification with her daughter further alienated her husband; and, I suspect his inadvertent "rough handling" of his daughter was likely motivated by conscious and, in large part, unconscious aggressiveness, stemming from his own feelings of rejection and sexual frustration in the relationship with his wife.

I strongly recommend that, in addition to the efforts which I understand are under way to help Mr. and Mrs. J. develop child-rearing skills, they both obtain psychotherapeutic help for the purpose of resolving their basic marital problems. If this is not done, I fear that the same set of dynamics will exist following the return of Jeannie, with possibly the same, or more traumatic, results. My suggestion would be that Mrs. J. be seen individually for awhile to help her work through her sexual problems. At a later time, she and her husband could be seen together.

I recommend that Jeannie not be returned to her parents, considering the circumstances of her hospitalization, until they are well on the way to resolving the problems related to their sexual difficulties and toward achieving an understanding between them regarding Mrs. J.'s adequacy as a wife, a mother, and a person.

This case should be reteamed prior to returning Jeannie home.

John R. Bond, Ph.D.
Clinical Psychologist

Psychological Evaluation Condensed into Problem-Oriented Format

1. Mother's emotional problems (16-year-old).
   —placid, impotent, dependent personality.
   —unable to protect her baby from her husband.
   —tendency to spoil the baby.
   —negative attitude toward sex.
   Recommendation: individual psychotherapy.
2. Mother's intellectual limitations.
   —Wechsler I.Q. test—81.
   —associated feelings of uncertainty and lack of confidence.

—completed ninth grade.

Recommendation: keep future expectations reasonable and explanations simple.

3. Marital problems.

—poor sexual relationship.

Recommendation: marital therapy after wife progresses with regard to her sexuality in individual psychotherapy.

Table 1. *Psycho-developmental evaluation*

INFANTS AND PRESCHOOL CHILDREN (AGE 1 MONTH TO 4 YEARS)

Instrument	Age Range	Purpose	Typical Time Required (minutes)	Comments
1. Vineland, Social Maturity Scale	1 month– adult	To assess 6 areas of ability contributing to social maturity	3–10	Based on observations of parents or other guardian, most useful for children under 10 and older retardates
2. Denver Developmental Scale	1 month– 6 years	To assess development levels in 4 areas: 1. gross motor 2. fine motor-adaptive 3. language 4. personal-social	10–15	Child examined directly, but reports from knowledgeable guardians are helpful
3. Cattell, Infant Intelligence Scale and/or	2 months– 5 years	To assess development and estimate intelligence	15–30	Particularly useful up to about 3 years of age
Stanford-Binet Intelligence Scale	2 years– adult	To measure intelligence	30–60	Similar to the Cattell in the 2 to 5 year range, may be used as an extrapolation of the Cattell
4. Beery, Developmental Test of Visual-Motor Integration	2–15 years	To assess visual-motor skills	3–5	A task requiring the copying or imitating of geometric figures
5. Human drawings (e.g., person-family)	When capable	To assess fine-motor skills, self-image, and psychosocial dynamics	1–2	Within the capability of some 4-year-olds

continued

TABLE 1. *(continued)*

Instrument	Age Range	Purpose	Typical Time Required (minutes)	Comments
1. Vineland Social Maturity Scale	1 month–adult	To assess 6 areas of ability contributing to social maturity	5–15	(see above)
2. Wechsler Preschool and Primary Scale of Intelligence or	4–6½ years	To measure intelligence	20–60	Both standardized and universally utilized individual tests of intellectual ability, used with different age groups of children
Wechsler, Intelligence Scale for Children, Revised	6–17 years	To measure intelligence	40–60	
3. Graham-Kendall, Memory-For-Designs Test	8½ years–adult	To assess visual-perceptual abilities	7–15	Indication of possible CNS dysfunction, utilizes objective criteria and consideration of age and intelligence
4. Wide Range Achievement Test	5 years–adult	To measure level of academic achievement	15–25	Brief assessment of phonetic reading, spelling, and arithmetic skills
5. The Blacky Pictures and/or	When capable	To assess personality dynamics and attitudes towards parents and siblings	10–30	Projective technique most effective with children under 12, psychoanalytic orientation
Rorschach	When capable	To assess personality dynamics	15–40	Projective technique usually utilized with adults but useful with some children down to 6 or 7 years of age

continued

TABLE 1. *(continued)*

Instrument	Age Range	Purpose	Typical Time Required (minutes)	Comments
6. Human drawings (e.g., person-family)	Any age	To assess fine-motor skills, self-image and psychosocial dynamics	1–10	May offer insights about self-image, developmental level and perceived family dynamics

OLDER ADOLESCENTS AND ADULTS (AGE 17 AND OLDER)

Instrument	Age Range	Purpose	Typical Time Required (minutes)	Comments
1. Wechsler Adult Intelligence Scale	17 years–adult	To measure intelligence	40–70	(see above)
2. Graham-Kendall Memory-For-Designs Test	8½ years–adult	To assess visual-perceptual abilities	7–15	(see above)
3. Wide Range Achievement Test	5 years–adult	To measure level of academic achievement	20–30	(see above)
4. Human drawings (e.g., person-family)	Any age	To assess fine-motor skills, self-image, and psychosocial dynamics	1–10	(see above)
5. Minnesota Multiphasic Personality Inventory (MMPI)	16 years–adult	To assess personality dynamics	60–90	Paper and pencil test, objectively scored and useful as an aid in differential diagnosis, may be unreliable with adolescents or adults with below average I.Q.
6. Rorschach	Any age	To assess personality dynamics	30–60	An unstructured projective technique useful in exploring deep-seated, personality dynamics
and/or				
Thematic Apperception Test	Any age	To assess personality dynamics	30–60	A more structured projective technique than the Rorschach

11

The Developmental Specialist's Evaluation of the Child

Pamela J. Boggess

The child development specialist is the child's strongest advocate. Therefore, he or she must clearly delineate the child's developmental status and needs. Often the child's needs are obscured by the parents' needs and desires and the system's inefficiencies. For these reasons, the child development specialist must focus on the child's present, as well as future, development and adjustment.

The child development specialist should have comprehensive training in normal and deviant development, especially personality development. Thorough training in the use of interviewing skills, evaluative skills (developmental testing), integrative skills, interpretive skills, and case management skills is essential. The child development specialist must understand and be able to utilize concepts, such as, attachment, individuation, trust, object constancy, separation, identification, self-image, coping mechanisms, and anxiety. These concepts represent the essence of personality development. Although the purpose of this chapter is not to outline a course in developmental pediatrics, the examples given illustrate ways in which these concepts can be used in thinking about a child and his development.

Persons who might qualify as child development specialists, depending on their additional training, include: pediatricians, child psychiatrists, child psychologists, pediatric nurses, psychiatric social workers, and early childhood educators.

Indications for Child Development Specialist

A child development specialist could be involved in all cases of child abuse, but he or she is particularly helpful in cases of emotional abuse and neglect. The child development specialist can document and confirm the existence of emotional abuse and the effects of deprivation and neglect. He can also evaluate the emotional status of those children who have been physically abused, those who exhibit behavioral problems, or those with disturbed parent-child relationships. In addition, the child development specialist can document developmental delays and determine the etiology of the delays. Finally, the child development specialist can assist in planning both short- and long-term intervention for the child and his family.

Evaluation—History

In order to understand the child's present status and needs, an appropriate history detailing the quality of life experiences is essential. This information can be most readily obtained by assessing daily routine activities such as feeding, sleeping, playing, and relating to people and objects. Obtaining a thorough and meaningful history requires sensitive interviewing skills. The resulting document should portray a vivid picture of the child and the life he leads. If a parent cannot recall specific information about the child, usually the parent was not available, either physically or emotionally, to the child at the time. The historical information should assist the child development specialist in determining the child's status regarding attachments, individuation, trust, object constancy, independence, separation, identification, self-image, affect, coping behavior, degree of anxiety, and general developmental level.

The following is an outline of historical items. All of the items should be reported from the standpoint of ways in which they influence the child's development.

EVALUATION: HISTORY OUTLINE

A. Medical History
   1. Pregnancy—abnormalities, planned parenthood, attitude toward pregnancy, expectations, and feelings about parenthood
   2. Labor—abnormalities and feelings about and during labor
   3. Delivery—events and feelings
   4. Neonatal course—condition, problems, illnesses, and kind of infant

5. Health—hospitalizations, surgery, accidents, ingestions, immunizations, and illnesses

B. Parental History

1. Family unit—who lives with family, finances, living arrangements, marriage, expectations, conflicts, and influence of extended family
2. Mother and father—education, work history, health, social adjustment, personality, impression of self as person and parent, and background (parents, siblings, significant events, relationships, problems, impressions of parents, and discipline)
3. Relationship to child—awareness of child's feelings and response to them, response to child's distress or pleasure, feelings about child, what does parent like about child, what does parent not like about child, expectations of child, and ability to adapt to child

C. Child Care Practices

1. Environment—safe, stimulating, protective, atmosphere, variety, consistency, and stability
2. Feeding—who feeds, how, pleasant, unpleasant, problems, mood, diet, mouthing, self-feeding skills, messages from child, and pica
3. Sleeping—arrangements, naps, bedtime rituals, nightmares, and sleep walking
4. Toys and play—space, materials, opportunities, appropriate, safe, cooperation, imagination, role play, themes, and problem-solving
5. Discipline—for what, who, how, reactions, results, frequency, reasons, appropriateness, limits, and consistency
6. Toilet training—philosophy, response, amount of choice of child, independence, negativism, masturbation, enuresis, encopresis, and hoarding
7. Separations—age, duration, circumstances, reactions, reactions to babysitters, and preschool
8. Caregivers—stable, fulfill needs, depriving, chaotic, consistent, organizing influence, responsiveness to child, and comfort measures

D. Developmental History

1. Milestones—sit, walk, smile, words, and grasp
2. Activity—motor skills, quality, sensitivities, physical contact, need for activity, and use of activity
3. Language and communication—early noises, hearing, words, meaning, convey needs, express self, amount, appropriateness, uses, books, and as social partner
4. Personal-Social—fears (people, animals, and water), sensitivities, anxiety, frustration, and pleasure (when, what, amount, and reaction), what upsets child, what makes child happy, how child deals with changes, self-destructive, headbanging, rocking, affection, sense of identity, pronouns, independence, dependence, self-care tasks, imitation, autonomy, aggression, relationship to parents, adults, peers, siblings, primary attachment (who comforts, how, get permis-

sion, and share joy), and how adults are used (protection, direction, ideas, partner, comfort, teasing)
E. School History
  1. General history—grades, attendance, interests, interactions, behavior, problems, strengths, weaknesses, and parents' views and reactions

A SAMPLE EVALUATION HISTORY

The following history illustrates many of the concepts discussed.

Name: Peter N.   #1940
Birth Date: 4/14/71   Age at Examination: 56 months
Date of Examination: 12/17/75   Examiner: Pamela Boggess, M.D.

A. Medical History.
    Peter was the third planned child born to Mr. and Mrs. N. The pregnancy was complicated by premature delivery. The neonatal course was stormy and parents did not visit during the two-month hospitalization, because they did not want to attach to him, only to lose him later. The first few weeks at home he was irritable, difficult to comfort, and always hungry. He has had no major health problems other than a hospitalization at 18 months for dehydration and failure to thrive.
B. Parental History.
    Mr. and Mrs. N. were married in 1968. They currently live in a small apartment and finances are a problem. The boys, ages seven, six, and four, share a room. The mother is 28 years old and works in the home. She lost her parents when she was seven years old and grew up in several different relatives' homes. She has never described herself as a happy person and takes life as it comes. The father is an unemployed truck driver. He has difficulty maintaining a job because of his temper. He grew up in a military family where discipline was inconsistent but obviously brutal. He feels life has been unfair to him for his 30 years.
C. Child Care Practices.
    The environment for Peter has been chaotic, and often the major adults in his life have been out of control, with anger directed at him and others. Peter has experienced numerous caretaker changes and inconsistency in expectations and management.
    Peter was described as always being hungry the first two years of his life. During this time, he was fed only baby food and formula. At 18 months of age, he was hospitalized for failure to thrive with no organic abnormalities uncovered. At two years of age, when he had access to food, he began gorging and hoarding food in his mouth. The father stopped this activity by shoving food down Peter's throat at two and one-half years. Peter now vacillates between refusing food and gorging himself.

Peter did not sleep through the night until he was nine months old. At three years of age, he began sleep walking and recently has had nightmares. He has no bedtime ritual and is afraid to go to bed. He often falls asleep in front of the television set.

He plays well with younger children, though most play is parallel play. Appropriate play material is sparse. Most toys available to Peter are too complicated for him, and he is forbidden access to more appropriate toys and household items. He is encouraged to play alone and never receives instruction or encouragement.

The parents' major concern is their inability to discipline Peter. Both parents easily become angry at Peter, and often, by their own admission, they lose control, spank Peter, and scream at him. They are often angry and uncontrolled with each other as well. The parents complain that even though Peter is spanked, he has no fear of punishment, and his behavior is unaltered by it.

Peter began toilet training at two years of age by being placed on the toilet every hour. The parents were discouraged and angry at Peter when he did not show any progress. At four years of age, while staying with his grandmother at his mother's request, Peter was easily trained and was dry until he returned home. His father then spanked him whenever he was wet. Peter has no choices regarding behavior, dress, food, or activity.

Peter has experienced many separations from his parents. The major ones include birth and the nearly two-month hospitalization. The next occurred at 18 months, when he was hospitalized for 11 days. He also stayed with his grandmother for over a year at the parents' request, because they were unable to tolerate Peter's behavior. With his grandmother, Peter was toilet trained, ate well, and was not considered a discipline problem. The parents complained that Peter was "spoiled" by his grandmother. Peter now often talks of "being left."

Peter's development was initially delayed as detailed by the following milestones:

> turn over at 10 months
> sit alone at 15 months
> stand alone at 1½ years
> walk at 20 months
> words at 2½ years
> sentences at 3 years

He was also described by his mother as uncoordinated. He could do nothing well, and the parents were irritated whenever he fell. He began speaking at two and a half years; but at age four years, often whispered instead of speaking in a normal volume. Hearing is adequate.

Peter is very dependent on his mother for direction and approval. At the same time, he often protects her, usually from father, and waits on her much as a little mother. He dresses and feeds himself. He craves affection and often gets it from complete strangers.

Interpretation

From this history it is clear that Peter has experienced caretaker change and inconsistency, adult loss of control, ambivalence of feeling toward him, unrealistic expectations, and traumatic separations, any of which might result in a child with emotional problems depending on the child's additional strengths and reactions to these conditions as well as the total affective atmosphere.

Evaluation—Examination

After an adequate history is obtained from any and all sources, confirmation or refutation of initial impressions can be obtained by observing the child in a variety of situations. The developmental testing sessions provide an opportunity to observe the child in a formal, structured setting in which the examiner determines the activity. Also the test results provide a profile of skills and deficiencies in several areas, depending on the tests used.

The Bayley Scales of Infant Development is a test which documents motor, mental, language, and personal-social development for children under three years of age. Many other tests are available and are discussed elsewhere in this and other books. The test results are norms and only a part of the necessary observation data. Formal test results from a variety of sources (psychologist, school, and nursery) can often be utilized, but additional information obtained by observing the child's interactions with people and objects is usually more productive. Informal play sessions provide an opportunity to observe the child in a free-flowing situation in which the child is the initiator of activity, thus providing some access to the child's thoughts and concerns. The interaction between parents (or adults) and child must be noted on every occasion. The following outline is one way of organizing observational and test data.

EVALUATION: EXAMINATION OUTLINE

A. General Observations.
   1. Validate expectations from history—health, appearance, size, outstanding characteristics, and reaction to examination.
B. Motor Skills.
   1. How child uses body—what can child do with body (roll over, sit, stand, walk, run, climb, and skip), unusual movement patterns (rocking and head banging), quality of movement, tempo, confident, awkward, graceful, clumsy, restless, inhibited, free, and smooth.

2. How child uses hands—grasping patterns, eye-hand coordination, hand integration, dominance, abnormal movements, precise, hesitant, fumbling, and over or under-reaching.

C. Adaptive Skills.

1. How child learns and plays—use of objects, sight, concepts (size, color, shape, numbers, and puzzles), imagination, ideas, problem-solving, interest, likes, dislikes, approach to problems, pleasure, frustration, persistence, curiosity, indifference, organization, alternatives, apathy, and impulsivity.

D. Language Skills.

1. How child communicates—what can child say (vocabulary, sounds, phrases, sentences, and appropriateness), what can child understand (identify, actions, and questions), nonverbal communication, hearing, articulation, syntax, and quality of sound.

E. Social Skills.

1. How child views self—wash, dry, dress, safety, rules, imitate, role play, distinguish real and unreal, reaction to body, mouthing, rocking, masturbation, range of feeling for age, how expresses (anger, anxiety, frustration, aggression, pleasure, fear), mood lability, view of self, reaction to feelings, comfort measures, and coping mechanisms (avoidance, submission, and impulsivity).

F. Parental Observations.

1. Parent-child interactions—helpful, intrusive, uninvolved, battles, babies, overwhelms, withdraws, and attitude toward skills.

A SAMPLE EVALUATION EXAMINATION

The following is an observation summary describing pertinent behavior of Peter N., the child previously discussed.

A. General Observations.

Peter was a sturdy, appealing, nearly five-year-old child in dirty, odorous, soiled clothes. He came with his mother, who was well groomed. Peter was obviously very anxious throughout the examination. His anxiety was manifested by chewing his nails, chewing his tongue, grinding his teeth, and masturbating. His anxiety interfered with his ability to function. The only tasks he could do were those concrete, obvious tasks like puzzles, and he attempted them only after checking with his mother and the examiner for permission to do so. He became more anxious at any change of task or position of persons in the room, even though he was prepared for the changes. The examiner could do nothing to decrease Peter's anxiety. This testing is not felt to be an adequate documentation of his capacities because of his overwhelming anxiety. The mother reported his performance to be typical of his functioning and behavior.

B. Motor Skills.

Peter was conspicuous in his gross motor movements. He could not sit still, except for very short periods of time when he was attempting a specific, concrete task. Otherwise, he needed to be in continuous motion, surveying the room and altering his body postures in expectation. When he was able to concentrate on a task, he could perform, although the quality of task completion was poor. Again, his overwhelming anxiety prohibited him from smooth, coordinated, skillful gross motor function. No abnormal movements were noted.

He used his hands relatively well, especially when the task was obvious and he could concentrate without worrying about reactions of the people in the room or the test itself.

C. Adaptive Skills.

As stated earlier, his anxiety completely overwhelmed him and prohibited him from attempting tasks or completing them successfully. He performed best with items that were very concrete and obvious, and these he did with skill and organization. He was also able to imitate tasks and build from models at an appropriate age level. He was unable, however, to complete any of the items reflecting body image and self-awareness as well as interaction with other people. He was obviously concerned about broken and missing body parts. An outstanding characteristic of his performance was his lack of pleasure in any of the tasks completed or attempted. Although he was able to accept help and guidance from the examiner, at no time did he indicate that he expected such help. He was also unable to adapt the formboard, which is often characteristic of constricted, inhibited children.

D. Language Skills.

Peter had many words, but his articulation was poor, and he obviously did not use language or any other method to communicate needs or desires. He heard and comprehended much of what was said to him. During the language test, additional fears and bodily concerns became obvious. His comprehension and use of words was immature.

E. Personal-Social Skills.

Peter was reportedly able to do many self-care tasks. He did not participate in imaginative play or verbalization of his activities and ideas. He also did not know his own sex and displayed a poor image of himself and other people. He was indiscriminately friendly though, at the same time, when approached in any way, he physically recoiled to the touch, no matter how slow, gentle, or anticipated. He hoarded material and food as children who are deprived often do.

Impressions

Peter is a pathetic little nearly five-year-old boy whose past history of frequent changes and inconsistent care has resulted in overwhelming anxiety which prohibits him from appropriately learning and interacting. Although a complete statement cannot be made about his intellectual capacity, because his anxiety prohibits him from performing fully, he does complete several significant items in the adaptive area at an age-appropriate level. Peter exhibits characteristics of deprived, inhibited, constricted children. His overwhelming anxiety, bodily concern, poor self-image, and inappropriate relationships indicate the beginnings of a severely disturbed child.

Alerting Patterns of Behavior

There are currently no agreed upon criteria which, if present, justify the diagnoses of emotional abuse or neglect. The most common definitions, however, usually include delayed or deviant development secondary to a noxious environment as experienced by the child. Emotional abuse or neglect can be identified by a variety of combinations of behaviors, depending on the particular child and the predominant modes of abusive interaction. Some behaviors and personality characteristics occurring in emotionally-abused children include: impulsivity; loss of control; extreme lability of mood; inappropriate independence and dependence; lack of acknowledgement of pain or pleasure; constriction and inhibition of thought, action, or affect; and immobilizing anxiety.

The general effect of either emotional abuse or neglect is to divert energies required for learning and development to the continual struggle of maintaining a sense of self, however deviant or inadequate. An adequate environment provides enough stability and predictability to permit a child to feel comfortable at exploring his world and enough variety so that learning occurs from such exploration. A child who is worried about himself or what will happen to him next, for whatever reason, is not free to learn from his environment or develop normally.

Pitfalls

There are three major pitfalls in evaluating and planning for children who have been abused. The first major pitfall is making decisions with insufficient data, as well as not making decisions when sufficient data exists. The second major pitfall occurs when priorities are not considered. For example, in considering placement for a child, the status of his attachments should influence the placement more than any developmental delays. It is often better to experience inadequate attachments than none at all. Attachment status should also influence therapy decisions. The third major pitfall occurs when long-range goals are forfeited in favor of temporary solutions. Detrimental neglect and emotional abuse are chronic problems, and immediate solutions are unrealistic.

Court Testimony

In court, the child development specialist must clearly present the child's present status, the etiology of developmental or emotional deviations, the future needs of the child, and the most appropriate environment in which those needs can be met. Before appearing in court, the child development specialist must reach a decision about what would be best for the child. For this judgment to be meaningful, adequate information must have been gathered.

The following are my personal guidelines for considering removal of a child from his parents for emotional abuse or neglect. Physical safety is discussed elsewhere in this book.

1. The child's development must be adversely affected by his present environment. If the child is developing adequately and his life is not in danger, then he should not be removed.

2. All available community resources must have been tried and failed. An appropriate time limit (six months or less) is essential. If a mother takes several years to convince a judge she cannot be an adequate mother, even with all known help provided, then that is too long for the child to be in limbo regarding his future. Community resources must be effective within a reasonable period of time.

3. The child's present environment must be more detrimental to him than several foster home changes. It must be kept in mind that the current system of foster care often results in three or more placement changes before final decisions are made regarding home versus termination of parental rights. The system of intervention must not make the problem worse. Therefore, removal of a child from his home should be done with caution. The child's meaningful attachments must be preserved and enhanced. If the child will eventually be returned to the care of his parents, then that attachment must be encouraged, not discouraged.

Summary

Development is complicated. Whatever happens to a child, either physically or emotionally, affects that development. Developmental problems are the result of many interdependent factors, and there are no easy solutions. Considering meaningful attachments in all long-range planning is most helpful in assisting abused and neglected children.

Acknowledgment

I wish to thank my teacher, Dr. Sally Provence, for her knowledge, ideas, interest, and concern.

Developmental Evaluation Checklist

A. Historical Data.
    1. medical history.
    2. parental history.
    3. child care practices.
    4. developmental history.
    5. school history.
B. Developmental Data.
    1. motor skills.
    2. adaptive skills.
    3. language skills.
    4. social skills.
    5. personal skills.
C. Conclusion—Emotional Status.
    1. attachments.
    2. separations.
    3. object constancy.
    4. independence.
    5. identification.
    6. self-image.
    7. coping mechanisms.
    8. affect.
    9. anxiety.
D. Etiology of Conclusions.
E. Plans.
    1. acute.
    2. long term.

Sample Developmental Evaluation

Name: Jeffrey C.
Birth Date: 12/7/72
Date of Exam: 2/7/75

#1946
Age: 2 years 2 months (26 months)
Examiner: P. Boggess, M.D.

Jeffrey was referred for developmental evaluation by Mrs. Carol W., social worker for the Department of Welfare, because of his poor growth and general developmental delay. The evaluation consisted of history from the social worker and foster mother, physical examination, developmental testing, and observation in the clinic and foster home.

PERTINENT HISTORY

Jeffrey is the fifth child born to Mr. and Mrs. C. She had one prenatal visit and delivered Jeffrey at home at 36 weeks gestation. He weighed three pounds and one ounce at birth and had a stormy neonatal course. He was discharged from the hospital at three months of age and was readmitted in two weeks in a moribund, dehydrated state. Diagnoses at that time included severe failure to thrive and neglect. He continued to grow poorly after release from the hospital and was placed in foster care at the age of eight months. He remained in foster care for one year and did well in all areas of development. In the care of his parents the last six months, he has not grown or developed.

PHYSICAL EXAMINATION

Jeffrey appeared in the emergency room on 2/1/75 as a pathetic, malnourished waif with numerous bruises, in various stages of healing, over his face and body. He was indiscriminately friendly, preoccupied with food, and unable to tolerate any stress.

DESCRIPTION AND ADJUSTMENT TO THE EXAMINATION

Jeffrey was a thin, sad looking, malnourished little boy with no means of coping with even minor stress. He was accompanied to the testing session by his foster mother of eight days, but he showed no attachment to her.

TEST RESULTS

Jeffrey was unable to participate formally in the tests. He attempted several tasks, but, after the candy pellets were presented, he could not be diverted to any other activity. He ate voraciously anything in his immediate vicinity, as he had done in the previous clinic visit. The following are some additional observations.

Gross motor development.   Jeffrey could walk and climb, but the quality was poor. He had a wide-based gait but no persistent primitive reflexes. He used his body only to find food or for other independent activity. He was, for the most part, lethargic and immobilized under stress of any sort.

Fine motor development.   He used his hands well, especially to obtain food. He was not interested in other tasks. No unusual movements were noted.

Adaptive development.   Jeffrey's interest in test items was limited to food items. He did exhibit firm object permanence and good memory and ingenuity in obtaining food. However, when thwarted in his attempts to get food, he had no means of handling stress and literally disintegrated. In fact, he would have fallen off the chair if he had not been caught by the examiner. Though his intellectual potential cannot be determined at this time, he did demonstrate ability to learn and imitate at age level.

Language development.   Jeffrey did poorly in this area. He understood much of what was said to him but said only a few words. All the words he did say pertained to needs, especially those involving food. He communicated wants by pointing and was interested in communicating only his need for food. Hearing was intact.

Personal-social development.   Jeffrey did poorly in this area. He exhibited indiscriminate friendliness and excessive independence regarding basic needs. He hoarded materials, especially food. He had no awareness of his own body image, and, as stated earlier, he disintegrated both emotionally and physically under any stress.

IMPRESSIONS

Jeffrey is a two-year-old boy who is severely deprived both emotionally and physically. His failure to thrive is secondary to maternal neglect and inappropriate mother-child interaction. Development in all areas is delayed, again secondarily to inadequate environment. His personality development is especially deviant.

RECOMMENDATIONS

Jeffrey is in desperate need of a long-term, nurturing, emotionally-invested environment which can also provide appropriate stimulation. He has survived several traumas, but he has no reserve. All his energy is currently directed toward survival. Without a great deal of assistance, he may lose even that battle.

DEVELOPMENTAL SPECIALIST'S EVALUATION CONDENSED INTO PROBLEM-ORIENTED FORMAT

1. Developmental delay
—delays in all areas, but most seriously in speech
Recommendation: environmental stimulation program
2. Emotional problems
—indiscriminately friendly
—preoccupied with food
—immobilized by any stress
Recommendations: 1. foster placement in nurturing environment
2. adoption as soon as possible

References

Bowlby, J. (1966): *Maternal Care and Mental Health.* Schocken Books, New York.

Bowlby, J. (1969): *Attachment and Loss, Vol. I: Attachment.* Basic Books, Inc., New York.

Fraiberg, S. (1959): *The Magic Years.* Charles Scribner's Sons, New York.

Frankenburg, W. and Camp, B. (1975): *Pediatric Screening Tests.* Charles C. Thomas, Springfield, Ill.

Goldstein, J., Freud, A., and Solnit, A. J. (1973): *Beyond the Best Interests of the Child.* The Free Press, New York–London.

Mahler, M., Pine, F., and Bergman, A. (1975): *The Psychological Birth of the Human Infant.* Basic Books, Inc., New York.

Martin, H. P. (1976): *The Abused Child: A Multidisciplinary Approach to Developmental Issues and Treatment.* Ballinger, Cambridge, Mass.

Provence, S. and Lipton, R. (1962): *Infants in Institutions.* International Universities Press, Inc., New York.

12

The Law Enforcement's Role in Evaluation

Harlan R. Bockman and Claudia A. Carroll

The role of law enforcement in child abuse should be seen as part of the total community approach to this problem. Like other community agencies, the police and the district attorney are interested in protecting the child and improving family functioning.

Police Functions

The police department is frequently one of the initial agencies to come in contact with child abuse cases. In all fifty states, by law, the police have some role in the investigation of alleged child abuse or neglect cases. The role of law enforcement agencies must be carefully thought out. Some children are in real danger and require immediate, assertive intervention by the police. The majority of children, however, are relatively safe and it is critical that the police deal with all parents in a nonthreatening manner so that they come through this initial experience receptive to therapy rather than hostile to future agency contacts.

Because child abuse involves a highly specialized area of investigation, it is strongly suggested that each police agency have specially trained officers who are familiar with both the psychology of child abuse and the procedures involved in reporting it. This training should be multidisciplinary in nature so that police have a broad perspective on this complex family problem. On-going training and consultation are also essential for effective handling of these cases. Law enforcement officers should be well aware of the other agencies in the community which can be called upon to provide services to the family. Each officer should have a phone referral list of agencies that can help in times of crisis (county protective service unit on-call workers, hospital child protection team consultants, emergency receiving homes, crisis nurseries, etc.).

A viable communication system and working agreement between the law enforcement agency and the Department of Social Services should be established and maintained. There must be a clear definition of roles and responsibilities and consistent interpretation of the law within the identified community. This communication system and working agreement should be in writing. There should be liaison people identified within each system. Open communication between the police and the Department of Social Services usually brings about the best resolution of the case for the family. For instance, if the police know from the Department of Social Services that a family is responding to treatment, they may be more inclined to recommend that criminal action be dropped or deferred. By contrast, if the parents are unwilling to use treatment services, criminal action may be necessary.

Among the guidelines and written agreements between the law enforcement agency and the Department of Social Services, an important one should be the delineation of in which cases the police will be involved in initial investigation and in which cases this is not necessary. In our experience the police do not need to be involved in all cases of child abuse. Cases of minor injury and where the parents are motivated for treatment are examples of such situations. However, with abuse of a more serious nature (e.g., death, life-threatening injuries, sexual abuse, and repeated abuse), the police and child protection worker need to be involved in investigation concurrently.

In the early stages of an investigation the main decision the law enforcement officer may have to make is whether or not to remove the child from the family and place the child in protective custody. If the police officer has a working relationship with the protective services worker and the Department of Social Services, this important decision should be a joint one. Whenever possible, when police are called to assist a social worker (e.g., removal of a child from the home or accompanying the social worker on a potentially explosive situation), this should be done with a "low-profile." This includes the use of unmarked cars, nonuniformed officers, and specially trained officers.

A communication system was developed between the Social Service Department and the law enforcement agencies at Adams County, Colorado, that proved to be helpful. Selected reports of nonserious child abuse were sent to the police department labeled "for information only." If the police, upon receipt of a "for information only" report, felt comfortable that no police intervention was necessary, they did not contact the family.

If, on the other hand, the police felt uncomfortable in not participating in the investigation, a police officer would contact the social worker, request additional information on the case, and then decide if police investigation was needed. Another helpful system was sending a feedback report from the Social Services Department to the law enforcement officer who made the initial report to social services. Often the law enforcement officers felt they did not know what happened when they made referrals to the department. To alleviate that, a form was developed which simply stated the name of the family, the date received, the name of the assigned worker, the name of the supervisor, the worker's phone number, and what action was taken. In this way the police officer knew that the referral had been received and that something had been done. Often relations among agencies can be greatly improved by such communication techniques.

In cases where criminal action is anticipated (e.g., third party abuse), the police should always be involved from the earliest moment possible. The police are the agency designated to collect the evidence necessary to establish a criminal case in court. The police crime lab should obtain pictures of both the crime scene and the injuries. Photographic evidence is often very important in the courtroom. Law enforcement officers are also more experienced in the collection and preservation of the physical evidence which may establish the abuse. Further, the police have the ability to obtain search warrants when necessary to collect physical evidence which might otherwise be lost.

Office of the District Attorney

A county-wide plan for law enforcement involvement in child abuse cases should be sanctioned and promoted by the district attorney's office. With many different law enforcement agencies in each county, it is helpful for the district attorney to serve as a coordinating body for legal procedures regarding child abuse. Optimally, this office would also be involved in helping to define the appropriate roles of police officers and child protection workers in the initial investigation of these cases. The prosecuting district attorney has the authority to file the suspected abuse case as a criminal abuse case and/or as a civil dependency and neglect case. The prosecuting attorney's office, therefore, is the coordinating agency which should receive all the reports from both law enforcement and the Department of Social Services and is in a position to make the appropriate filings. Further, it should be the responsibility of his office to promote liaison between the other two agencies. The prosecuting attorney's decision to file either a criminal or civil case should be controlled by the following factors: (1) the severity of the injury, (2) the ability to prove an actual abuse case, (3) the attitude and conduct of the parents, and (4) whether the parent(s) is amenable to assistance.

We have frequently seen the effectiveness of using the juvenile court action in preference to the criminal action, and would suggest this approach in most cases of child abuse. This stems from the differential purposes of each action. The purpose of a juvenile court or civil action is protection of the child; the purpose of criminal court is the punishment of the perpetrator.

Finally, it is most helpful in our experience for the district attorney's office to have a representative sit on the county multidisciplinary team. This not only enhances communication between the law enforcement and the other community agencies, but also improves the effectiveness of managing the more difficult cases.

13

The Coordinator's Role in Evaluation

Candace A. Grosz and Marilyn R. Lenherr

The Coordinator's Goals

Three major goals outline the coordinator's responsibilities in the assessment phase. First, the coordinator aids in gathering information for the team's diagnosis and evaluation process, insuring that a complete data base is collected for each family. Second, she provides consultation and support to others in the community who are requesting aid in case management for abusive and neglectful families. Third, she plans the dispositional conference so that it will be an effective and worthwhile meeting.

DIAGNOSIS AND EVALUATION DUTIES

1. *Arrange evaluations.* When the coordinator receives the initial referral, she immediately contacts the physician and the social worker to initiate their evaluations. She clarifies the availability of the family for interviews and, when necessary, helps to arrange appointments for the physician and the social worker to see them. If the case is an unusual accident, she makes certain the physician is involved first. If he concludes that the injury is accidental, the team social worker is spared an evaluation.

2. *Gather information.* The coordinator supplements information from the pediatrician and the social worker who have interviewed the family directly by contacting other related agencies, including previous medical resources such as clinics, hospitals, private physicians, and visiting nurses.

153

Primary questions include: Has the child experienced past injuries? What was the history of the injury, the date, and the treatment received? Were there any suspicions about the circumstances of the past injury? A record of well child care, acute illnesses, chronic medical conditions, and growth and development parameters is also obtained.

Since this medical information is frequently confidential, a good approach for a coordinator to use to obtain it is to explain that another hospital or physician is currently treating the child. If someone is reluctant to share the information, an offer can be made to obtain a release of information. Or, the information can be subpoenaed if medical records will check to see whether the child has been there or if they have available any information worth subpoenaing. Another approach is to develop some trust and rapport with a contact person at the primary medical resources in the area who will locate the information and share it verbally. Then, if any of the data seems important, it can be subpoenaed. When these resources begin to know that the coordinator is seeking the information in the child's best interests, the reluctance to share information is usually diminished.

Many state laws are also making provisions to aid in easier information gathering in cases of suspected child abuse and neglect. Telephone contacts should also be made with the Central Registry for Child Abuse, the county Department of Social Services where the family lives or has previously lived, the police, or other agencies who have recently been involved. Inquiry should include the nature of the involvement, assessment of the family's functioning, concerns for neglect or abuse, and the services the agency can provide the family. When making calls to county Departments of Social Services, it is helpful to clarify the specific interest of open or closed financial, family service, or child welfare records. For checking records, it is important to have available parents' names, children's names, and names by previous marriage. A contact person such as a protective services secretary, intake worker, or supervisor for each county frequently called is helpful because it can be difficult to elicit detailed information from the general records department.

3. *Report suspected abuse and neglect.* When it is determined that the injury is nonaccidental, a call is placed immediately to the county Department of Social Services or other agencies designated to receive these reports. Reporting a case of suspected child abuse and neglect can be difficult. Again, it is most helpful to develop a key person, such as an intake worker or supervisor, in each agency to decrease anxiety about reporting cases and improve cooperation and service between agencies.

Common anxieties about reporting seem to focus on a wish to avoid an angry reaction from the parents, the fear that reporting will only cause more stress rather than offer support for the family, and the reluctance to lose control of the case by turning it over to others. Increasing the predictability of the response following reporting helps decrease anxieties and promotes the development of trust and cooperation between agencies.

The coordinator also needs to be certain that the physician completes and signs an official, typed medical report. It is usually mailed to the county Department of Social Services within 48 hours of the child's medical evaluation, unless the report is needed for immediate court action.

4. *Schedule special tests.* The coordinator may need to schedule appointments for family members with psychiatry, psychology, specialty physicians, or for laboratory work and X-rays. Some cases will also require photographs by police photographers for court documentation or medical photographers for teaching purposes. Polaroid® pictures may be taken to have a quick reference and to enable team members to view the injuries. The coordinator needs to be able to expedite these procedures by knowing when parental consent is required according to the state law and how all the necessary consultations can be completed without conflicts.

It is advisable to prepare the personnel in the area, such as nurses, foster grandparents, ward clerks, or other physicians, that photographs will be taken and to explain the need and use for pictures. Preparation should also include explaining the procedure to the child. When state law does not require parents' consent, it is much easier to arrange that the photographs be taken when the parents are not present; however, the parents should be advised that they have been taken and that they may possibly be used in court. It is important to insure that the parents receive careful explanation regarding consultations, medical procedures, and hospital policies, and clear communication of appointment times and locations.

5. *Provide liaison with hospital staff.* If the child is hospitalized, it is important to keep physicians, nurses, and ward clerks informed of any change in status, for example, when a police hold is obtained, the projected date for discharge, whether the child will be going home or to foster placement, specific recommendations for the family, and the current cooperation and emotional status of the parents. It is also important to notify the admissions or billing office if there is a change in financial responsibility, such as the placement of a child in the custody of the county Department of Social Services.

When a child does not require hospitalization for medical treatment, the coordinator attempts to expedite placement in a receiving home as soon as possible to shorten or avoid hospitalization. When foster home plans are finalized, the coordinator facilitates placement by making arrangements between county workers and the hospital staff regarding discharge time and procedures.

It is usually necessary for the foster parents, case aide, or social worker picking up the child for discharge to have proper identification as well as clarification that the Department of Social Services does have the authority to place the child and that he can be discharged to the designated person. A clearance for release frequently can be a letter on the department's letterhead to indicate the date and provisions of voluntary placement or court action.

Care should be taken to clarify who will prepare the child for foster placement, that is, a social worker or nurse, since this can be easily overlooked. The coordinator also keeps hospital staff informed of times and places of any court hearings at which they may be needed to testify. This includes negotiation with attorneys regarding who needs to testify, when written reports can be submitted to the court record, and arrangements for the possible witnesses to be on call and available within short periods or make appointments to testify to avoid prolonged waiting in court.

Frequently, this liaison work will require extra time to help hospital staff understand the dynamics and actions of parents and children involved in child abuse and neglect. It is important that all hospital staff, not just professionals, be given the chance to receive education in this area. Frequently, the most meaningful orientation and education comes with case-by-case teaching on a one-to-one basis.

The coordinator often aids protective service workers and visiting nurses by helping them contact physicians or others who have cared for a family. In a large medical facility, it is hard for a community person to determine the appropriate person to call, to reach a specific busy physician, or to contact the appropriate clinic. The coordinator can support direct services, assist continuity of medical care for the family, and ease the frustrations for the community workers by checking hospital records for recommendations and helping protective service workers and visiting nurses contact hospital staff.

When the police or a social worker brings a child to the clinic for medical documentation of physical abuse, the coordinator can expedite the process by helping them understand and anticipate the procedures—such as, explaining what information to have available, who is needed to provide treatment consent, how to obtain a clinic card, where to check in, and when to expect a written report.

6. *Keep child protection team records up to date.* The major focus is to implement a system that can be efficient and facilitate the follow-up process. Our system includes a card file for quick reference, a data sheet for yearly statistics (Table 2), and an individual family file. The family file includes a face sheet, and an intake data base checklist to show the dates certain actions were completed by the physician, social worker, and coordinator (see Appendix A1). A problem-oriented team report, social history, psychiatric evaluations, on-going brief notes regarding the current status, and follow-up sheets are also included in the family file. A separate card file divided by months helps to order the follow-up system and shows which cases need review each month (see chapter 25).

CONSULTATION TO OTHERS IN THE COMMUNITY

Many calls are received from private doctors, visiting nurses, school personnel, or social workers requesting guidance in case management. These are cases where the hospital child protection team may not be involved with the family directly, but where consultation is needed by those providing direct service. Calls are also received from relatives and neighbors who are concerned for a family.

1. *Suspected cases.* If a child has received injuries, the coordinator can arrange for the child to be brought immediately to a hospital or clinic for medical evaluation and possible reporting. This would require that another person (e.g., a nurse, social worker, or teacher) accompany the child and his parents to the clinic to insure that the child is brought in. While it is not necessary at this point for the community person to tell the parents that abuse or neglect is suspected, it is important that the parent know the child is being taken in for medical evaluation and for them to participate in the evaluation when possible. If the parents cannot accompany the child to the clinic, the person bringing the child in must have the legal authority to do so or the consent of the parents (usually written). Schools and day care centers may require this consent when the child is enrolled.

The physician will usually need to ask the parents certain questions about the injury in order to reach conclusions about the diagnosis. The child may need to be hospitalized for further evaluation, and the reporting process can be explained. When a child does not require hospitalization, a protective service worker is called to come to the clinic and initiate the evaluation with the family. The community protective service worker can then evaluate the safety of the home and the possible need for temporary placement of the child in a receiving home.

2. *Potential cases.* When it is not known if the child has received injuries, or when there is concern regarding the potential for child abuse and neglect, it is best to obtain the identifying information and a summary of the current situation from the community person without asking them to call someone else. Then, the coordinator can call the appropriate community resource and make the referral or report for the community person. This course of action is recommended to show support for the community person making the referral and to eliminate as much red tape as possible for them. In this way, the community person is encouraged to report other cases, and the report goes to the appropriate person more quickly. If the community person is faced with road blocks or red tape in making this call, he may frequently choose not to report cases. Common rationalizations for not reporting an injury can include that the injury seems minor or that the community person can work with the parents on his own. In this case, it is important to help the community person consider his own limits in time, skills, and emotions and compare those limits with the probably great needs in many problem areas of the family. It can also be important to document minor, repeated injuries which can become more serious.

Anxieties can also prohibit reporting and include concerns such as: What will the family's reaction be? Will I have to testify in court? Do I still need to report if I'm not sure it is child abuse? Will the child be removed from his home? What will happen to the other children in the family?

When the coordinator can offer reporting service to others in the community and make reporting an easier process, cases are usually reported at an earlier stage, perhaps sparing some children more serious injuries or permanent damage.

It is important to explain the coordinator's tentative plan to the community person making the referral. After the coordinator has made the referral, she should then let the community person know the name of the person who will be responding and what specific action is planned. In most cases of this type, all appropriate services may be already in effect, and the coordinator may need to listen and share the worry about the situation with the community worker and offer him encouragement.

3. *Self-referrals.* Parents may call at a time of personal crisis to ask for services. The goals in managing these cases are to offer support and arrange for someone to contact the family directly and assess the situation. Usually, this requires patience, and, often, an extended phone call with the parent to offer reassurance and develop enough rapport and trust so that the parent will share his name, address, and telephone number. The coordinator then calls the appropriate agency to arrange an immediate home visit by a social worker. It is important to share with the parent that a social worker will be requested to see them immediately. Specific approaches and interviewing techniques to facilitate this process are outlined in chapter 8, *"Social Worker's Evaluation."*

PREPARATION FOR THE DISPOSITIONAL CONFERENCE

1. *Contact participants for each family to be discussed.* All persons who are currently involved, as well as those who will be receiving referrals for future involvement with the family, should be contacted to attend the dispositional conference. If someone cannot attend this meeting, the coordinator should, nevertheless, contact the person, obtain information about his involvement with the family, share with him the tentative recommendations, and identify his questions for discussion.

Persons who cannot attend this meeting because of distance can be included in the discussion with the use of a speaker-phone—an attachment to the microphone and speaker of a regular dial phone which allows the person not attending the meeting to hear the discussion and to be heard by the team. (Cost of installation is approximately $33.00 with an additional charge of approximately $9.00 per month.) To facilitate smooth utilization of a speaker phone, a preliminary call should be made to the person who will not be attending the meeting to arrange the call and summarize the discussion anticipated at the meeting. This preliminary call is also helpful because it enables the coordinator to better anticipate the reactions of this person and facilitate the conference call. At the beginning of the speaker-phone call, it is important to introduce the person not attending and those who are present, going around the table giving names, professions, and involvement with the family. It is effective to pause after each presentation or at various times throughout the discussion to allow the person not at the meeting to ask questions and make comments regarding his position on various issues, since it may be difficult for him to feel comfortable when interrupting the discussion. The speaker-phone is not recommended as a substitute for having people meet together personally. It is, however, particularly useful when someone is at a great distance, has a tight schedule, or is needed for a case that is going to be reviewed only briefly. For review with workers in another community, it can be prearranged for several people to be on extension phones, and, thereby, they can all contribute to the discussion.

2. *Prepare problem-oriented team report.* Prior to the meeting, the coordinator prepares the typewritten, problem-oriented team report. She completes this report by listing diagnostic impressions and team recommendations for each of the persons who have performed a direct evaluation.

3. *Bring pertinent materials.* The coordinator needs to anticipate and have available all the materials the team will need to adequately discuss the case. These include: case records, hospital charts, photographs, X-rays, and information about previous medical care or services provided to the family.

4. *Share team's decisions and evaluation information.* Following the dispositional conference, the coordinator revises the problem-oriented team report and mails it, with evaluation reports from the physician, social worker and others, to persons providing ongoing service—usually county social service workers, visiting nurses, private physicians, or mental health workers. If the juvenile court is involved, it is also helpful to send a copy to the county attorney for the Department of Social Services and the guardian *ad litem.* Confidentiality does not have to be a major concern in child abuse cases, since many state laws provide for sharing of information in these cases. While consideration is needed for family privacy, the main foci are to provide protection for the child and integrated treatment services for the family. These objectives require sharing team diagnosis and recommendations. The coordinator should also inform the person providing the data for the report (i.e., pediatrician, psychiatrist, or social worker) of its distribution.

5. *Schedule team recommendations.* Frequently, follow-up appointments are needed for health care, psychiatric or developmental problem evaluations, or both. The coordinator helps to schedule these and implement other treatment services. Calls are made within two or three weeks following the dispositional conference to determine if services are being provided and if the diagnostic information has been received. Subsequent follow-up calls are made on high risk or serious cases, according to the particular case needs (see chapter 25).

Qualifications of a Coordinator

Qualifications that prepare a coordinator for his or her role in evaluation and treatment tasks can be considered in four areas. These qualifications are pertinent regardless of the coordinator's base—that is, hospital, community, or agency.

EDUCATION

A degree in behavioral sciences is preferred, with majors of social work, psychology, sociology, or family/child development. This should also be supplemented with education in the specific area of child abuse and neglect, which is an area not usually included in routine college courses. The additional training can be gained by involvement in continuing education classes, specialized workshops or seminars, directed reading, and use of specific audio-visual materials.

WORK EXPERIENCE

Direct services to families such as protective services are a primary desired experience. Also pertinent are jobs in other settings such as hospitals, day care centers, residential treatment centers, private family service agencies, schools, or mental health clinics. Many kinds of work with parents and children can provide benefits to a child protection team coordinator. The primary focus should be direct exposure to the dynamics of both normal and abnormal family life.

Public relations work and experience in communication, both speaking and writing, are experiences that increase the coordinator's effectiveness. Persons coming to the job with deficits in previous experiences should receive a comprehensive orientation to broaden their experience base. This can include direct observation of social work interviews, medical examinations, psychiatric evaluations, and court hearings, as well as accompanying intake workers, lay therapists, or visiting nurses on home visits or providing ongoing supportive services to a family.

KNOWLEDGE OF THE COMMUNITY

Personal knowledge of specific resources within the community for social, legal, psychiatric, and health care services are particularly helpful. When making referrals, the coordinator needs to know intake procedures, quality and types of services provided, response of agencies to requests for services, provisions of the state law, and resources for specific needs, such as emergency child care, transportation, or financial assistance. This awareness is best provided by work experience in a particular community.

Knowledge of the general functioning and interrelationships of systems in the community, such as social services, juvenile, district and criminal court, hospital and health care, in-patient psychiatric treatment, and law enforcement, are also needed. Experience in another community can be beneficial, since the basic structure of these agencies is generally similar. One way to update and supplement knowledge of the community is to schedule on-site visits to pertinent agencies and build rapport with the many people the coordinator will need to routinely deal with by phone.

PUBLIC RELATIONS SKILLS AND ATTITUDES

The coordinator must be able to confidently refer families for a wide range of services in the community. She must be able to contact the person who can do the job appropriately, relate the pertinent information and facts concisely and accurately, and clearly outline the services requested.

The many demands of her job require that she continually reassess priorities to balance job responsibilities. On very busy days, it can seem that reassessment needs to be done every few minutes. She also must be able to flexibly respond to other's demands as they require her attention, rather than as she would like to set her own schedule. One of the primary values of having a person identified as coordinator is to have that person available for consultation or immediate help in case management.

Flexibility also extends to skills in responding to various individuals on many different levels, including a demanding professional, an upset and overwhelmed parent, or a routine information seeker. This flexibility requires good skills to organize and keep track of the many loose ends of varied activities.

The need to respond to others, both professionals and families, requires management of an uneven work flow—that is, demands may be exceedingly heavy or light. The coordinator needs to be able to push herself when the work is slow and catch up for the next busy time. The nature of the job is primarily that of an ongoing process, so she must be able to find rewards in her ability to control the process rather than having expectations of completing tasks. During days when a great majority of time is spent talking with people in person or on the phone, the coordinator may feel that little is accomplished. A different perspective is needed to reemphasize the value of this type of consultative work.

A delicate balance is required between operating either dependently or independently. The coordinator must be able to make decisions and take action immediately in many situations. She must also constructively and appropriately use consultation from other team members. She is not effective if she must check with someone each time or if she consistently acts with no consideration of the repercussions for others.

On an emotional level, she must have resolved her own personal feelings towards parents who inflict injuries upon their children if she is to cope effectively with the angry feelings parents may direct at her during the intervention phase. In addition, other professionals may at times displace their anger to her or criticize her. She, as well as others, must be able to discern inappropriate criticism, understand the underlying dynamics, and not be personally devastated. Some situations require that she be quite assertive and directly address issues even at the risk of provoking anger in others, both professionals and parents.

SUMMARY

Education, work experience, community knowledge, public relations skills, and attitudes come together to help create some of the essential qualities for an effective coordinator. She must have a good reality base for child abuse and neglect which includes: a sense of what is needed for adequate protection; what needs immediate action; the response of parents, children and agencies; and how to initiate effective intervention. The coordinator must be a person who is not seeking a job with a large amount of patient (parent or child) contact. Her primary role in contacts with families is as an informational resource, not as a lay therapist or social worker. This is needed to prevent other job tasks from getting squeezed out and neglected. She can participate in a limited number of training activities or provide therapy to one or two families as a means of preventing the emotional drain that can come with this job, building in more rewards, and gaining a wider experience base.

TABLE 1. *Diagnostic Tasks of the Coordinator*

A. Diagnosis and evaluation duties.
   1. —arrange evaluations.
   2. —gather information.
   3. —report suspected abuse and neglect.
   4. —schedule special tests.
   5. —provide liaison with hospital staff.
   6. —keep child protection team records up to date.
B. Consultation to others in the community.
   1. —arrange immediate medical evaluation if child has injuries.
   2. —arrange immediate social work home visit for potential cases and self-referrals.
C. Preparation for dispositional conference.
   1. —contact participants for each family to be discussed.
   2. —prepare problem-oriented team report.
   3. —share team's decisions and evaluation information.
   4. —schedule team recommendations.

TABLE 2. *Intake Statistics for Annual Report*

CHILD PROTECTION TEAM
Colorado General Hospital
INTAKE STATISTICS FOR ANNUAL REPORT

NAME	AGE	DATE	COUNTY	REF BY: Self	CGH staff	Police	Social Service	Other	SEEN IN: CCC	Ward	Consult	Chart Review	INJ: Potential

Neglect	Accidental	FTT	Bruise	Burn	Fx	Subdural	Sexual	Other	PERPETRATOR:	Mother	Father	Boyfriend	Stepfather	Other	Unknown	EVAL.: Pediatric	Soc. Wk. CPT	Soc. Wk. CGH	Psych: Mother	Psych: Father	Psych: Child	Psych: Other	Developmental	CWS-59	Police Hold-CGH	P.H. in effect	Filed in Court	HOSPITAL-3 days	4-7 days	more than 7 days

continued

TABLE 2. *(continued)*

CHILD PROTECTION TEAM
Colorado General Hospital
INTAKE STATISTICS FOR ANNUAL REPORT

NAME	AGE	DISPOS.-home	Foster Care-Vol.	Foster Care-Ct.	Other	REF: Ch. Welfare	VNS	REC: Termin.	REV: F-U #1	Follow-up #2	Follow-up #3	No review ind.	Financial asst.	Cards made	Info. complete

PART III

Child Protection Team Conferences

14

Ground Rules for Effective Team Conferences

Barton D. Schmitt and Candace A. Grosz

The Multidisciplinary Team Conference

The most critical component of team functioning is the multidisciplinary team conference. The professionals who have actually evaluated the family are present, such as the hospital social worker, the protective service worker, the pediatrician, and the public health nurse. Also present are the consultants who make up the permanent diagnostic consultation team; and these may include: a pediatrician, psychiatrist, psychologist, and lawyer. At the multidisciplinary team conference, the individual professionals pool their knowledge and understanding of a given family. They attempt to assimilate and analyze all of their data. Finally an accurate picture of the family's strengths and weaknesses comes into focus. At this point a reasonable treatment plan can be designed.

The multidisciplinary team conference requires ground rules if it is to be productive and efficient. The guidelines in this chapter can be written down and enforced, because they occur at an intellectual level. In contrast, the guidelines found in chapter 17 relate more to attitudes and, in general, cannot be enforced so easily. The following 24 ground rules help to bring about a meaningful multidisciplinary team conference.

GROUND RULES FOR TEAM CONFERENCES

1. *Hold regular conferences.* Teams should meet on a scheduled basis so that the meeting time becomes built into the members' schedules. Most

169

teams meet weekly. It is much easier to cancel an occasional meeting if it is not needed than to schedule each conference separately.

2. *Discuss all cases.* It is important to expose members of all disciplines to the full spectrum of child abuse and normal accidents. The more cases that are discussed, the more accurate and efficient the team becomes. It is extremely important that cases of reabuse or death are fully discussed, much as one would insist upon a medical inquest.

3. *Have all team members present.* This is important for two reasons. First, each member then has input into the final decisions. Second, it prevents an absent member from later vetoing the team's decision. This is especially important in terms of having the juvenile court's attorney present, so that he fully understands the reasons for seeking court action. However, the team must be able to move ahead with recommendations if members are absent.

4. *Have presenters come fully prepared.* Before the meeting, all participants should have collected a complete data base in their area. Also, prior to the meeting, each should have thoroughly analyzed their data and made as many decisions as possible. Ideally, each participant should already have met with his supervisor. Making up one's mind in advance about the existing problems and tentative recommendations allows for more in-depth team discussion.

5. *Have agency representatives come with decision-making power.* The person who attends the meeting must have the power to agree or disagree with team decisions without checking with his supervisor. An agency person not present at the meeting should not have veto power over the consensus recommendations.

6. *Appoint team leader to enforce 7–24.* Every team needs a leader or moderator to be in charge of case management discussion, pacing the meeting, and keeping to the time schedule. The team leader should also foster an informal, democratic atmosphere with free give-and-take discussion.

7. *Conference time limit—two-hour maximum.* By two hours everyone is exhausted. The meeting must have an agenda and a time table so that it stays on schedule. The team leader should adjourn the conference early whenever possible.

8. *Case time limit—30-minute maximum.* It is very important to stay within the time deadline for individual cases, so that all members are still present when the final decisions on that case are made. Complicated cases take 20 to 30 minutes to review. These time limits are usually difficult to adhere to without implementation of the problem-oriented record (see chapter 15).

9. *Formal presentation time limit—three-minute maximum.* Most of the case time should be reserved for open discussion. All formal presentation, both medical and social, should be precise and prepared in advance. It should concentrate on pertinent findings, current problems, tentative recommendations, and available treatment resources. Usually, the medical pre-

sentation can be limited to two minutes, describing the medical findings and how they allegedly occurred. The social work and psychiatric presentations may require four minutes; but these presentations should stay with a capsule view of the personalities, and these individuals should be told of the time limit in advance of the conference. Distillation of essential data is usually more important for social workers and psychiatrists who frequently have volumes of materials and anecdotes that could be presented on each family.

10. *Start on time and stay on schedule.* The meeting that starts late is unlikely to ever catch up. If a time schedule is adhered to, direct service workers can attend the portion of the meeting discussing their particular family without being kept waiting unduly.

11. *Present the evaluation in a logical sequence.* It is helpful to develop a basic sequence for presenting each case. Our usual sequence is medical diagnostic information, information from the reporting source (for example, public health nurse, police, or teacher), social work information, psychiatric information, and then other agencies involved with a particular family. This sequence can be modified when it is not appropriate for a specific case.

12. *Utilize the problem-oriented record (POR) format.* This subject is fully discussed in chapter 15. It involves identifying and numbering the total problems in each family under discussion by the team. Ideally, this is done prior to the team meeting. If a family-problem list with tentative recommendations is available at the start of a case, the participants require about one minute to read it before beginning the presentation and discussion. It is also important that visitors bringing cases to the team for consultation prepare their cases in this style. As a bare minimum, an agenda should contain the child's name, age, category of child abuse, father's characteristics, mother's characteristics, legal action planned, and names of responsible professionals for each case. It is very difficult to do a quick review of a case without having this core data available.

13. *Address all comments to a specific problem number.* The participants should be encouraged to preface their comments and questions with a specific problem number. For example, the participant may say, "My comments relate to treatment for number 3, the mother." This helps keep the meeting focused. Team-functioning problems may come up during this meeting, but their full discussion should be tabled until case discussion is complete and a staff meeting can be held.

14. *Record the team's recommendations during the meeting.* This is preferably done on a chalk board or somewhere visible to all the participants. The person recording this data should be someone who is not presenting on that specific family, since it may be difficult to do both. Often, this person can be the team leader. In addition, a secretary or some other willing person should be simultaneously recording the chalk board recommendations on paper for later typing before they are erased.

15. *Focus on critical decisions.* The main purpose of the meeting is to coordinate therapy; decisiveness and setting priorities are two of the hallmarks of an effective team. The team should spend a maximal amount of time on serious deliberations about four major decisions:

a. Is the home safe for the child, or is foster care required?

b. What are the optimal treatment recommendations for this family? The team should be certain that each identified problem has a plan.

c. Who will be responsible for each treatment recommendation?

d. Is the data base complete, or have some problems been overlooked?

16. *Consultants must give practical recommendations.* It is important that the advisory members offer attainable advice rather than idealistic advice.

17. *One consultant cannot overrule a primary member's diagnosis.* The consultant can try to persuade the primary team members that an injury was not accidental; however, they should not have veto power on this matter. A case should not go to court when the team of experts cannot make up its mind about the diagnosis, because, in such a case, one cannot expect the court to resolve a diagnostic question. Obviously, a case cannot go to court without knowing exactly who abused the child.

18. *One consultant can demand a court hearing in a confirmed case regarding a treatment question.* If any team member feels a child should be removed from his home for his safety, that team member should be allowed to overrule all the other team members in this regard, at least to the point of giving the child his day in court. This is the kind of treatment decision that judges are prepared to make. A guardian *ad litem* should be appointed, and a hearing date set.

19. *Give a five-minute warning before closing case discussion.* This provides the team members a last opportunity to raise important questions.

20. *Summarize the team's recommendations at the end of a case.* This should be done by the same person who leads and directs the overall meeting. It is very difficult for someone to summarize if he has not had the power to clarify all his own questions during the case discussion.

21. *Gain team's approval of recommendations.* Although the team is rarely unanimous in its decisions, one should expect the majority of the team members to form a consensus about recommendations.

22. *If the team does not approve the recommendations, the recommendations should be modified at this point, until they are acceptable to the majority of people.* The discussion of a case should never close until a consensus has been expressed. Occasionally, the team leader must force this decision solely by a show of hands regarding two alternative situations.

23. *Set a date for case review by the team.* Often, this follow-up report will take only two or three minutes.

24. *Have the team's final recommendations typed and distributed to all involved professionals and agencies.* It is very important that the Child Protective Service's attorney receive a copy of the team's deliberations, so that he might

better prepare his case for court and, possibly, submit these documents into the court's record.

SPECIAL ASPECTS OF TEAM CONFERENCES

1. *Crisis cases.* People may try to pressure the team to review serious cases (for example, a fatal reabuse case) immediately. Such crisis meetings are usually very unproductive. The team should not get rushed into holding a meeting until a complete data base is available to the team. This usually takes several days. Also, the team should not be a forum for crisis counseling of individual professionals. Their grief and anger around a particular case should be worked through at a different place and time.

2. *Too many cases.* As the case volume increases, it may be difficult to discuss all cases at a team meeting. There are several possible ways of handling this problem. First, an additional review team could be developed to handle half the cases. Second, all the cases could be presented, but priorities could be set on the time allotted for each case. Only complicated cases would require the full twenty- to thirty-minute review. Minor, straightforward, or unconfirmed cases would receive only a three-minute review. Third, only the complicated cases could be reviewed by the team, and the other cases would not be presented at the team meeting at all. However, the cases that are not reviewed by the team should, at least, have a miniconference between two or more people. The miniconference could simply be a phone call between the case worker and the physician on the case to ascertain that they are in agreement about the management plan.

The criteria for selecting the cases to be reviewed by the full team should be agency or hospital policy and not left to the discretion of the individual worker. Chapter 16 has a section on guidelines for team conferencing that carefully delineates these criteria. While it may seem to be more comfortable for the worker to retain almost sole responsibility for treatment decisions, experience has shown that this is a short-lived benefit, and one that can be devastating for the family and worker if treatment fails.

3. *Key participant cannot attend.* If one of the key people who evaluated a family is unavailable for the meeting, the team must decide how to proceed. One approach would be to have the coordinator gather the information and recommendations from the missing team member prior to the meeting as completely as possible. The person who has missed the meeting must also be willing to stipulate to the team's recommendations or bring the recommendations back to the team to renegotiate major conflicts.

Sometimes certain professionals, such as, the private physician, protective service worker, or public health nurse, cannot attend because of a tight schedule or distance factor. They can be included in the team discussion by use of a speaker-phone. This allows them to hear the discussion of all the team members as well as to have a chance to ask questions and share information of their own. While it is preferable to have people attend in person, a speaker-phone can be of great benefit, especially in brief, follow-up reviews of cases that have been previously presented. (The cost of a speaker-phone is approximately $33.00 for installation fee and $9.00 additional per month. One can be obtained by calling the Telephone Company's business office.)

4. *New participants.* Any professional attending the team meeting for the first time or who does not come on a regular basis should be introduced to the other team members. He should also be seated near one of the permanent team members who knows him or, at least, is involved with his case. The new participant should be made as comfortable as possible so that he can freely share his information and opinions with the team.

5. *Visitors.* In general, visitors are not allowed at team meetings because of the confidential nature of the information being discussed and because they can impede the team's ability to get work done. Team members may feel more reluctant to be frank about their opinions or to negotiate their position when there are spectators present. Visiting professionals in the field of child abuse are allowed to attend meetings but only in small numbers. To help professionals not involved with child abuse or laymen understand the process of a team meeting, a video-tape, *Dispositional Conference,* has been made and is available for viewing and discussion.

6. *Confidentiality.* The team must decide how it will handle the confidentiality of the information discussed. One alternative is to limit the meeting to those professionals directly involved with the family under discussion. In such a setting, names and sensitive information can be discussed fully. A second alternative is not to use identifying information in presenting the case, but rather to assign each family a number or use initials for the presentation. The team must periodically be reminded of the confidential nature of the written information used during case discussion unless it does not have any identifying data on it. These written agendas should be collected at the end of the meeting from any visiting professionals not directly involved with the family under consideration. It is also useful to check the specific state laws on the sharing of confidential information in situations of child abuse. Many states, including Colorado, abrogate confidentiality in cases of suspected child abuse and neglect and permit transfer of this information among involved professionals even without the parents' permission.

15

The Problem-oriented Record and Team Reports

Barton D. Schmitt

The Problem-oriented Record

The problem-oriented record (POR) is a new form of medical recordkeeping. Those who use it feel that it leads to more logical thinking, write-ups, presentations, and meetings. It was introduced by Dr. Lawrence Weed in the late 1960's. [1,2] It has become immensely popular in medicine, and many predict that it will become the universal means of communicating in the world of medicine. [3,4] The POR has four components. The first is the complete data base, which includes history, physical exam, and laboratory findings. The second component is the active problem list. After all data is collected, the physician is expected to identify and fully define the patient's problems. These are then recorded on an active problem list, and each is given a permanent number. An example of an active problem list on a 52-year-old man could be (1) diabetes mellitus; (2) obesity; (3) pneumonia; (4) hearing loss, left ear; and (5) recurrent eczema. The keystone to the POR is the active problem list, and it is placed in the front of the chart to serve as a table of contents. The third component of the POR is the plan for each problem, and these are also marked with the same permanent numbers. The fourth component is a progress note on each problem; these are also cross-indexed using the same numbers. Therefore, no notes are made unless they relate to a problem, which avoids the recording of trivial data in the chart. At any time, new problems can be added to the problem list by introducing a new number.

The POR has recently been gaining wider acceptance in psychiatry. [5-10]

An example of an active problem list on a psychiatric patient could be (1) depression; (2) suicidal thoughts; (3) temper outbursts; (4) marital conflicts; (5) difficulty expressing feelings; and (6) chain smoker. Again, all progress notes in the patient's chart should be prefaced with the appropriate problem number to which they relate.

The Problem-Oriented Record in Child Abuse and Neglect

This chapter will discuss three years of experience utilizing the POR in child abuse and neglect cases at Colorado General Hospital. To the author's knowledge, there are no previous references in this area. Until now, medicine and psychiatry have applied the POR to the analysis of a single patient. In child abuse and neglect the problem-oriented record must analyze an entire family. Therefore, any individual family member receives a maximum listing of two problems—physical and emotional.

The critical step in problem orienting a child abuse and neglect case is the step called formulation of the problems. There is always one point in time where the professionals involved in a case will never again have more data available to them. This may vary from 48 hours to two weeks into a case. At that time, it is important that an active problem list be drawn up. It should be clear that the POR does not ask the caseworker to change her social evaluation or narrative social summary. Instead, it requires that the worker reanalyze her data and go one step beyond it.

THE MASTER PROBLEM LIST

Child abuse and neglect is a symptom of family unit problems; and, therefore, the entire family needs evaluation in order to arrive at rational treatment decisions. The master problem list contains standard nomenclature for family unit diagnosis in child abuse and neglect. There are a maximum of twelve problem areas.

1. Specific child abuse/neglect category (for example, physical abuse, failure to thrive, sexual abuse, medical care neglect, intentional drugging or poisoning, emotional abuse, abandonment, lack of supervision, severe physical neglect, high-risk child, or true accident).

2. Patient's physical problems.

3. Patient's emotional problems or status (for example, discipline problems, deprivational behaviors, depression, and developmental lags).

4. Siblings' emotional problems or status.

5. Parents' or siblings' physical problems.

6. Mother's emotional problems or status.

7. Father's emotional problems or status.

8. Perpetrator's emotional problems or status (if other than parents).
9. Marital problems or status (for example, discord, separation, desertion, or divorce).
10. Environmental current crises (for example, inadequate home, heat, water, food, job, medical insurance, or child support payments).
11. Extended family's problems.
12. Safety of the home (that is, composite data from above that relate to all legal decisions such as foster care placement).

These categories were arrived at by revising the list many times until any type of family dysfunction or problem could be fit into it. Problems were split when each of them required different treatment recommendations. Problems were consolidated when they shared a common therapeutic approach. Obviously, the majority of cases will not have all twelve problems operational. Problem 1 will be present in all cases, because it is a description of the specific kind of child abuse or neglect that has taken place. The mother or father's emotional problems that pertain to their roles as parents are listed under 6 and 7. The mother's and father's problems as spouses are listed under 9, marital problems. The data for 10, environmental crises, may not be uncovered until a home visit has been carried out. Problem 12 is an important category that should be present in all cases, namely, a listing of the data that pertains to the safety or danger of the home in terms of the likelihood of a life-threatening recurrence of abuse.

THE MASTER TREATMENT LIST

The master treatment list contains the treatment options for the specific problems listed in the master problem list. There are a broad range of possible recommendations for each of the problems. In any given case, only a few of the possible treatment recommendations will be chosen. Some treatment options are used commonly; others are used rarely. However, they all have indications. In this manner, treatment is individualized and tailor-made for particular people and families. For convenience, the medical follow-up plans are always listed under 1, the child abuse and neglect category. Also, legal decisions are always listed under 12, safety of the home. The presence of this extensive list of treatment modalities makes it incumbent upon the multidisciplinary team to consider indications and contraindications for each. Of the treatment options available, the only two universal types of intervention are follow-up by a child protective service caseworker and a primary physician or nurse.

The treatment options on the master treatment list are:
1. Child abuse or neglect category.
   —report to child protective service (CPS).
   —routine medical follow-up by private physician, house staff physician, or neighborhood clinic.
   —increased medical visits, if not in foster home.

2. Patient's physical problems.
   —pediatric specialty clinic for evaluation, treatment or both.
   —obtain release of information for evaluation done elsewhere.
   —dental services.
   —special instructions for parents regarding home medical care if child has chronic disease (for example, cerebral palsy).
3. Patient's emotional problems.
   —CPS follow-up.
   —child-rearing or discipline counseling by CPS worker, pediatrician, public health nurse (PHN), young mothers' group sessions, parent education classes, or Parent Effectiveness Training (PET).
   —infant stimulation program, day care center, or nursery school (especially for developmental lags).
   —MHC referral for individual psychotherapy (for example, play therapy).
   —therapeutic play schools or day care.
   —foster grandmother in the hospital.
   —child companion or Big Brother or Big Sister programs.
   —speech therapy or physical therapy.
   —CHIN's or PIN's petition.
   —recreational activities (for example, community recreational center or youth group).
   —give phone number of crisis center or lifeline to adolescent patients.
4. Siblings' emotional problems.
   —same as 3.
5. Parents' or siblings' physical problems.
   —medical specialty clinic for evaluation, treatment or both.
   —dental services.
6. Mother's emotional problems.
   —CPS case work and follow-up.
   —PHN services.
   —parent aide/lay therapist counseling.
   —group therapy (e.g., Parents Anonymous, drug abuse group, Alcoholics Anonymous, or other self-help groups).
   —individual psychotherapy (clinic versus inpatient unit; psychologist versus psychiatrist versus social worker).
   —family counseling.
   —crisis outlets (24-hour hotlines, crisis nursery, install a phone, provide child protection team [CPT] members' home phone numbers, and emergency home visits).
   —job training, have the mother return to work.
   —homemaker services, babysitters.
   —family planning.
   —psychotropic drugs.
   —suicidal precautions.

7. Father's emotional problems.
   —same as 6 plus the following:
   —reality therapy: forbidden to babysit by staff physician or police warning or court order.
8. Perpetrator's emotional problems.
   —same as 6.
9. Marital problems.
   —marital counseling, sexual counseling.
   —file for divorce.
10. Environmental current crisis.
    —environmental crisis intervention (that is, financial assistance, legal assistance, emergency funds, food stamps, food, shelter, and transportation). (Note: These items should have first priority in order to restore some equilibrium to the home.)
    —training in how to receive appropriate community services in the future.
11. Extended family's problems.
    —same as 6 plus the following:
    —help parents to deal with their relatives more effectively.
    —exclude relatives as potential foster parents.
12. Safety of the home.
    —close CPS supervision on voluntary basis and child in the home (for example: close follow-up via school, day care, PHN, or MD using total body surface exams weekly).
    —adjudicate juvenile court petition as soon as possible.
    —court order of above treatment plan.
    —court-ordered supervision, child in home.
    —court-ordered supervision, child with relatives.
    —voluntary foster home.
    —court-ordered foster home (short term versus long term).
    —indepth CPT review before any return to natural home.
    —encourage voluntary relinquishment for adoption.
    —initiate termination of parental rights petition (include team's vote).

EXAMPLE OF A PROBLEM-ORIENTED CHILD ABUSE AND NEGLECT REPORT

The following is a copy of a problem-oriented summary of a multidisciplinary team diagnostic conference. This family has eight problems that have been detected, and each has been assigned a permanent number. The positive or abnormal data that prove the existence of each problem are listed under it. Under the emotional problems of a particular person, an attempt is made to also list that person's strengths or assets. These might include special work skills, character strengths, family ties, and close friendships. Each of these eight problems has a recommendation written for it with an identical number. This fulfills one of the prerequisites of the problem-oriented record, namely, that every problem must have a treatment plan. There is also a section called "Additional Data," which includes important, normal interview findings. This is where the other categories from the master problem list are placed when they are normal. A final statement is recorded regarding when the child protection team wants to review the case.

Multidisciplinary Conference Problem-oriented Summary

Dispositional Conference, 5/6/75

DOB: 11/15/73	Barton Schmitt, MD, Child Protection Team
CGH #	Marilyn McDonald, MD, Colorado General Hospital
County: Adams	Barbara Knapp, JFK, Nutritionist
17-month-old boy	Kathy Bancroft, SW, Family Learning Center
	Karen Schaffer, SW, Adams County
	Pat Beezley, SW, Child Protection Team

Problems and Recommendations:
1. Physical abuse.
   —33 bruises (one strap mark, some grab marks); trauma X-rays negative.
   —mother admits father caused several of the bruises.
   Recommendations:
   —report to CPS.
   —medical follow-up at Fitzsimons Peds Clinic, Dr. Spaulding.
2. Question of failure to thrive.
   —height and weight third percentile (father also short).
   —poor appetite, no gain in first four days.
   —gained 600 gm in three days but only with behavior modification.
   Recommendations:
   —no validation of underfeeding; final diagnosis is short stature.
3. Siblings' emotional problems.
   —two girls (ages 3 and 4) take care of mother and fearful of father.
   —strength: not afraid of adults in general.
   Recommendations:
   —day care arranged.
4. Father's physical problems.
   —severe headaches, blurred vision, occasional unconsciousness, untreated since 1969, probably psychogenic.
   Recommendations:
   —thorough neurologic and physical workup at Fitzsimons.

5. Father's emotional problems.
    —currently "under a strain" at work, acutely depressed for more than nine months.
    —possible thought disorder.
    —history of deprivation; father died when his son was six years old.
    —high-risk score of 85.
    Recommendations:
    —full psychiatric evaluation and urgent intensive psychotherapy at Fitzsimons.
    —consider hold and treat order for psychiatric hospitalization.
6. Mother's emotional problems.
    —does not protect three children from father; high expectations of children.
    —pervasive denial and avoidance of conflict.
    —beaten by father; domineering mother.
    —high-risk score of 52.
    —strength: has long-standing, close friend who is supportive.
    Recommendations:
    —treatment at Family Learning Center or Adams MHC.
    —CPS counseling and follow-up; give three phone numbers for crisis or suggestion of suicide in husband.
7. Environmental problems/crisis.
    —mother returned to work recently.
    —father must babysit evening hours.
    Recommendations:
    —father must not babysit; mother work days or arrange other sitting arrangement.
8. Safety of the home.
    —severe bruises, different ages.
    —young age of child.
    —father is dangerous person currently.
    —mother not protective of children.
    Recommendations:
    —temporary foster care, court enforced.
    —projected duration: at least three months.
Additional Data:
    —patient's emotional status: Denver Developmental Screening Test normal.
    —marital status: allegedly both parties satisfied with marriage.
Review:
    —one week.

All future progress notes made on this family in the child protection team's chart will conform to these numbers. Ideally, there will be an active problem list in the front of the chart to serve as a table of contents for all entries. The previously described problems will be condensed on this list to three-word descriptive diagnoses.

Active Problem List For Smith Family

Date of identification	Number	Problem	Date of resolution
5/75	1	physical abuse—numerous bruises	
5/75	2	patient—short stature, familial	5/75
5/75	3	sibs—fearful	
5/75	4	father—recurrent headaches	
5/75	5	father—chronic depression	
5/75	6	mother—passive, nonprotective	
5/75	7	father babysits while mother works	
5/75	8	safety of the home—very unsafe	

IMPLEMENTATION OF THE PROBLEM-ORIENTED RECORD FORMAT AT MULTIDISCIPLINARY TEAM CONFERENCES

The first step in implementation is to have all team participants agree upon a standard nomenclature for case problems. The previously listed twelve problems have gone through several revisions and are a good starting point. Ideally, a tentative listing of problems and recommendations should be prepared prior to the team meeting. This requires that each professional who evaluates any member of the family (for example, the pediatrician, social worker, or psychiatrist) submit his tentative problem list and recommendations to the team coordinator. The premise behind this approach is that if a person can perform a standard evaluation, he can also condense his findings into conclusions with a brief listing of the hard data that substantiate these conclusions. The coordinator then combines these problem lists prior to the meeting into a tentative team summary. Each case discussion starts with two minutes of silence while the team members read the case summary. This permits the meeting time to focus on major decision making. After a full discussion, the recommendations are usually modified and retyped.

Another method of implementing this system is to have one team member, who is familiar with the problem-oriented format, record the main points of the dispositional conference on a chalkboard during the meeting. After all the involved professionals have presented their evaluations, the team leader can focus people's attention on the data as he has recorded it. The team should then be encouraged to modify the data until it agrees with their viewpoint. A team member who is not presenting can write down the final version of the problem-oriented notes as they appear on the chalkboard. These can be typed after the meeting and distributed to all participants. The least desirable method of implementing this system is to have one person write up the results of the multidisciplinary meeting in a POR style after the meeting is over.

ADVANTAGES OF THE PROBLEM-ORIENTED RECORD IN CHILD ABUSE AND NEGLECT

The advantages of the POR are numerous.

1. It improves the efficiency of team meetings. It helps to focus meetings on relevant issues and get more accomplished in less time and it prevents digression into extraneous material.

2. It focuses meetings on group decision making. When one considers how expensive it is to have this many professionals in the same room at the same time, it is imperative that the time be spent on high-level decision making, not on helping someone reorganize his evaluation. Major decisions cannot be made until each professional has clarified his own position. There is no reason why this cannot be done prior to the meeting.

3. It improves the accuracy of team communication. The standard nomenclature for problems provides a common language which permits a more precise description of problems and goals.

4. It provides a focus for latecomers. A person can arrive at the meeting late and quickly bring himself up to date by reading the problem-oriented handout. Also, nonattending agencies will receive a clear synopsis of the meeting and its decisions.

5. It encourages collection of a complete data base. Because the master problem list looks at family diagnosis in a comprehensive way, it prevents problems from being left out. On some occasions, the discussion at the meeting may unveil an inadequate data base, such as, the need for a pregnancy test, a developmental exam on the child, or a psychiatric evaluation of the father.

6. It encourages the process known as scientific reductionism. The professional collects lots of data, but he must condense it before the meeting into the main points. This homework requires extra input by the individual, but it saves time for all the other professionals attending the dispositional conference.

7. It encourages accountability for recommendations. Recorded problems are more likely to be solved if the person responsible for each problem is designated.

8. It encourages realistic recommendations. When recommendations are recorded and accepted by the entire team, it is much more likely that they will be practical and attainable than if they are made unilaterally. The conflicting recommendations that are seen when separate reports and recommendations are filed are also prevented by this composite report.

9. Supervision becomes more productive. Since the caseworker's prob-

lem definition and treatment plans are clearly outlined, the supervisor can easily recognize errors and excellence.

10. It provides a mechanism for follow-up at predetermined intervals (for example, three months and nine months after the dispositional conference). The recommendations that have been laid out can be reassessed to determine whether or not they were implemented. Over time, many of the numbered problems should become resolved if treatment progress is really being made.

11. It also provides a mechanism for audit. If a child abuse and neglect system for a given population wishes to audit its performance, one efficient method for doing so is to examine the results that have been achieved for each numbered problem in 50 cases at random.

Summary

The problem-oriented record can be useful in the management of child abuse and neglect cases. The two prerequisites are: (1) a standard nomenclature for family problems and (2) a willingness of professionals to organize and condense their data to fit this format. Once implemented, multidisciplinary team dispositional conferences can become more relevant and efficient.

References

1. Weed, L. L. (1968): Medical records that guide and teach. *N Engl J M*, 278:593.
2. Weed, L. L. (1968): Medical records that guide and teach (concluded). *N Engl J M*, 278:652.
3. Ways, P. O., Jones, J. W., Hansbarger, L. C. (1973): Use of the problem-oriented record in pediatrics. In: *Advances in Pediatrics*, Vol. 20, edited by I. Schulman. Yearbook Medical Publishers.
4. Neelon, F. A. and Ellis, G. J. (1974): *A Syllabus of Problem-Oriented Patient Care.* Little, Brown and Company.
5. Gilandas, A. J. (1973): The problem-oriented record in psychiatry. *Aus NZ J of Psychiatry*, 7:138.
6. Ryback, R. S. and Gardner, J. S. (1973): Problem formulation: The problem-oriented record. *Am J Psychiatry*, 130:312.
7. Novello, J. R. (1973): The problem-oriented record in psychiatry. *J Nerv Ment Dis*, 156:349.
8. Sehdev, H. S. (1974): Adapting the Weed system to child psychiatric records. *Hospital and Community Psychiatry*, 25:31.

9. Smith, L. C., Hawley, C. J., and Grant, R. L. (1974): Questions frequently asked about the problem-oriented record in psychiatry. *Hospital and Community Psychiatry*, 25:7.

10. Mazur, W. P. (1974): *The Problem-oriented System in the Psychiatric Hospital*. Trainex Press.

16

Team Decisions on Case Management

Barton D. Schmitt and Leimalama Lee Loy

The purpose of this chapter is to set forth in a concise manner the guidelines for making the most common decisions confronting multidisciplinary teams. By looking at these case management decisions as a group, interdecision consistency is more closely achieved. These guidelines should not be considered as absolute criteria, for there will always be some exceptions to them. However, they should provide the younger team with some of the mental pathways that more experienced teams have found to be helpful. The two most important and complicated decisions are: when is foster care required and when can the child be safely returned to his natural home.

The sixteen case management decisions that will be outlined are:

   I. Guidelines for intake (that is, investigation).
  II. Guidelines for diagnosis (that is, definitions).
 III. Guidelines for psychiatric/psychological consultation of parents or child.
  IV. Guidelines for police consultation.
   V. Guidelines for legal consultation.
  VI. Guidelines for multidisciplinary team conferencing.
 VII. Guidelines for safe home.
VIII. Guidelines for temporary foster care placement.
  IX. Guidelines for taking a case to court.
   X. Guidelines for criminal investigation of the offender.
  XI. Guidelines for multidisciplinary team reconferencing.
 XII. Guidelines for transfer to the child protective services follow-up unit.
XIII. Guidelines for returning child to natural home from foster care.

XIV. Guidelines for unsupervised home visits.
 XV. Guidelines for case closure.
XVI. Guidelines for termination of parental rights.

I. *Guidelines for intake.*
  A. Acceptance for investigation.
    1. A symptom or finding is present that suggests child abuse/neglect (see II, Guidelines on diagnosis, for 10 types).
    2. An incident occurred that suggests child abuse/neglect (see II, Guidelines on diagnosis, for 10 types).
    3. Factors placing the report at higher risk.
      a. Recent (Note: An incident that reportedly occurred months ago may still require investigation).
      b. Recurrent.
      c. First-hand information.
      d. Child under age five.
    4. Current threat in past confirmed child abuse/neglect case.
    5. Homicidal threat by parent (child usually less than one year old).
    6. When in doubt as to possibility of suspected child abuse/neglect. Note: It is assumed that all cases investigated by CPS and found to be suspicious or confirmed will also be evaluated by a physician or nurse.
  B. Nonacceptance for investigation.
    1. Reverse of above list (that is, no symptom, finding, incident, or threat that suggests child abuse/neglect).
    2. Families or children that are reported as nuisances in the neighborhood (for example, prejudices, grudges, harassment, or petty complaints).
    3. Unreliability of complaint (for example, reporting person is incoherent, inconsistent, or confused).
  C. Referral of non-child abuse/neglect situation to more appropriate resource.
    1. Crying baby: public health nurse.
    2. Other minor medical neglect: public health nurse.
    3. Chronic truancy: school social worker.
    4. Custody disputes: lawyer.
    5. Run-aways without abuse: child guidance clinic, mental health clinic, child and family service, or juvenile court.
    6. Parent-child emotional problems: child guidance clinic, mental health clinic, or child and family service.
    7. Spouse physical abuse: mental health clinic or marital counselor.
II. *Guidelines for diagnosis.*
  A. Definitions of child abuse/neglect.
    1. *Physical abuse.* Physical injuries inflicted by a caretaker, sibling, or

babysitter. Also called nonaccidental trauma. These could be rated as *mild* (a few bruises, welts, scratches, cuts, or scars), *moderate* (numerous bruises, minor burns, or a single fracture), or *severe* (large burn, central nervous system injury, abdominal injury, multiple fractures or any life-threatening abuse). In its extreme, the result is death. Often the injury stems from an angry attempt of the parent to punish the child for misbehavior. Sometimes it is an uncontrolled lashing out at a child who happens to be in the adult's way when some unrelated crisis is occurring.

Since physical punishment and spanking are acceptable in our society, physicians must have guidelines as to when it is excessive and, therefore, represents physical abuse. Corporal punishment that causes bruises or leads to an injury that requires medical treatment is outside the range of normal punishment. Bruising implies hitting without restraint. A few bruises in the name of discipline can easily spill over into a more serious injury the next time. Although discipline is necessary to prevent spoiled children, harsh discipline is not. Even when there are no signs of injury, an accident that includes hitting with a closed fist or kicking the child represents physical abuse. Likewise, a history of past inflicted injuries should be reported if the perpetrator still lives in the household. (Note: rough handling, spanking, yanking, or pushing are not physical abuse in themselves.)

2. *Nutritional deprivation.* Underfeeding (caloric deprivation) causes over 50 percent of cases of failure to thrive (underweight) in infancy. This is documented by a weight gain in the hospital of over two ounces per day sustained for at least a week. A smaller gain is diagnostic if it far surpasses the gain during an equivalent period of time at home. These cases do not include failure to thrive secondary to organic causes (30 percent) or a feeding error on the parents' part (20 percent). (The three percent or more of normal children who are short but well nourished are not included.)

3. *Medical care neglect.* When a child with a chronic disease has serious deterioration in his condition or frequent emergencies because the parents repeatedly ignore medical recommendations for home treatment, reporting and foster placement may be indicated. Serious acute diseases where the parents refuse treatment can usually be dealt with by a court order to treat, rather than the child abuse laws. (Incomplete immunizations, diaper rashes, flea bites, missed medical appointments, and other types of suboptimal health care should be handled by the public health nurse. Only if repeated offers to help are not accepted should the case be referred to CPS.)

4. *Intentional drugging or poisoning.* Drugging children with adult sedatives, sharing narcotics or other dangerous drugs with children, and intentionally poisoning children. In other words, parents who purposely drug children. .

5. *Sexual abuse.* Any sexual exploitation of a child under age 18 by a family-related adult. This may include molestation, exposure to sexual acts, masturbation, incest, oral-genital contact, and sodomy. Molestation can be defined as intentional touching of the genitals or breasts (females only) of a child, the presence or absence of intervening clothing being irrelevant. Incest should not be confused with rape, which usually involves a stranger and considerable force or threats of harm. (Note: Family preferences regarding nudity and sleeping arrangements should not be included.)

6. *Emotional abuse.* The continual scapegoating and rejection of a specific child by his caretakers. Severe verbal abuse and berating is always part of the picture. Psychological terrorism is present in some cases (for example, locking a child in dark cellar or threats of mutilation).

   Diagnostic criteria of emotional abuse:
   a. Severe psychopathology and disturbed behavior in the child documented by a psychiatrist.
   b. Treatment offered to the family on at least two occasions.
   c. Treatment refused by the parents at least twice.
   d. Situations where the only parent is floridly psychotic, and hence, inadequate to care for the children; or severely depressed, and hence, a danger to the children, should also be included and reported.

7. *Abandonment.* The parents have left the child with no obvious intentions of reclaiming him.

8. *Lack of supervision.* When young children under age 12 are left without an adult or babysitter in attendance. Also included are children over age 12 continually left alone overnight.

9. *Physical neglect.* Mild cases of this type should not be included under child abuse and neglect. However, in flagrant cases of smelly children and a filthy home, investigation is important and will usually uncover a very depressed or withdrawn parent. Physical neglect that is consistently confined to one child in a family also requires investigation, regardless of the degree.

10. *Education deprivation.* Laws to guarantee school attendance for children have long been in effect. With proper education, many a child can escape even a severely adverse home environment. If parents do not respond appropriately to counseling regarding school phobia or keeping a child home for housework or babysit-

ting, full investigation is required. (Note: truancy should not be included here, unless the parents are promoting it.)

B. Definitions of non-child abuse/neglect.

Note: The following categories are too easily confused with poverty and ignorance to be of much value as diagnostic categories. Including them in child abuse investigations will dilute the efforts of CPS in more serious cases and lose them the respect of parts of the community. By and large, they should be approached in a helping way, with no mention of child abuse and neglect.

1. Clothing neglect: Mild (for example, torn pants or no raincoat).
2. Meal neglect: Mild (for example, unbalanced meals or cultural food preferences).
3. Hygiene neglect: Mild (for example, dirty face or hair).
4. Home environment neglect: Mild (for example, unclean home or poorly-washed dishes).
5. Cultural deprivation or intellectual-stimulation neglect (e.g., not enough creative toys or children not talked to enough).
6. Emotional neglect (for example, child not given enough parental time or love).
7. Safety neglect (that is, usual and unusual accidents).

III. *Guidelines for psychiatric/psychological consultation of parents or child.*

A. Severe abuse especially if premeditated or sadistic (See decision VIII-1).
B. Reabuse cases after initial report and intervention.
(Exception: few bruises in child over age 5 on one or two occasions).
C. Parent suspected of being dangerous.
1. Psychotic (for example, bizarre ideas, paranoid ideas, fanaticism, inappropriate affect).
2. Suicidal.
3. Homicidal.
4. Sociopathic (for example, prison record, multiple arrests, violent temper outbursts, or threats with a weapon).
5. Drug addiction or severe alcoholism.
6. Past psychiatric hospitalization.
7. Past intensive psychotherapy without improvement in personality.
8. Past suicide attempt.
D. Parent suspected of having intellectual limitations (obtain psychometrics).
E. Perpetrator: uncertain (evaluate both parents).
F. Child:
1. Appears severely emotionally disturbed.
2. Recipient of longstanding, profound child abuse/neglect regardless of symptoms.

      3. Claims sexual abuse or other severe child abuse/neglect without any evidence.

      4. Parent claims child is severely disturbed without any evidence.

      5. Psychometrics when intellectual limitations are suspected in the child.

  G. Recommendations include criminal investigation (see decision X).

  H. Recommendations include permanent severance of parental rights (see decision XVI).

   I. Parents demonstrate ongoing resistance to intervention and treatment.

IV. *Guidelines for police consultation.*

      1. Serious accusations of abuse and parents refuse entry.

      2. Parents refuse to admit a child to the hospital or threaten to remove him from the hospital and a police hold is needed.

      3. Child is under legal custody and is unexpectedly removed from hospital or foster home by the parents.

V. *Guidelines for legal consultation.*

      1. Serious accusation of abuse, and parents refuse entry, and police refuse to help.

      2. Parents refuse treatment for child with life-threatening disorder, and court order to treat is needed (most expeditious approach is to talk directly to Juvenile Court judge).

      3. Interpretation of state laws is needed for complex case.

      4. Considering taking the case to Juvenile Court (see decision IX).

      5. Considering request for criminal investigation (see decision X).

VI. *Guidelines for multidisciplinary team conferences.*

The following types of cases should be routinely reviewed by a multidisciplinary team. When the team is one that reviews all cases, the cases on this list should be allotted the most time (for example, 20 to 30 minutes each). Minor cases not on this list may only require five minutes of discussion each.

      1. Severe physical or sexual abuse (for example, life-threatening abuse, multiple injuries, head injuries, large burns, sadistic injuries, incest, severe malnutrition, or deliberate poisoning).

      2. Reabuse cases, all failures (exception: few bruises in child over age five on one or two occasions).

      3. Severe emotional abuse—child severely emotionally disturbed and totally rejected/unwanted by parents.

      4. Child less than one year old with any physical abuse.

      5. Parent suspected of being dangerous (see decision III-D).

      6. Cases requiring police consultation (see decision IV).

      7. Cases requiring legal consultation (see decision V).

      8. Considering foster care placement or foster placement has been accomplished (see decision VIII).

      9. Considering termination of parental rights (see decision XVI).

10. Specific questions exist regarding diagnosis or treatment.
11. The recommendations of different professionals or agencies are in conflict.
12. An unusual number of professionals and agencies are involved in a multiproblem family situation.
13. Educational cases (present briefly).

VII. *Guidelines for safe home.*

A. Perpetrator removed, lives elsewhere, or has definitely left town (must be more than promises to not let a boyfriend in).

B. A combination of all of the following:

1. Minor injury (for example, bruises, confined to buttocks, back, and legs).
2. Cause (inflicted in name of discipline for specific misbehavior).
3. Frequency (once or twice only).
4. Older child (greater than two years old).
5. Child is not unduly provocative or obnoxious.
6. Parent is not a dangerous person by initial evaluation.
7. No major home crises, according to the initial evaluation.
8. The parent admits to problems and is willing to accept counseling and close supervision by child protective services agency (especially if the parents have accepted and utilized help in the past).
9. The nonperpetrator parent is protective of the child and will not leave the child alone with the perpetrator parent (i.e., angry at perpetrator parent).

C. Factors Increasing the Safety of the Home.

1. Child is over age five.
2. Child has many lovable qualities in the parents' viewpoint.
3. The perpetrator is openly remorseful about his loss of control.
4. Both parents have good health and normal intelligence.
5. The father has a stable job.
6. The marriage is stable (for example, the parents are supportive of each other and can relieve each other in child care and housework).
7. Lifelines are available, preferably in the home. Ideally, each parent has a friend or relative to whom he can turn.
8. Other professionals, agencies, or relatives provide collateral confirmation that this home is safe.

VIII. *Guidelines for temporary foster care placement.*

1. Severe physical or sexual abuse.
   a. Physical abuse (usually any case requiring hospitalization for the extent of the physical injuries), death of a child, life-threatening abuse (for example, central nervous system injury, abdominal injury, or large burn), multiple fractures, sadistic abuse or mutilation (deliberate assault), or beating with a weapon (aggravated assault).

    b. Failure to thrive to severely malnourished level.

    c. Deliberate poisoning with intent to kill (premeditated murder).

    d. Sexual abuse (incest or any type using force).

2. Evidence for repeated and frequent abuse by history, physical examination, or X-ray, even though not previously reported.

3. Reabuse after initial report and intervention (exception: few bruises over age 5 on one or two occasions).

4. Severe emotional abuse (child severely emotionally disturbed and totally rejected/unwanted by parents; for example, kept in a closet).

5. Child less than one year old with any physical abuse.

6. Child has behavior which is unduly provocative or obnoxious to the parents.

7. Child is extremely fearful to return home with valid cause.

8. Adolescent refuses to return home and is beyond parents' control.

9. Parent is dangerous (see decision III-C).

10. Nonperpetrator parent is not protective (for example, stood by while abuse occurred).

11. Parent wants child placed after appropriate counseling.

12. Parents persistently refuse intervention and treatment services from onset.

    a. Parents persistently deny diagnosis.

    b. Parents persistently state that physical abuse is necessary and justified to correct misbehavior.

    c. Parents consistently refuse treatment services with open hostility, passive-aggressiveness, or total indifference.

13. Multiple, ongoing crises.

IX. *Guidelines for taking a case to court.*

Even when the parents agree to voluntary foster care, some children deserve a court hearing to provide the CPS worker with the power to assure the child's protection.

1. Severe physical or sexual abuse (for example, life-threatening abuse, multiple injuries, head injuries, large burns, sadistic injuries, incest, severe malnutrition, or deliberate poisoning).

2. Reabuse after initial report and intervention (exception: few bruises over age 5 on one or two occasions).

3. Severe emotional abuse (child severely emotionally disturbed and totally rejected/unwanted by parents).

4. Parent is dangerous (see decision III-C).

5. Parents persistently refuse intervention and treatment services from onset.

    a. Parents persistently deny diagnosis.

    b. Parents persistently state that physical abuse is necessary and justified to correct misbehavior.

      c. Parents consistently refuse treatment services with open hostility, passive-aggressiveness, or total indifference.

    6. Parents initially accept intervention, but voluntary efforts have been nonproductive for more than three months.

X. *Guidelines for criminal investigation of the offender.*

  A. Severe physical abuse (that is, assault and battery).

    1. Death.

    2. Life-threatening injury (for example, abdominal injuries or brain injuries not due to shaking).

    3. Numerous fractures.

    4. Beating with a weapon (aggravated assault).

    5. Gunshot wound.

  B. Premeditated physical abuse (for example, numerous cigarette burns or serious dunking burns) or torture (that is, mutilation or sadism).

  C. Nonsevere physical abuse, but where previous sibling was killed by parent and parent was not prosecuted.

  D. Sexual abuse plus physical injuries (that is, family-related rape).

  E. Deliberate poisoning with intent to kill (premeditated murder).

Note: Criminal filing should be strongly considered as a way of enforcing treatment when the offender is an unrelated adult (for example, boyfriend, day care center worker, teacher).

XI. *Guidelines for multidisciplinary team reconferencing.*

    1. Any major question or decision mentioned on the conferencing list that is still unanswered or pending.

    2. A court hearing is imminent, and the team's recommendations to the court are incomplete, or the recommendations of different agencies are still in conflict.

    3. The child has not been placed, but the parents demonstrate ongoing resistance to intervention and treatment.

    4. The initial team treatment plan is ineffective.

    5. Reabuse occurs in a previously confirmed case.

    6. Consideration is being given to returning a child in foster care to his natural home, and reevaluation of the safety of the home is in order.

    7. Consideration is being given to closing a serious case because the family is moving, or the case is being reviewed by another team.

Note: Reconferencing is usually required indefinitely in cases where the team recommends termination of parental rights, voluntary relinquishment, or long-term foster care.

XII. *Guidelines for transfer to the child protective services follow-up unit.*

  A. The following guidelines pertain to cases that require long-term follow-up and, hence, in some communities a transfer from the crisis unit to a follow-up unit.

    1. Child in foster home (see decision VIII).

    2. Reabuse.

3. Reported physical abuse suspected but unconfirmed; needs minimum six months' surveillance for possible documentation of abuse.
4. If home conditions have not changed enough to prevent further abuse/neglect, but with help the family could improve.

B. Proper timing of transfer.
   1. Investigation of actual complaint is completed and an appropriate and specific treatment plan, which is acceptable and realistic to parents and social worker, is ready to be implemented.
   2. Referrals to other professionals (for example, the psychiatrist) are complete, and their recommendations for treatment are clear.
   3. Team conferencing has occurred, and their recommendations are clear.
   4. Court hearing has occurred, and the Court's disposition is clear.
   5. Don't transfer children placed in foster home until certain that specific home will work out.

XIII. *Guidelines for returning child to natural home from foster care.*
   Prerequisites:
   1. If either parent was diagnosed as severely disturbed on a previous evaluation, this person is permanently out of the home; *or* a recent evaluation has been done and finds the parent no longer dangerous.
   2. If the child was provocative, his behavior has improved.
   3. A team conference has been held regarding this decision.
   4. Follow-up services by CPS will be continued for at least one year and preferably until school age.
   5. Telephone lifelines with several resources (and preferably a crisis nursery) will remain available, and the parents have a phone.
   Note: The contract with the parents should make clear from the beginning that the child's return is not going to be based on any time schedule, but relates strictly to the attainment of the following behavioral changes.

   In these cases, all of the following guidelines apply:
   A. Parents are utilizing therapy (for example, they keep appointment keep contracts, talk freely, consider therapy valuable, and no long use denial).
   B. Child management is improved. The CPS worker, or other profes sionals, have documented many specific improvements in the paren ability to cope with their child.
   1. Parents can talk about alternative ways of dealing with anger.
   2. Parents have demonstrated impulse control.
   3. Parents can tolerate the child's expression of some negative feelings toward them (for example, "I hate you.").
   4. Parents use discipline techniques that are fair, nonpunitive and consistent.

5. Parents have asked for advice regarding child rearing and were able to implement some of this advice.
6. Parents have recognized and solved specific problems of child rearing.
7. Parents are beginning to recognize the child as an individual with needs, desires, and rights of his own, and their expectations of him are also realistic.
8. Parents speak in positive terms about the child.
9. Parents keep all scheduled visits with their child.
10. Parents interact positively with their child during supervised visits. The parent smiles at his child.
11. Child is no longer fearful of parents.
12. Perpetrator has shown the most improvement in these skills.
13. Perpetrator can recognize potentially dangerous situations and knows how to remove himself from the child at these times.
14. Nonperpetrator has demonstrated an ability to intervene on child's behalf.

C. Crisis management is improved.

The CPS worker or other professionals have documented specific improvements in the parents' ability to cope with crises.

1. Parents no longer live in the chaos of multiple, overwhelming, ongoing crises (for example, one parent has a stable job).
2. Marriage is stable. The parents are supportive of each other and can relieve each other in child care or housework.
3. Parents can talk about alternatives to dealing with crises.
4. Parents have solved specific crises.
5. Parents have asked for help during crises and have been able to utilize it.
6. Parents have recognized and solved specific stresses, before they turned into major crises.
7. Interpersonal relationships have increased; isolation has decreased. The parents have a friend or relative who is supportive and available.

XIV. *Guidelines for unsupervised home visits.*

1. Very similar to the guidelines for returning the child to his natural home. Several definite improvements must be seen, especially before any overnight visits. The most common error is permitting unsupervised visits before any signs of improvement.

XV. *Guidelines for case closure.*

A. Indications: the gains mentioned under XIII (guidelines for returning a child to his natural home) are maintained or increased after the child has been home for a certain period of time.

1. Low-risk cases—three months or more of follow-up.
2. High-risk cases—one year or more of follow-up.
   Note: High-risk cases are listed under IX, guidelines for taking a case to court.

B. Technique.
   1. Gradually withdraw services.
   2. Even after closure, clarify with the parent that "the door is always open" for them to request additional treatment services.

XVI. *Guidelines for termination of parental rights.*
   A. Indications.
      1. Abandonment for over two years.
      2. Voluntary placement for over two years without visits by the parents.
      3. Both parents institutionalized with child in foster care for over one year (for example, psychotic or criminal parents).
      4. A combination of all of the following:
         a. Severe abuse or reabuse (see decision VIII-1-4).
         b. Both parents have dangerous psychiatric diagnosis (see decision III-C).
         c. No improvement after one year of therapy, or repeated resistance at receiving therapy for over six months (that is, incurable by present means of treatment).
   B. Technique.
      1. Have recommendation stated on the initial court petition.
      2. Have written statement from physician regarding severity of the physical abuse. Severe emotional abuse of a child should be confirmed by a child psychiatrist or developmental specialist.
      3. Have written statement from both a psychiatrist and a social worker experienced in the field that the parents are relatively incurable, and that abuse is likely to continue in their home.
      4. Have documentation of treatment attempts and failures. This can be done by outlining a strict treatment plan at the first hearing and having rehearings regarding the parents' progress or lack of progress every three months.
      5. In some states, adoption planning has to be completed before the court will consider termination of parental rights.
         Note: Persuading the parents to agree to voluntary relinquishment for adoption is often the more efficient course of action.

Acknowledgement. The authors are extremely grateful for the input of the Child Protective Services Crisis Unit Workers in Honolulu, Hawaii during June and July 1975 in the initial development of these guidelines, namely, Henry Kikuta, Suzanne McPherson, Agnes Truman, Allen Wine, Rodney Hee, Maxine Reiter, Luanne Murakami, and Joyce Rumel. Members of the Child Protection Team at Colorado General Hospital have also contributed to improvements in these guidelines.

17

Human Aspects of Teamwork

Barton D. Schmitt and Claudia A. Carroll

Team Attitudes

The ability to participate on a team requires more than competence in one's discipline. Team work requires people with helpful and positive attitudes. These attitudes cannot be implemented by policies such as those discussed in chapter 14. The purpose of this chapter is to describe team attitudes which help to attain optimal team functioning and team decision making. It will also review some pitfalls which lead to team failure.

HELPFUL ATTITUDES

The effective team members usually share a philosophy composed of the following premises. First, everyone wants to do a good job. Everyone wants to learn techniques which will help them to do an even better job. Professionals who are not well informed would like to be better informed and would welcome education in specific areas. Second, everyone who joins a child protection team realizes they are permitting measurement of their performance, and that any vulnerabilities they might have can be exposed. This increased visibility requires considerable trust of one's professional peers and ought to be responded to with patience and support by fellow team members. Third, even the best of professionals make some mistakes. Team members must be accepting of this for themselves and for others. Even with optimal team input, all child abuse deaths cannot be prevented. It is tragic, however, if a death occurs because of a reluctance to diagnose abuse or a lack of treatment and follow through. Fourth, even the best of teams have some disastrous team meetings. There are too many factors involved to be able to control or predict all of them. The number of poor meetings will decrease with time, and usually much is learned from poor meetings. Fifth, gratification in the field of child abuse is minimal and is not to be expected from the families themselves, by and large. Therefore, professionals involved must provide the recognition and support for each other which are required to keep people involved in this trying field.

CHARACTERISTICS OF A TEAM MEMBER

There are certain basic characteristics of the type of person who can successfully be involved in team dynamics. It is critical to keep team members who have these characteristics. It is also critical to look for these characteristics when recruiting new team members.

Experienced. The seasoned, experienced person, who has been a direct-service provider in the field of child abuse, will usually be a very practical and understanding team member. Ivory-tower type people, who have never gotten their feet wet in this field, do not make good team consultants.

Broadly educated. Although each team member can only be an expert in one discipline, he must have a good basic knowledge of the medical, legal, social, and family dynamic aspects of child abuse and neglect so that he can properly utilize the other disciplines. He should understand the place of child abuse and neglect in society at large. Therefore, generalists do better in child abuse teams than subspecialists.

Family oriented. It is best if the team member understands families, their strengths and their stresses. Child abuse must be looked upon as a problem in family dysfunction, and treatment must be regarded as an exercise in family rehabilitation. Professionals who are not polarized into child advocates or parent advocates do best with team interaction.

Flexible. The team member needs to be flexible in his thinking and willing to change his position, if it proves to be wrong. He must be able to accept criticism and learn from it. He must not be defensive about his conclusions.

Trustful. The ability to trust other professionals and to respect other accomplished people is critical to good team functioning. Team members must be able to listen carefully to each other. The permanent team must trust the line worker to implement the team's recommendations; on the other hand, the line workers must trust the permanent team's judgement and seriously consider their recommendations.

Supportive. People who are struggling with difficult problems and family dilemmas need full support from their colleagues. Criticism must be used sparingly and constructively.

Reliable. The team member must be reliable in terms of team attendance as well as following through on commitments he makes related to team business (that is, expediting services to a family from his agency).

Anger-resilient. Team members must be able to handle anger from parents and, occasionally, colleagues. Anger must not be taken personally nor result in any counter-attack.

DESTRUCTIVE ATTITUDES

When any team member has some of the following attitudes, they can undermine the team's effectiveness and even its survival.

Impractical. An inexperienced or overly-optimistic team member can insist upon unattainable recommendations which result in team friction.

Rigid thinking. Some professionals have a lack of understanding of the skills and standards of disciplines other than their own. They are caught up in their specialized training, allegiances, and viewpoint. Usually, this narrow, misinformed viewpoint will respond to education and experience.

Distrustful. Sometimes teams become purely investigatory, suspicious bodies looking for flaws in the direct-service provider's evaluation and treatment plan. Yet, the same professionals will emphasize the great need for professional-client trust. It seems unlikely that professionals can teach parents how to trust other people if professionals are unable to trust each other. It would seem important that professionals establish mutual trust in professional relationships before trying to instill it in deprived and mal-treated clients.

Highly Critical. Some teams get into a vicious cycle of criticism. Consultants criticize the primary team, and the primary team criticizes the child protective service unit or other agencies. There should be no putdowns or attacks on people in this stress-laden field. The proper use of authority is to work in a constructive and supportive way.

Controlling. Power struggles, hidden agendas, territorial imperatives, and ego-problems are bound to occur in team dynamics. In its mildest form, controlling is manifested by competition, rather than cooperation, and subsequent lack of sharing of information. In a more advanced stage, it concerns the inability to share status, such as, physicians representing a high power group who are not interested in really integrating with a lower power group, such as, social workers. At other times, it is an inability to share power, such as, the child protective services caseworker being possessive of his decision-making power and continuing to make decisions unilaterally. In the most severe stage, control becomes domination, and one member attempts to have more than one vote on every question and, on some occasions, to have total veto power. A team cannot continue to function under such circumstances.

Indecisiveness. When several team members are ambivalent and indecisive about the best course of action, no action will be taken. In some cases, a difficult decision is referred to a judge or psychiatrist, when it is actually a decision the team should be able to make. This is usually true for decisions regarding whether or not child abuse actually happened. A court cannot make a decision that the team cannot when the real difficulty is an incomplete data base.

Fostering Teamwork and Team Rapport

An effective team leader can prevent many of the human problems of team functioning. He should always attempt to maintain an informal, democratic atmosphere. He can include and involve everyone at the conference, including nurses, lawyers, psychiatrists, and the advisory team. Therefore, no one should feel unwanted or left out. He should pace the conference so that it doesn't run on interminably and lead to mental exhaustion in the participants. In addition, he can counteract the more serious types of negative attitudes mentioned in the previous section. He can look after human rights and protect people from any attacks or destructive criticism. He can end any domination by a specific team member. He can call a halt to infighting and unnecessary power struggles. And, he can prevent indecisiveness by forcing the team to make up its mind (that is, by taking a vote). On occasion, it may be necessary for the team leader to talk with one of the team members privately, if that member continues to manifest a destructive attitude which impedes team functioning.

Effective team functioning should not be viewed as the sole responsibility of the team leader. Each member of the team carries his share of the responsibility. For example, if the discussion of a case becomes tangential, another team member can, and should, refocus the discussion on the issue at hand.

Teamwork is also enhanced by good communication. Basically, this requires staff meetings that occur at a separate time from case management discussion meetings. Protocols can be discussed at these staff meetings. Feelings should also be discussed, especially concerning the issue of trust and mistrust. Team members can be reminded that teams do not acquire good team play until they have worked together for several years. Communication can also be increased by a good coordinator who shares and distributes information among all the agencies involved in cases. It is important that agencies do not become bogged down in confidentiality issues which prevent proper data sharing.

Trust comes mainly with the passage of time and shared experiences. It is important that team members have some social interaction. They must try to find time to have a cup of coffee together. Occasional luncheons without a structured agenda may be beneficial.

Summary

For maximum team effectiveness, it is necessary to view the team and its functioning as a fluid, open process which encourages growth and change.

PART IV

Treatment Tasks

18

The Court's Role

Brian G. Fraser

The Juvenile Court

This chapter describes the Juvenile Court's role in a child abuse case. More specifically, it is about how the Juvenile Court works, and what its components are. The term "Juvenile Court" will be used throughout this chapter, although children's courts have different names in different jurisdictions, that is, District Court with Juvenile Jurisdiction, Family Court, and Probate Courts. The term "child abuse" will be used, for purposes of a simplified writing style, to include the elements of a nonaccidental physical injury, neglect, sexual molestation, and mental injury.

It is important to note that the Juvenile Court reacts *after* a child has been abused. For the most part, it does not anticipate. Also, the Juvenile Court does not activate itself to react. It is a passive participant until some person or agency sets the legal mechanism in action.

How well the Juvenile Court reacts depends upon:

1. Knowledge of child development.
2. The information that it receives about the abusive incident.
3. How well the information is presented.
4. How knowledgeable the court and the other participants are concerning the rather complex issues of child abuse.
5. What resources are available within the community for dispositional purposes.

When the Juvenile Court is viewed in this manner, it is easy to conceptualize it as one part of a system.[1] It is a mistake to view the Juvenile

Court in a vacuum. It is a part of a rather complex system; and it can only work as well as the total system works.

The system begins when a report of suspected child abuse is received. Every state has a law which mandates certain persons or certain groups of persons to report suspected incidences of child abuse.[2] That same law identifies at least one agency to receive the reports and to investigate them. That agency is usually the Department of Social Services, Department of Protective Services, Department of Family Services or Social and Rehabilitative Services.[3] Most states require that the investigation be made promptly once a report of suspected child abuse is received. It is not until an investigation has been completed that a determination of child abuse can be made. If an investigation is made promptly and thoroughly, it should resolve two issues: (1) Is this child currently in danger in his home environment and (2) can the child's injuries or the parent's behavior be classified as child abuse under state law? The proper investigation should resolve both issues separately.

A current danger to a child and child abuse are not the same thing. Both have a common element: a child in peril. Both should result in protective services for the family. However, only child abuse permits a petition to be filed successfully in the Juvenile Court. To put it in a slightly different manner, direct services should be offered whenever a child is in danger; but it is only when a child's injuries or the parent's behavior can be classified as child abuse under state law that the option of the Juvenile Court becomes available.

A decision to utilize the option of the Juvenile Court usually rests upon a consideration of four factors:

1. How serious are the injuries to a child?
2. Is there a history of past abuse?
3. Are the parents willing to try and work through their problems?
4. What is the possibility of successful treatment, even if the parents accept such treatment?

There is no fixed rule governing which case will be presented to the Juvenile Court, and which case will not. If the child's injuries are serious, if there has been a history of past abuse, if the parents are uncooperative, or if the possibility of successful treatment is minimal, a decision to use the Juvenile Court is usually made.

It is a patent mistake not to file an appropriate case in the Juvenile Court. It is a dangerous mistake to second guess the Court and decide that a case would not be an appropriate one to file, because the judge is hostile to the local department of social services, the judge consistently rules in favor of the parents, or the docket is crowded with more serious cases. A decision to file a case of child abuse rests solely upon the facts in that particular case, not the personality of the judge.[4] Judges do change their minds and their personal ideologies. A case well presented can be a teaching tool. However, until the case is presented, the facts are not known, and the status quo is not challenged. No case can be appealed until it is first filed and heard by the appropriate local court.

It should be apparent that the court hears facts and resolves the issues on the basis of those facts. If the data base is insufficient, incorrect, or slanted, there is little chance that the issues will be resolved appropriately.

The investigation is the single most important element in resolving a case of child abuse. A poor investigation results in a poor data base; and a poor data base precludes proper disposition.

The better and more thorough the investigation, the better the chances are of developing the correct diagnosis, prognosis, and treatment plan.

1. *Diagnosis.* Is this child in danger in his current home environment? Can the child's injuries or the parent's behavior be classified as child abuse under state law?

2. *Prognosis.* What is the probability of successful treatment for the family?

3. *Treatment plan.* If the prognosis is favorable, what treatment should be offered to the family, and what treatment is available within the community?

It is only when a thorough investigation has been made that a decision to utilize the option of the Juvenile Court can be made. The Juvenile Court is used to ensure that the most appropriate treatment plan for the family is followed.

THE PURPOSE OF THE JUVENILE COURT

The Juvenile Court[5] is a special type of court that deals with the complex issues of children. The purpose of the Juvenile Court is to help young people in trouble. Children in trouble, for the purposes of the Juvenile Court, are divided into three rather broad categories:

1. *Juvenile delinquents.* A child who has violated a criminal statute in a particular state. Except for the fact that he/she is a child, the case would be heard in a criminal court.

2. *Status Offender.* A child who behaves in a manner that is not condoned by society, but would not be considered criminal (or actionable) if committed by an adult, is a status offender; e.g., is sexually promiscuous or fails to attend school (called C.H.I.N.S. or S.I.N.S.).

3. *Neglected Child.* A child whose life or health is seriously threatened by the acts or omissions of his caretakers (that is, child abuse) is a neglected child.

Juvenile delinquency and status offenses result from the actions of a child himself. Child neglect, on the other hand, is a status which results from the action of another. This would include child abuse.

The philosophy of the Juvenile Court rests upon the presumption that children should be protected, guided, and cared for, not punished. Children are different from adults. They do not have the wisdom, the knowledge, or the expertise which comes with age. Because they do not have that knowledge, wisdom and expertise, they should not be held accountable to the same degree that an adult is. Children, because of their age, do not have the ability to articulate their needs, desires, and hurts. It occasionally becomes necessary for some third party to articulate a child's needs, desires, and hurts, and ensure that the interests of a child are fully protected.[6] The purpose of the Juvenile Court is to provide guidance, care, and support. It is not to punish. It is to allow children to grow into adulthood with some degree of protection and to become productive citizens.

Because the Juvenile Court does not punish, it is often referred to as a civil court. In actuality, it is a rather unique combination incorporating civil law, the principles of the English Courts of Equity, and its own rules and procedures.[7] Since the establishment of the first Juvenile Court in America at the turn of the century until today, the Juvenile Court has constantly undergone change. As it was originally conceived, the Juvenile Court simply acted in the child's interests. To give the Juvenile Court the flexibility that was needed to forge a highly individualized treatment plan for the child, rules of evidence and procedure were waived. A gross abuse of discretion by the court in regard to children's rights and a recent interest in the individualized rights of children have led to a more structured, more formalized Juvenile Court. Although the Juvenile Court does not exhibit the formal, strict structure of the criminal courts, it no longer retains that aura of unbridled, unrestricted discretion.

The Juvenile Court is a special court that deals with the extremely sophisticated and complex problems of children. The issues are not strictly legal.[8] A good Juvenile Court utilizes a rather unique blend of social work, psychology, childhood development knowledge, medical pathology, and legalese. Its practitioners should be highly trained and competent. In most cases, unfortunately, they are not.

TERMINOLOGY

Like many other disciplines, the law has developed its own terminology. To understand what a lawyer is saying and doing (and what he is not saying and not doing) and how the court works, it is prudent to have at least a working knowledge of legal terminology.

1. *Petition.* A petition is a piece of paper which initiates a Juvenile Court proceeding. It informs the Court why it has the right to hear the case (jurisdiction) and what allegations are being made.

2. *Petitioner.* The petitioner is the person or agency filing the petition in the Juvenile Court and making the allegations.

3. *Respondent.* The respondent is the person who must respond to the allegations contained in the petition.

4. *Burden of proof.* The burden of proof is the degree or amount of evidence that must be presented by the petitioner to prove the allegations.

5. *Preponderance of the evidence.* A preponderance of the evidence means a greater weight of the credible evidence. It is what most Juvenile Courts require to establish a case of child abuse. It is a balancing of the credibility of both arguments.

6. *Expert testimony, expert witness.* An expert witness refers to a particular type of witness who is entitled to give expert testimony. An expert witness is someone with skill or knowledge in a particular area that is both beyond the understanding of the average person and will aid the Court in determining a complex issue. An expert witness can offer his opinion or draw a conclusion. A lay witness cannot.

7. *Cross examination.* Cross examination refers to the opposing counsel's right to question the same witness with regard to his testimony. The right to question the same witness about testimony he has just presented offers the Court an opportunity to establish a witness's credibility.

8. *Advisory hearing.* An advisory hearing is a legal proceeding at which the respondent is formally notified of the allegations made against him and his rights.

9. *Setting.* A setting is a legal proceeding at which all parties agree upon a date and a time to resolve the allegations contained in the petition.

10. *Adjudicatory hearing.* An adjudicatory hearing is a formal proceeding at which the allegations contained in the petition are resolved. In an adjudicatory hearing involving child abuse, the issue to be resolved is whether or not the child's injuries or the parent's behavior can be classified as child abuse under state law.

11. *Dispositional hearing.* A dispositional hearing is a formal proceeding to determine how to ultimately resolve the case. In a dispositional hearing involving child abuse, the issues to be resolved are who will have custody of the child, and what treatment will be offered to the family.

12. *Continuance.* A continuance means that a hearing, which has been scheduled for a particular time, is rescheduled for some future time.

THE PROCESS[9]

When a report of suspected child abuse is received, it will be investigated. That investigation should determine if the child is currently in danger in his home environment, and if the child's injuries or the parent's behavior can be classified as child abuse under state law.[10] If a child is in danger in his home environment, protective services must be offered. If a child's injuries or the parent's behavior can be classified as child abuse under state law, a decision must be made of whether or not this case should be filed in the Juvenile Court. The decision to file a petition in the Juvenile Court is usually made by the petitioner, the local department of social services. The person who actually files the petition with the court and presents the evidence is the city attorney, the county attorney, or the corporation counsel.

When a petition is filed with the Juvenile Court, the Court will set a date for the *advisory hearing* and will notify all parties. At the advisory hearing the respondents (usually the parents) are formally notified of the allegations contained in the petition, and their rights are noted. In most jurisdictions, the respondents are entitled to retain their own attorney, and they may request that the case be tried before a jury. At the advisory hearing, the Court should appoint independent representation for the child.

At the *setting*, the county attorney, the parent's attorney, and the child's independent representative are asked to agree upon a date and a time to resolve the allegations. The date is set on the Court's calendar, and all parties are notified.

There is only one issue to resolve at the *adjudicatory hearing*. Has the child been abused, as abuse is defined under state law?[11] It is the obligation of the petitioner to go forward and prove the allegations contained within the petition. The burden of proof is a preponderance of the evidence. If the petitioner cannot prove the allegations contained within the petition by a preponderance of the evidence, all legal proceedings cease.

If the petitioner can establish the validity of the allegations contained within the petition, the Court will find the child abused and order that a date be set for the dispositional hearing.

The only issues to be resolved at the *dispositional hearing* are who will have custody of the child, and what treatment will be offered. The dispositional hearing should identify the needs of the child, the parent, and the family. The Court should then attempt to link those needs to available resources within the community. The Court may choose to leave the child in his own home under the Court's supervision, it may place the child in a foster home, and, in some states, if the facts warrant, it may permanently sever the parent-child relationship.

If the child is left in his own home or placed in a foster home, there is a presumption that treatment will be successful. The prognosis is favorable. The Juvenile Court may set limits concerning visitation and require that certain treatment be sought, and it will set a date to formally reconvene and review progress. At the *review hearing*, if treatment has been successful, and if the child would be safe in his home environment, the Court may formally withdraw. All legal proceedings cease. If treatment has not been successful, and if the family environment has not stabilized, the Court may request that the treatment be continued or that new treatment be initiated, and it will set a date for a new review hearing.

At any time during the investigation or the legal proceedings which follow, the department may request a hearing for *temporary custody*. If the department feels that a child's health or safety is in imminent danger in his home environment, it may request that the Court remove the child until the issue of his safety can be resolved. Upon receipt of a petition for temporary custody, the Court must balance two conflicting issues; the possibility of future harm to a child if he remains at home versus the known harm to a child that results from a forced separation from his parents. If the Court is convinced that the possibility of future harm to a child in his home is greater than the damage of a forced separation, it will place the child in the custody of the Department of Social Services. The child will remain in temporary custody until the issue of his safety is resolved.

The Juvenile Court does not become involved in a case of child abuse until someone sets the legal mechanism in motion.[12] Someone must file a petition alleging child abuse. But, even when that mechanism is set in motion, the Court, in most states, assumes a rather passive role. The Court does not receive a report of suspected child abuse; it does not complete an extensive intake; and it does not make its own investigation. By the time a case of child abuse reaches the Juvenile Court, someone else has completed the intake and the investigation and has decided that this is a case of child abuse. The Court is asked to make a formal evaluation of the case based upon all available data.

The Court is a tool; and it is meant to be used. How well it is used depends upon the quality and the depth of the investigatory data and the skill of the attorney who presents that data.

Some persons would include a third factor—the knowledge of the judge. The judge's lack of knowledge about child abuse however need not be fatal. A good attorney can present his case and educate the Court at the same time.

THE ROLE OF THE COUNTY ATTORNEY, THE RESPONDENT'S ATTORNEY, THE GUARDIAN AD LITEM, AND THE JUDGE

The County Attorney

The county attorney[13] presents the petitioner's case to the Court. The role of the county attorney is quasi prosecutorial in nature. We may say that a child abuse case proceeding is civil in nature, that it is nonadversarial, and that the purpose is to keep the family unit intact whenever possible. But the fact remains, if the petitioner wants to move into the dispositional hearing, he must show that the child has been abused. He must establish culpability. It is the county attorney's obligation to prove the allegations in the petition. The function of the county attorney should be that of a consultant to the local Department of Social Services (or whatever other agency is mandated to handle these cases) at all points leading up to the filing of a petition. He should offer his expertise in developing the diagnosis, the prognosis, and the creation of a treatment plan and help in deciding the feasibility of filing a petition in the Juvenile Court. He should prepare the petition, interview the witnesses, and help prepare all witnesses for Court.

Like many things today, however, what ought to be usually is not.

Respondent's Attorney

The role of the respondent's attorney[14] is to show that the respondent is not culpable. His function is to give the often inarticulate respondent a vehicle through which to address the court. He should ensure impartiality at all proceedings by acting as a counterbalance to the emotional hostilities and pressures which often seem to flourish around the issues of child abuse. He should ensure that all elements of due process are preserved. He should interpret countless procedures and hearings to the respondents which are often quite alien to them. He should ensure that expert medical testimony and expert psychiatric testimony are based upon expertise and not the nearest available medical student. He should insist that all of the allegations contained within the petition are proven by whatever quantum of proof the law requires. Again, what ought to be usually is not.

The Judge[15]

At the moment that a petition is filed in the Juvenile Court, the child who is the subject of that petition becomes, for all practical purposes, a ward of that Court. To put it in a slightly different way, once a child is properly before the Court, the Court becomes the child's guardian. As the child's guardian, the Court (the judge) must ensure that the child's interests and safety are fully pursued and protected. However, the role of the judge is to hear both sides of the case, to impartially balance all of the facts, and to arrive at an equitable decision.

In the majority of cases of child abuse, it is the parents who are the respondents. It is the parents who are alleged to have abused the child. The parents' interests and the child's interests (at least in the adjudicatory hearing) are in direct conflict. If the Juvenile Court judge actively pursues and advocates the child's interests, he loses that air of impartiality that is necessary to equitably resolve the issues. In all states, the Juvenile Court judge does have the option of appointing a guardian *ad litem* to represent the child's interests.[16] In some states, in a case of child abuse, the Juvenile Court judge is obligated to appoint a guardian *ad litem* by law.

When the Juvenile Court appoints a guardian *ad litem* to represent a child's interests, it temporarily transfers its own obligation to pursue the child's interests. The transfer is, however, a temporary one. The Juvenile

Court can never abrogate its responsibility to ensure that the child's safety and interests are fully protected.

The role of the Juvenile Court judge is to impartially balance all the facts and render a decision that is equitable to all parties. By putting the judge's role in these terms, it is assumed that the judge does not begin with the unrelentable presumption of parental rights. In many cases, that may be a poor assumption to make. One of the Juvenile Court judge's functions is to ensure that the guardian *ad litem* is fully pursuing and protecting the child's interests.

The Guardian Ad Litem[17]

The guardian *ad litem* is a "special" guardian appointed by the Court to protect the child's interests. A guardian *ad litem* does not, by definition, have to be an attorney. In most cases, however, he is. The guardian *ad litem* has, in point of fact, absorbed the responsibility of the Juvenile Court; and, in this respect, he is an officer of the Court. The guardian *ad litem* is not responsible to the county attorney or the respondent's attorney. He is responsible to the Court that appointed him. As a special guardian, his obligations begin at the time he is appointed and end at the time all issues before the Court are resolved. Because the Juvenile Court itself is ultimately responsible for the child's safety and interests, the guardian *ad litem* has no power over the child's person or his property. He cannot consent to open heart surgery, for example; nor can he order a review of the child's stock portfolio.

The guardian *ad litem's* role is to fully protect the child's safety and interests in all legal proceedings. In his pursuit of the child's interests, the guardian *ad litem* has four *functions*. He is:

1. an *investigator*, whose task it is to ferret out all relevant information. This means he should conduct his own independent investigation.[18]
2. an *advocate*, whose task it is to ensure that all relevant data is before the Court.
3. a *counsel*, whose task is to ensure that the Court has before it all of the available dispositional options.[19]
4. a *guardian*, in the simplest sense of the word, whose task is to ensure that the child's short-range and long-range interests are fully protected.

The guardian *ad litem* must be actively involved in the case. He should be appointed at the first point in time when the child's interests may be jeopardized. He should be appointed at the advisory hearing or the hearing for temporary custody, whichever occurs first.

The actual impact that the guardian *ad litem* does have is hard to determine. At the close of each hearing, the guardian *ad litem* may make recommendations to the Juvenile Court based upon the child's best interests. The

Court, however, is under no obligation to accept those recommendations. The degree to which the Court does accept the recommendations will no doubt depend upon the guardian *ad litem's* knowledge of the case, his knowledge of the complex issues of child abuse, and how well he can articulate the Court's options.

WHY WHAT OUGHT TO BE, USUALLY IS NOT

In most jurisdictions, it is the local Department of Social Services which receives the report of suspected child abuse. Then, the local department completes the intake and makes the investigation. On the basis of the investigatory data, the local department decides if this is a case of child abuse, what the prognosis is, what the treatment plan ought to be, the feasibility of petitioning the Juvenile Court, and, in some jurisdictions, actually prepares the petition and subpoenas the witnesses. The county attorney is simply a vehicle through which to move the case into the Juvenile Court and to perpetuate the department's decisions.

Child abuse is, however, a rather complex issue. To determine what child abuse is and to evaluate such a case necessitates common sense, some knowledge of medical pathology, psychiatry, law, and social work. The idea that we have any one social worker (or any other individual for that matter) who has enough substantive expertise in all these areas is unrealistic. Decisions involving the complex issues relating to child abuse, child development, and a child's safety should be made jointly. The expertise of different disciplines should be utilized. The task is to build on others' expertise to maximize potential strengths through a joint effort and to minimize current weaknesses inherent in a single-discipline approach.[20]

The number of identified and reported child abuse cases has been growing rapidly over the past few years. The number of cases that are identified will, in all likelihood, continue to grow over the next few years. While the number of reported cases has risen, agency personnel that are mandated to receive and investigate the report, treatment programs, and protective services have not kept pace. The result is a system which slowly is becoming unable to cope.

Every state requires that suspected cases of child abuse be reported. Every state identifies and mandates at least one statewide agency to receive and investigate those reports. As the number of cases continues to increase, while the number of agency personnel remains somewhat stable, the time and the personnel available to investigate suspected cases of child abuse drop proportionately. When investigations are done poorly, there is an inadequate data base; and when there is an inadequate data base, there is little hope of reaching and developing the proper diagnosis, prognosis, and treatment plan.

The Juvenile Court has never attracted the best and most skilled attorneys. It has remained on the bottom of the legal profession's priorities. Lawyers, like doctors, sell their time. Juvenile law does not pay well; therefore, it does not attract skilled practitioners. Because it has rarely attracted skilled practitioners, juvenile law has come to be regarded with disdain by the rest of the legal profession. It is a cycle that perpetuates itself.

Unlike corporate law, criminal law, and civil law, children's law and the Juvenile Court process, for the most part, are not taught in schools of law. The Juvenile Court is a rather unique blend of civil law, concepts of the old English Courts of Equity, and has its own rules and procedures. For those practitioners who want to practice in the Juvenile Court, the process is one of becoming involved and learning through trial and error, a dangerous process.

Juvenile Courts are crowded. There is not sufficient time nor personnel to deal adequately with these cases. If the respondents are poor, they are represented by legal aid. But the legal aid attorney, like the Juvenile Court, is swamped. He simply does not have the time to adequately prepare and present. The county attorney not only represents the county in cases of child abuse and neglect, he represents the political entity in a wide range of non-child-related conflicts. Like the Juvenile Court and the legal aid attorney, in many cases, the county attorney does not have the time necessary to adequately prepare and present the case. The role of the guardian *ad litem*, therefore, must be developed and expanded.

CONCLUSION

The Court is one part of a system. It offers one option to be considered in dealing with cases of child abuse. If any part of the system is weak, it affects the whole system. There are presently a number of weak components in the system. It is a patent mistake to believe that the Juvenile Court by itself will identify issues and conflicts and resolve those issues and conflicts. It will not. The Juvenile Court can be used effectively, but it must be used wisely. For the most part, it is a rather passive tool. Like a computer, what you get out is a factor of what you put in and how you put it in. If the Court is provided with an accurate and comprehensive data base, it can formally and legally identify the child's injuries or the parent's behavior as child abuse and develop and implement an appropriate treatment plan.

Notes

[1]For a thorough discussion of how the court interfaces with the whole state delivery system in Colorado, see: Fraser, B. G. (1976): *Colorado: Child Abuse and the Child*

Protection Act. The National Center for the Prevention and Treatment of Child Abuse and Neglect, Denver, Colorado.

[2]See: Fraser, B. G. (1974): A pragmatic alternative to current legislative approaches to child abuse. *American Criminal Law Review,* 12(1):103.

[3]For purposes of a simplified writing style, the term "Department of Social Services" will be used to denote that state agency which is mandated to receive and investigate reports of suspected child abuse, even though the actual agency varies from state to state.

[4]For a good article which proposes standards for intervention and court involvement in cases of child abuse, see: Wald, M. S. (1976): Standards for removal of children from their homes, monitoring the status of children in foster care and termination of parental rights. *Stanford Law Review* 28(4):623. Also, Paulson, M. G. (1962): The delinquency, neglect and dependency jurisdiction of the juvenile court. *Justice for the Child.* Edited by M. Resenheim; and Wald, M. S. (1975): State intervention on behalf of neglected children: a search for realistic standards. *Stanford Law Review* 27:985.

[5]In general, see: Mennell, R. M. (1972): Origins of the juvenile court: changing perspectives in the legal rights of juvenile delinquents. *Crime and Delinquency* 18:68.

[6]See: Fraser, B. G. (1976): The parent and the child: a delicate balance of power. *Child Abuse and Neglect: The Family and the Community.* Edited by C. H. Kempe and R. E. Helfer. Ballinger Press, Cambridge, Mass.

[7]See: Kleinfield, J. (1970 and 1971): The balance of power between infants, parents and the state. *Family Law Quarterly,* 4:320 and 5:64.

[8]See: Fraser, B. G. (1976): Advocacy for the child in a case of child abuse. *Child Abuse: A Developmental Approach.* Edited by H. Martin. Ballinger Press, Cambridge, Mass.

[9]See: Besharov, D. (1974): *Juvenile Justice Advocacy.* Practicing Law Institute.

[10]Every state defines child abuse differently. See Footnote 2 above.

[11]See: Burke, K. M. (1974): Evidentiary Problems of Proof in Child Abuse Cases: Why the Juvenile Courts Fail. *Journal of Family Law,* 13(4):819.

[12]For a more complete and technical discussion of the proceedings in a child abuse case in the juvenile court, see: Fine, A., Fraser, B. G., MacDonald, D. P. (1974): The battered child. *Colorado Lawyer* 3(6):33.

[13]See: Kay, R. and Segal, D. (1973): The role of the attorney in juvenile court proceedings. *Georgetown Law Journal* 61:1401.

[14]See: Isaacs, J. L. (1972): The role of the lawyer in child abuse cases. *Helping the Battered Child and His Family.* Edited by C. H. Kempe and R. E. Helfer. J. B. Lippincott, Philadelphia.

[15]See: Delaney, J. J. (1972): The battered child and the law. *Helping the Battered Child and His Family.* Edited by C. H. Kempe and R. E. Helfer. J. B. Lippincott, Philadelphia.

[16]The court does not have to appoint a guardian *ad litem* in all states. In some states, in a case of child abuse, the court must appoint a guardian *ad litem*. The author has

used the term "guardian *ad litem*" because it is the most common form of independent representation for the child.

[17]See: Fraser, B. G. (1976): Independent Representation for the Abused and Neglected Child. *California Western Law Review* 13(1):14. See also: Kaplan, E. N. (1972): Appointment of counsel for the abused child. *Cornell Law Review* 58:177.

[18]For a detailed explanation of how that investigation ought to be conducted see footnote 17.

[19]To understand and delineate a child's needs and interests, see: Martin, H. (1976): *Child Abuse: A Developmental Approach.* Ballinger Press, Cambridge, Mass.

[20]To see how such a system can be created legislatively, see: *Colorado Revised Statutes Annotated* (1976): §9-19-101 through §9-10-113.

19

The Protective Service Social
Worker's Role in Treatment

Claudia A. Carroll

There are three possible roles of the protective service worker: (1) evaluation (discussed in chapter 8); (2) direct treatment, and (3) case coordination. The main focus of this chapter will be discussion of direct treatment with abusive parents.

To briefly mention the third role, case coordination is an extremely important skill that the worker must develop, because, optimally, there will be a variety of agencies and service providers involved with any one family. Carrying the legal responsibility for the family also entails coordinating tasks, such as, enlisting a public health nurse or mental health worker when the need exists. In some situations, the family may refuse to work with the Department of Social Services but is agreeable to working with another agency. This is acceptable as long as there is ensured communication between the two agencies. Effective service delivery requires the ability of the social worker to work cooperatively with a variety of people and agencies.

Treatment of the abusive family will take time, commitment, and great resiliency on the part of the social worker. It is the arduous task of helping the parents grow psychologically. What will be discussed here is a personal approach to treatment which has evolved through my own trial and error methods and feedback from peers and, most importantly, parents with whom I have worked. This chapter is written "in the process of becoming," and it is not intended as a final statement on the subject.

Protective service work is complex and difficult. The social worker must be able to deal with client hostility, being on call for emergencies, after-hours work, personal feelings about abuse, and a bureaucratic morass of forms. In addition, caseloads are typically considerably higher than is reasonable. Given the recent nationwide concern about child abuse and neglect, as well as budget freezes which portend a fiscal glacier, it appears that caseloads will continue to increase. Recognizing that there are currently such formidable hurdles in providing treatment to abusive families, and that the future does not appear to be much brighter, this chapter will attempt to highlight some guidelines which may be used in effective service delivery to families.

Knowledge and Skills Necessary to Provide Treatment

In addition to the seven areas of skill and knowledge discussed in chapter 8 for the evaluation of abusive parents, the seven following areas are helpful in the treatment phase with the abusive family.

KNOWLEDGE AND SKILL IN USE OF VARIOUS TREATMENT MODALITIES

Based on a sound assessment and diagnosis of the family, a treatment plan should be implemented, drawing in such modes of treatment as individual therapy, marital counseling, group therapy, parent educational groups, behavior modification techniques, lay therapy, and day care. Much of the direct therapy can, and should be, part of the services of the Social Service Department. Leaving all of the "treatment" to other agencies, and assuming the posture of "monitoring, managing, and/or only supervising" is, in my opinion, a grave mistake, often leaving the family receiving little, if any, therapy. Unquestionably, other agencies such as mental health should be involved in treatment with abusive/neglecting families. However, other agencies should not replace the significant role of the protective service worker in the provision of direct therapy to families. Direct therapy must be a concerted effort of many agencies.

ABILITY TO MANAGE THE CASELOAD

Management of a protective service caseload requires considerable skill and flexibility on the part of the social worker. This is exacerbated by the high caseloads common in this work. By the nature of protective services, a social worker involved with a family in treatment must be predictable and reliable in keeping appointments and scheduling regular sessions with the family. At the other end of the continuum is the need to be responsive to crises which are eternally surfacing in the caseloads. Juggling these two often conflicting needs requires such skills as:

1. Setting caseload priorities—that is, identifying families who are treatable and those few who are not; spending more time with those who will benefit; if a family is not treatable, this must be recognized; making realistic goals and plans on cases and moving expeditiously to those ends; and weighting the caseload based on these and other criteria to identify levels of involvement (heavy, moderate, and low).

2. Setting priorities regarding other responsibilities in relation to casework responsibilities—for example, involvement in group leadership, speaking engagements, and paper work.

3. Scheduling in a way which allows for flexibility—for example, scheduling appointments every hour is setting the situation up for failure. It is necessary, whenever possible, to leave time open daily for the crisis situations which inevitably will present themselves.

4. Having a variety of treatment options from which to choose—for example, day care, groups, crisis nurseries, lay therapists, emergency provisions, housing and clothing, and therapy for individuals as well as the family unit.

SKILL IN EDUCATING

This is the ability to explain dynamics, consequences, treatment, legal procedures, and the like to others involved in a team treatment approach (for example, teacher, day care mother, and public health nurse), as well as to community groups (for example, service clubs, high school classes, and PTA's).

KNOWLEDGE OF COUNTY AGENCY'S POLICIES AND PROGRAMS

Knowledge of and skill in utilizing the county agency's policies, procedures, and programs is extremely important. A worker must know how to maneuver within his or her own system—that is, how and where it is possible to minimize the "red tape." If the system is confusing to the social worker, it is even more confusing to the client. Identification of people within the system who can answer questions related to particular areas is helpful.

KNOWLEDGE OF THE COMMUNITY

This area addresses understanding of community perceptions of child abuse and neglect as well as the perception of the Department of Social

Services within the community. Is child abuse and neglect perceived to be a community problem and not only the responsibility of the Department of Social Services? What cultural practices of child rearing and notions of family autonomy affect community definitions of abuse and neglect? Which agencies, public and private, are involved in service delivery, and what are their levels of commitment? Who are significant people in each agency? Which groups have not been adequately addressed (for example, Newcomers and Jaycees) in terms of education and support for protective services work? Who are the untapped resources?

KNOWLEDGE AND SKILL IN USE OF RESOURCES

This is knowing what professional and lay resources are available for the prevention and treatment of abuse and neglect and having skill in advocacy, effecting quid pro quos, or whatever else it takes to gain the benefits of these often scarce resources for clients. In addition to obvious organizations and agencies, such as, the courts, schools, medical centers, mental health centers, Parents Anonymous groups, and the like, the worker should know the availability of less traditional facilities. These include vocational training, ladies day at the local movie, a ceramics class, and anything else which might be utilized to help parents cope with problems of being isolated with a child, loneliness, feelings of inadequacy and finances.

UNDERSTANDING THE DEPARTMENT OF SOCIAL SERVICES

Understanding the horizontal controls, vertical controls, and hierarchy of the Department of Social Services is important. Having some understanding of state and county legislative functions, in terms of legal and budgetary aspects of abuse and neglect, is necessary. A county Department of Social Services, for example, is accountable to their county commissioners, the State Department of Social Services, the local state legislature, and, at the federal level, the Department of Health, Education and Welfare.

SELF-AWARENESS

Underscoring these seven points is the idea of self-awareness and a positive use of self in working with abusive families. (This area is discussed in depth in chapter 20.) The attitude and interest the social worker is able to convey to the parents in large part becomes the main impetus to growth in these families.

Treatment with the Abusive Family

Child abuse is a family problem. It is not just the problem of the identified abuser or the child. It is a problem involving the entire family; and, as such, treatment must be available to each family member, including mother, father, abused child, and siblings. For too long, the focus in protective services has been to work exclusively with the mother. The children can develop emotional scars which may or may not be evident at the time the physical abuse is evident. Treatment with the child is covered in chapter 23. This chapter will discuss treatment with the parents.

THE PARENTS

The majority of treatment with abusive parents is done by social workers. Psychiatric treatment by a psychiatrist is not necessary nor available in most situations. Certainly, there are exceptions; however, the overwhelming number of families can be helped by social workers. Good psychiatric consultation is essential to assist social workers in providing treatment to families.

Perhaps one of the most difficult, inexplicable dilemmas of the therapist with abusive families is keeping oneself sensitive and open, yet, at the same time, remaining resilient. One's senses and feelings must be keen; but, in an effort to defend oneself against the human unhappiness and tragedy seen daily in this type of work, one must guard against the development of complacency, dormant feelings, and distancing oneself from the realities of child abuse situations. There are no easy answers to this dilemma of maintaining the amount and type of energy needed to work with abusive parents. Striking a good balance can be enhanced by good supervision and consultation, flexible compensatory time, a variety of protective services experiences available to the worker (see chapter 20 for further discussion of this point), and a good *esprit de corps* within the agency with abundant support given to the worker. Much also depends on the personal characteristics of the social worker, and this is also discussed in chapter 20.

Part and parcel to successfully being able to perform in the job is recognizing what type of client or patient one works with best. Some therapists are particularly skilled, for example, in working with a borderline, or more disturbed parent, whereas the very depressed, overwhelmed, yet neurotic patient is very trying to him. There must be awareness by both the social worker and the supervisor as to what type of client one works with best, and families should be assigned accordingly. Occasionally, it is necessary to transfer a family to a different social worker, sometimes at the request of the parent(s).

The worker should not become defensive about a family transfer and feel that he has failed because, in some instances, it is not possible for the family to work through the initial anger they have for the worker who may have initiated such steps as court action or removal of the children from the home. If, after both the worker and the family have tried to resolve the anger, this has not succeeded, there should be a flexible agency policy, whereby a new worker is assigned easily and smoothly. If, on the other hand, the family insists that they can work with no one and are continually requesting a new worker, a different situation is present; the request should not be granted, since it is simply a defensive maneuver, only postponing getting at the fundamental family problems which precipitated the abuse.

STAGES OF TREATMENT

A Treatment Plan

There should always be a treatment plan with the family, because without it, there is no direction to the activity between the worker and the parents. Periodic assessment and revision of treatment plans and priorities is critical. If a particular treatment modality turns out to be ineffective or unnecessary, it can be discontinued. If the treatment program seems to be bogged down, a new therapeutic approach should be considered (for example, adding a homemaker). Important treatment decisions should not be unilateral ones. For example, if a decision is being considered to return a child home from a foster home, there should be review by a multidisciplinary team or the juvenile court, or both.

Following evaluation of the family, the social worker must sort out all of the data gathered up to that point to gain a real feeling of the family and its problems. During this stage, the worker is continuing to try to develop rapport and confidence with the parents through finding ways of being supportive and helpful to them. Without the foundation of trust between the family and the social worker, nothing therapeutic will happen. Development of trust breaks down the loneliness of the parents and offers them hope in their lives. The social worker can anticipate that establishing a good relationship with the family will take time and testing, sometimes up to six months and more.

Mutual problem identification between the social worker and family becomes the next step, and this process must actively involve the parents.

Then, a priority of problems which the therapist and family are going to work on together must be established. It is essential that the social worker be realistic about the goals of the family; they must be attainable within the lifetime of all involved! We cannot expect total personality metamorphosis. We can, however, work toward helping the parents grow gradually in relation to each other and their adult needs, helping them see their children as children, and assisting them in developing alternative methods of discipline, thus removing the physical danger to the children. Hopefully, this will begin to cut through the emotional vicissitudes played out generation by generation in this vicious cycle. Abusive families, by and large, require that maximum treatment and supportive services be available to them for an average of one year.

Turning Points in Treatment

Key turning points in treatment become apparent in families in a variety of ways, but with the common positive theme of reaching out for help, often very subtly, and then feeling better about oneself. The first real turning point becomes the establishment of trust. (Examples of significant turning points would be calling the social worker at home for the first time and asking for reassurance, or opening the living room drapes which have previously been closed, perhaps for years.)

Following the beginning signs of trust is the feeling that the parent can make use of the worker's time and interest to feel better about himself. It is at this point that the parent may begin to share the many fears characterizing his life—fears about himself, his temper, and life in general. Once the fears of the parent are at least verbalized, compartmentalizing and dealing with associated problems can begin. This can free some of the parent's energy in more productive ways such as trying different ways of relating to their child (for example, different discipline methods). A following step is seen when the parents demonstrate an ability to reach out and use others (for example, lay therapist or neighbor) in addition to the social worker.

Slowly, the parent gains confidence in his or her ability to handle things. As the parents' coping skills improve, they are, in fact, having fewer crises, because they are dealing with situations before reaching crisis proportions. This enhances the parents' self-image. The entire process just described becomes, initially, one of great dependence on the worker by the parent. Eventually, the parents move to more independent functioning.[1] It usually takes months to go through these stages, and even small increments of improvement should not be discounted, but applauded!

One of the best examples of this process concerns a very depressed, suicidal mother who initially refused to see me. Gradually, we were able to work together, and eventually a very close working relationship resulted. Toward the end of my involvement with the family, there were two excellent indications that termination was not far off. Here was a previously isolated mother having a Tupperware® party, and also becoming the den mother for her son's cub scout group. When she took them to a baseball game she stated, "I didn't realize there was an outdoors before." This was a mother who was now having fun with her children, and her world had expanded immeasurably. Although we have terminated formally, I periodically hear from her when she is either needing a slight boost or, more frequently, to share with me some new aspect of her life.

TASKS OF THE SOCIAL WORKER

The tasks of the social worker are to mobilize the untapped abilities of the parents; the support of the extended family, if one exists; and the utilization of community resources, so that the unmet needs in the family will be met. The ultimate goals are good reality testing in terms of need gratification and enhanced feelings of self-worth. The social worker should only be involved with the family as long as fulfillment of these needs is necessary; then, the social worker should extricate himself from the family and their lives.

In a very real sense, the social worker becomes a role model for the parents, serving as someone with whom the parent can identify, emulate, and gain strength through ego-lending and the like. The social worker wears a variety of hats which are constantly changing—the teacher, showing the parent other ways of relating to their children; the parent, encouraging dependency, then independence; and always a caring friend.

TREATMENT TECHNIQUES

In part, my approach to treatment has developed through integration of many of the treatment ideas of Dr. Carl Pollock. The late Dr. Pollock served as consulting psychiatrist for the Adams County Department of Social Services from 1972 to 1975, and was one of the leaders in the development of the theory of child abuse. The following are treatment techniques he encouraged:

1. In the early stages of treatment, let the parents know you are very interested in them and want to know what feelings they are experiencing. Ask them what has happened in their lives in the past and at present. Empathize and understand that they have been through a lot. Diffuse their burden. Tell them some good things about themselves and their parenting abilities. Don't play detective. You don't care about that. What you do care about is them, that they hurt, and that they are in a crisis.

2. Initiate a spontaneous account from the parents of what they see their problems to be. Ask them in what way you could be of help to them.

3. Listen for someone who was good and giving to the parent(s) in their childhood and past. In other words, was there an identification with someone positive? If there was no such positive person in the parents' childhood, the prognosis for growth in the parent is poor.

4. A helpful organizing principle in treatment is looking at the need-meeting system of the family. Mentally assess "who is doing what for whom" in the family. Look at the family as an interaction of who is taking care of someone else's needs. Often in abusive families, the child is expected to take care of the parent. This assessment highlights areas needing to be addressed in working with the family.

5. Frustrate the parent in honest ways. For example, help the parent pretend that you will be gone (that is, you are taking a vacation) to help them learn how to handle things in your absence. The frustration can be growth producing to the parent, and it encourages their independence.

6. Listen to and determine the defensive maneuvers of the parents and don't support them. This will help to get at the real affect of the parent. Follow the feelings and affect of the parent in the treatment hour (that is, sadness, relief, or anger). In therapy, the importance of the emotional experience, through the expression of the affect, is critical to experience interpersonal growth. To be effective, the therapist must be in touch with his own affective state(s) as well.

7. Prevent interminable relationships between the family and the social worker. Say to yourself, "I want to help this parent learn one behavior as a goal." Realistic goals are essential.

8. Give the message to the parent(s) of confidence in their ability. Allow them to use their own ideas.

9. Visualize an image of the strengths of the parent and keep it out in front of you. In other words, envision the best of the client and strive with them toward that goal.

10. Some abusive parents, who developmentally are fixated at a more primitive level, characteristically "split" into all good or all bad significant people in their lives. Try to help them see the strengths and weaknesses in each person. Help them put together the good and bad in a person, thus accepting the humanness and individuality of the person as well as of themselves. This is part of working through the transference phenomena with the parent(s).

11. Give the parents hope, saying something like, "Here's how we are going to do something for you." This not only offers hope to them, but relief in the mutuality of effort inherent in such a statement.

12. Let the parent know that there is a healthy part of him or her—"I know you can handle this in some more useful way."

13. Let the parents know the final goal is a successful termination of therapy characterized by control and permission of their own lives, which they have never experienced before.

The message of therapy is synonymous with what we are striving for in the ideal parent-child situation; that is, "I hear you and I know where you are."

SPECIFIC STEPS OF TREATMENT

Treatment Steps with the Parents

It is futile to only lay out injunctions to the parents such as, "You can't discipline your child that way anymore, because it is against the law." It is absolutely critical that we help the parent find other more acceptable ways of not only correcting their child, but more importantly, relating to him. One of the best means I have found to do this is a small book called *Living With Children* by Gerald R. Patterson and M. Elizabeth Gullion. It is an easily understood behavior modification approach on how parents and children teach each other negative behaviors. This approach offers the parent a language and structure by which to concretely look at the relationship between themselves and their child. The behavior modification ideas contained in this book should certainly be coupled with discussion of the parents' feelings about the child and the individual child's needs. A pure behavior modification approach is not being advocated. The main behavior modification emphasis should be on reinforcement of positive behavior and ignoring negative behaviors. As a result of this two dimensional approach, the parent can engage himself in a more positive interaction with the child and often realizes the child's behavior isn't as negative as once thought. One way in which it is possible to encourage the parent to try something different is to help him identify that what he is currently doing (physical punishment) isn't working very well. For example, the parent will usually go into great detail recounting the many negative behaviors they perceive in the child. This is the worker's entree to engage the parent in taking steps to relate differently to their child.

Another important aspect of working with the parents is helping them anticipate problems both with their children and their lives in general. Many of these parents have never learned to do this. Innumerable "things" just "happen" to them, and they feel they have no alternatives from which to choose or act. An example of anticipating problems would be for the social worker to ask the parent to pinpoint what time of day the child most likely is abused and what behavior provokes the abuse. Help the parent recognize what his alternatives are when these factors are in operation. It is helpful to play out with the parent all the different situations of the day which could trigger the abuse, and what the parent could do (for example, putting the child in his room, closing the door, and telephoning the social worker). Another example would be listing on the refrigerator door all the reasons why a baby might cry, completely unrelated to the competency of the mother. The mother could then put the crying baby in her crib, go to the refrigerator, and read the list for suggestions (for example, heat up the baby's bottle). Establishing alternatives so that the parent does have good options from which to choose, and a sense of control over his life, can strengthen his impulse control.

A third area is helping the parents see the child as a child who cannot meet their adult needs. Instead of looking to their child for need fulfillment, help the parent identify those adults in their life who can meet those needs, and let the parents know it is all right to ask for, receive, and make use of help from other adults. This enables the parent to see the child more realistically. The child needs to be seen by the parent as a *growing* individual who, at nine months, for example, has different needs, such as for stimulation and protection from accidents, than he had at two months. A positive, empathetic, and realistic perception of the child by the parents is a good sign of improvement in the family.

Fourth, assist the parents in learning how to "negotiate" in this world. This includes both interpersonal relationships as well as expanding the parameters of their physical world. Most abusive/neglecting parents are extremely isolated, lonely individuals. Something such as driving across town may be overwhelming to them. They need help in finding "the out-doors," friends, pleasure, a baby-sitter, and the like.

Underlying all of this is the need for the social worker to be interested in the parents and to be able to listen unhurriedly to them. Social workers too frequently underestimate their importance to the families. The social worker must help the parent see that he or she is not going to be rejected by the worker. Abusive parents, because of their low self-esteem and past life experiences, may feel they are being rejected by the slightest action or inaction by the worker. This theme must continually be worked through with the parents during any stage of treatment.

Treatment Steps with Case Planning

Anticipating treatment problems and concomitant alternatives aids the social worker in good decision making. This is especially helpful if done in an anticipatory manner, rather than at the time of the actual crisis when sorting out viable alternatives is more difficult and clouded by the emergent situation. An example of this would be if a parent misses three appointments for a child's medical condition, the anticipated plan could be to ask for court ordered supervision and mandated medical care.

Finally, it is sometimes necessary for case movement to be initiated by the social worker taking a stand, through action or recommendations to the court, to bring a situation "to a head." Forcing an issue can bring about case movement. For example, if a child has been in foster placement for several months with little progress being made by his parents, yet a lack of legal evidence exists on which to move for more permanent planning, the social worker may need to return the child home, closely supervising the situation to determine whether the child can safely reintegrate into the home or must be placed for adoption. (This step should *not* be considered with an infant or in cases of serious abuse.) It is better to take some action than to allow a child to grow up in the oblivion of foster care, except in cases where returning the child home could be life threatening.

INDICATORS FOR A POSITIVE PROGNOSIS IN TREATMENT

There are four helpful indicators in assessing parents' positive prognosis for treatment:

1. The presence in the past of a person with a warm effect in terms of a

parenting role. This person would have been a warm and giving individual with whom the parent went through the process of identification.

2. Some kind of a good work history, since this requires something both in terms of reality testing and of conceptualizing one's needs and the ability to act upon those needs.

3. The ability to have used help in the past.

4. The parents or individual is wanting help, verbalizing that they are overwhelmed. One of the goals of therapy is the acceptance of help. As the parents are able to say, "I need help," and make use of the help available to them, the prognosis improves.

Termination of Parental Rights

The gravity of this recommendation requires punctilious attention to reviewing all aspects of involvement with the family by the social worker. It is a recommendation which should be made only after all other efforts have failed, and the parents have demonstrated no movement over a period of time (six months to a year). From the beginning of involvement with the parents, it is important to be honest with them that termination may be an alternative. Termination tends to occur in cases of more serious injuries or pervasive, ongoing minor ones.

In considering recommending termination of parental rights, it is important in the very beginning to have a good diagnostic assessment of the parents so that when termination becomes the recommended alternative, the court case is postured in such a way that legally termination is possible. Treatment plans should have clearly been presented to the court with sound documentation supporting termination based on the various opportunities the parents have had to change but have not done so. In addition, the court will also likely need a psychiatric evaluation of the parents buttressing the social worker's opinion that: (1) abuse will likely continue to occur in the home, and (2) that the prognosis for change in the parents is poor, even with therapy which would take more time than is possible in the child's timetable of needs (more than a year) (B. Fraser, *personal communication*, Feb. 1976). As indicated elsewhere in this book, not all families are treatable and termination of parental rights is a viable alternative in hopeless situations.

A court report recommending termination of parental rights contains the following elements essential to this serious recommendation:

1. The treatment plan has not been met by the parents, though it has been made available to them.

2. The parents may be verbalizing wanting the child returned home, yet their behaviors are indicating otherwise.

3. The physical, emotional, and developmental needs of the child are identified.

4. There is a supporting psychiatric statement recommending termination.

An example of such a report for a child burned by her parents is found at the end of this chapter.

Before leaving this subject, one final area bears mentioning. Undoubtedly, the social worker, or whoever is making the recommendation of termination, will initially have many conflicting and confusing feelings about taking such a strong position. The social worker will need an opportunity and means by which to articulate, sort out, and work through these thoughts and feelings to be able to then make an organized, clearly stated recommendation of termination. Consultation with peers, supervisor, psychiatric consultant, or all three is a helpful means of coming to grips with one's own feelings about such a recommendation to the court.

Conclusion

Effective treatment with abusive parents is crucial but difficult. It takes special people to sensitively and humanely reach out to abusive parents in the way that protective service workers do. They persevere in spite of discouraging setbacks and frustration, demonstrating patience, dependability, and skill. Indeed, it is valuable work with uniquely worthwhile human beings.

Sample Review Report to the Court

Ford, Courtney
Age: 4 years

Evaluation of the Present Situation

Since the last court hearing three months ago, the situation with Mr. and Mrs. Ford remains unchanged. Prior to and during that hearing the following were prescribed conditions in considering a return of custody to Mr. and Mrs. Ford:

1. That the Fords be willing to make a commitment to continue to work with the Adams County Department of Social Services and the Adams County Mental Health Center.

2. That the Fords follow through with additional visits with Courtney. Mr. and Mrs. Ford have continued to refuse to see psychiatrist Dr. Bruce Green and myself. Further, they have declined visitation with the child. (On September 24, 1975, Mr. Ford told me he wanted "no more appointments of any kind.")

Regarding Courtney, individual therapy began six months ago and has continued on a weekly basis. The purpose of this play therapy is to help the child identify appropriately with a female, and, further, to help her in the areas of autonomy, initiative, and trust. Courtney is seen as a child whose inner self is tenuous, at best, although she is able to make progress. She continues to thrive in her current foster home.

On August 17, 1975, Courtney's foster mother told me that the child returned from a home visit with her parents with a bruise on her left leg. The bruise was reported by the foster parent to be approximately three inches long and one and one-half by two inches wide. Courtney told Mrs. White, her foster mother, that her mother had hit her with a belt because she was "bad." I then talked with Courtney and asked her about the incident, and she told me the same thing.

Recommendations

In retrospect, it is my opinion that Mr. and Mrs. Ford have had a reasonable amount of time and opportunity to change. The prognosis of these parents to change and their capacity to care for Courtney appear poor, and it is my opinion that she cannot be returned in the foreseeable future. It is my recommendation that parental rights be terminated. This recommendation is based on the following:

1. The Fords continue to be ambivalent regarding Courtney; they continue to request more time before additional action is taken by the court, yet, they are not willing to follow through with any prescribed course of treatment. Courtney was referred to Adams County Department of Social Services for protective services 19 months ago by Colorado General Hospital with inflicted burns from boiling water and lateral bruises from a strap. She has been in foster care a total of 17 months.

2. I am very concerned regarding the Fords' denial and externalization of the problems. Mr. Ford stated to me, "Everything would be okay, once Courtney is back in the home." Courtney was returned once for a period of a month and removed again because of the high potential for reabuse feared by the then current worker, Mrs. Bernstein. The nature of these family problems and the seriousness of Courtney's problems require ongoing help to which the Fords are not receptive. Courtney has come from being a child exhibiting very severe and autistic-like behaviors to a child who is currently functioning quite well superficially, but in need of intensive work regarding interpersonal relationships.

3. Possible reabuse on last home visit.

4. The Fords were very much aware of our moving closer to returning Courtney prior to the last court hearing. They were expressing interest in this, and yet their actions and messages indicated otherwise; cancelling visits with Courtney, statements of "inconveniences in picking her up."

5. There has been open rejection of this young child. On August 28, 1975, Mrs. Ford told me, "It's better to lose one (Courtney) than the whole family." The Fords have refused visits with Courtney since September 1975.

6. The needs of this child are paramount. In her four years, she has had a variety of caretakers ranging from relatives to foster parents. It is imperative that Courtney be placed permanently as soon as possible. Because of the duration, nature, and poor prognosis of the family situation, it is my recommendation that Courtney be freed for adoptive planning and placement.

7. Dr. Bruce Green states in his letter to the court, attached to this report, that, "in the interests of the child, it would seem appropriate to place her in a permanent adoptive home, as her parents have not given evidence of the stability nor interest necessary to raise this child."

> Claudia Carroll, M.S.W.
> Principal Social Worker
> Adams County Department
> of Social Services

References

1. Pollock, C. and Steele, B. F. (1972): A therapeutic approach to the parents. In: *Helping the Battered Child and His Family*, pp. 3–21. J. B. Lippincott Company, Philadelphia.
2. Helfer, R. E.: *The Diagnostic Process and Treatment Program*. D.H.E.W. Publication No. (OHD) 75-69.
3. Martin, H., Ed. (1976): The abused child. In: *A Multi-Disciplinary Approach to Developmental Issues and Treatment*, Ballinger Press, Cambridge, Mass.
4. Patterson, G. R. and Guillion, M. E. (1968): *Living with Children: New Methods for Parents and Teachers*. Research Press Co., Champaign, Ill.
5. Steele, B. F.: *Working with Abusive Parents from a Psychiatric Point of View*. D.H.E.W. Publication No. (OHD) 75-70.

20

The Protective Service
Supervisor's Role

Claudia A. Carroll and Jane W. Berdie

The Supervisor's role can be broadly divided into two major areas: (1) administrative responsibilities and (2) direct supervisory responsibilities. The myriad of administrative responsibilities will not be covered, other than to say that administrative duties are realistically a part of the supervisor's duties. However, it is our premise that they should not preclude or take precedence over the direct supervisory responsibilities discussed in this chapter.

Supervision in a Social Service Department

A Social Service Department has traditionally been a one-to-one, hierarchic structure, which has perpetuated bureaucracy, lack of creative problem-solving, low morale, and a lack of autonomy.[1] In proposing guidelines for supervision in protective services, we will discuss this structure of supervision, partly because it is seemingly ubiquitous,[2] and partly because our experience has been that it can be advantageous to the maintenance of certain job performance requirements and an intra-agency support system for workers. Despite difficulties, we have found that this structure can become a means of helping workers attain and maintain the skills and knowledge necessary for protective service work. The ever increasing caseloads in protective service units are certainly not optimal; however, the supervisory process can help to make them more manageable. We suggest that the focus of County Departments of Social Services, at least for the present, be directed towards expanding the parameters of traditional supervision in social services. The model proposed here is one means of accomplishing this. It views supervision as a process of: (1) defining areas of knowledge and skills, (2) defining methods of acquisition and maintenance of knowledge and skills, (3) deciding where each worker is in terms of knowledge and skills, and (4) helping workers maintain their present skills and develop new ones necessary to effective child protective services work. The effectiveness of this process depends in great part on the supervisor's qualifications and his or her skill in carrying out the tasks inherent in this model.

QUALIFICATIONS OF THE SUPERVISOR

Recent Protective Service Experience

It is extremely important that the supervisor have recent or ongoing experience in direct work with abusing or neglecting families or both. This is necessary for one's own self-awareness, credibility with the workers, skill maintenance and development, and reality-based approach to protective services. Treatment with even one family on an ongoing basis can help in these areas.

Organizational Skills

In a county Department of Social Services it seems as if there is a neverending number of crises which must be addressed, a new morass of forms to be completed, and reports due. It is essential that the supervisor have the ability to set priorities in order to meet goals, as well as to maintain a sense of fulfillment. Further, the supervisor serves as a "buffer" for the workers, communicating that information which is relevant and important to them, and screening out that information which is not.

Good Background in the Principles of Psychotherapy

To be of assistance to the social workers who are dealing daily with very difficult clients, it is important that the supervisor bring a working knowledge of treatment and the issues of therapy. This knowledge helps the worker set realistic goals and be aware of what is operating in a family.

Personal Characteristics

Finally, there are personal characteristics which augment being able to do the job.

Good listener. The supervisee needs somewhere to go to vent frustrations and feel comfortable that these frustrations will generally be responded to in a supportive way.

Low anxiety level. If the supervisor generally functions in an anxious state, this will undoubtedly carry over to the workers and the general climate of the unit. We have heard supervisors, in assigning a family, say, "This could be the next dead child in the county," which, of course, immediately immobilizes the worker.

Flexibility. To encourage and allow growth, the supervisor needs to be sensitive to each individual worker's needs in supervision and his strengths and weaknesses. The supervisor must relinquish control, as the worker exhibits increased skill. The supervisor must be flexible, encouraging, and allowing for the worker's professional growth.

Decisiveness. There are times in protective services when a worker is having great difficulty sorting out what is happening in a family, establishing alternatives, and making a plan. In these situations, it is necessary for the supervisor to help the worker gain perspective on the case, look at additional areas of concern, arrive at mutual decisions, and establish a treatment plan. Discussing a family and not making any clearcut decisions only leaves the worker more frustrated.

GENERAL PRINCIPLES OF SUPERVISION IN PROTECTIVE SERVICES

In our experience, the most important tasks of the supervisor are the following:

Discuss and Share Decision Making

In attempting to delineate categories of skills and knowledge which the worker will need, as well as methods of their acquisition and maintenance, it is imperative that the process involve the workers. The supervisory process mutually engages both the supervisor and the supervisee. As Kadushin and Hawthorne have pointed out, supervision is highly susceptible to game-playing,[3] especially if the power disparity is viewed as arbitrary and unreasonable. In helping the worker assess information and make decisions about families with whom he is working, the role of the supervisor is to help the worker look at the situation in an enabling, rather than therapeutic way. It is not the role of the supervisor to become the worker's therapist; rather he encourages and promotes self-awareness in the worker, so that, in turn, the worker becomes more effective with families.

Support the Workers

Social workers in this field must be tied in with ongoing support systems, and one of the strongest of these should be with the direct supervisor. Given the draining nature of this work, the social worker must feel that his work is appreciated and understood as, unquestionably, he will not be getting this reinforcement from the families or the community in general. Frequently, parents displace inappropriate anger at the social worker. This is often coupled by slow progress in treatment. If the social workers feel support from their supervisor, they, in turn, can be supportive to each other. We are not advocating unconditional support, but rather support based on mutual trust and respect between the supervisor and supervisee, and shared problem solving on a direct and open basis. With these two components, critical discussion and honest evaluation of child abuse situations can take place. In large part, the support provided by the supervisor, other social workers, and the agency as a whole dictates the worker's effectiveness.

Influence the Agency's Administrative Structure

With the current public recognition of the immensity of the problem of child abuse and neglect, more and more cases are being identified. However, this is often just the "tip of the iceberg." Any supervisor in a county department must be a moving force in identifying child protective services as a priority social service of the department. These families require extensive manpower and resources and, thus, must be seen as a priority by the agency management. (It may be necessary for the supervisor to do considerable work outside of the agency educating the public as to the needs and, thus, generating support by the community to protective services for children.) The supervisor needs open lines of communication to the administration, so that current needs and problems identified by the workers are addressed, as well as insuring that communication occurs from the administration back to the workers. In addition, it is important that there be sanction by the administration for protective service workers to develop needed programs (within budget constraints), through such means as writing grants and cooperative work with other agencies and community groups.

Hire Protective Service Workers

The supervisor should be involved in the direct hiring of potential employees. To have a personnel officer without direct protective service knowledge making the decisions regarding hiring precludes looking at the unique characteristics which should be screened in hiring. (Refer to pages 200–201 regarding further discussion of these characteristics.) Before hiring, current protective service workers should talk with applicants to present, as realistically as possible, what it is like to do this work. Also, a probationary period in which the new worker's performance is evaluated for permanent status is helpful, since not every social worker has the ability to do protective service work.

Provide Case Back-Up for Workers

The protective service worker needs to feel that he can "get away" from the job from time to time. The supervisor plays an important role in back-up to the worker, being available to handle urgent matters, yet not usurping major decisions in the worker's absence.

Identify Specific Needs of Each Social Worker

We have identified the following fifteen knowledge and skill areas of the social worker in protective service work, and the supervisor should be aware of the worker's "cutting edge" or level in each. (These skills are discussed in more detail in chapters 8 and 19.)

1. Knowledge of child development.
2. Understanding of abuse and neglect dynamics.
3. Knowledge of legal and court procedures.
4. Understanding of hierarchy of Department of Social Services.
5. Skill in using agency's policies and programs.
6. Knowledge of the community.
7. Knowledge and skill in use of resources.
8. Ability to take referral information.
9. Ability to communicate through writing.
10. Skill in interviewing techniques.
11. Skill in educating other professionals and the general community.
12. Knowledge and skill in treatment.
13. Ability to manage caseload.
14. Ability to integrate diverse knowledge and skill areas.
15. Self-awareness of the worker.

Arrange Access to the Various Means of Skill Acquisition

Acquiring the knowledge and skills just identified can be accomplished through a variety of methods. The choice of methods depends on the (1) skill area, (2) level of worker functioning, and (3) availability of resources and constraints of the Department of Social Services.

It is the responsibility of the supervisor to arrange access to these fifteen skill areas. In a sense, the supervisor becomes a coordinator of continuing education for the worker. It is important to note that the supervisor need not always do all the leg work in providing the means of skill acquisition; he can delegate responsibilities to interested workers and coordinate the efforts. The various means of skill acquisition include the following:

1. One-to-one teaching by supervisor.
2. One-to-one consultation with supervisor.
3. Use of consultants (psychiatric, medical, legal, and educational).
4. Reading.

5. Unit meetings (organized discussion with peers). This is an opportunity to disseminate and discuss procedural information and treatment issues, as well as to increase group cohesiveness, openness, and trust.

6. Informal and spontaneous discussion with peers. Discussion is an extremely important vehicle for learning, decision-making, problem solving, and maintaining morale. It offers the worker an opportunity for feedback, encouragement, advice, reflection, sorting out, and setting priorities—all of which can be critical in decision making and problem solving.

7. Inservice training, conferences, workshops. This becomes a means of sensitizing and informing workers to issues, research findings, treatment modalities, and the like. This can also be a time to become "refueled." Workers should be involved in planning the training agenda, so that it is relevant to their needs.

8. Observation. Examples of observation would be watching video material and observing court hearings.

9. Participant-observation. Accompanying another social worker on activities such as an intake interview and placement and case conferences is an excellent form of learning.

10. Tandem supervision. This is a method of two workers "sharing" responsibility for a family, usually with one having primary responsibility and the other secondary responsibility. Discussions and decisions are made between the two workers.

11. Interagency team treatment. Treatment for the entire family often involves, in addition to the social workers, one or more of the following: public health nurse, pediatrician, psychologist, psychiatrist, teacher, home-maker, lay therapist, therapist for the child, and the like. This approach becomes an invaluable opportunity to develop knowledge of a wide spectrum of areas relating to abuse and neglect, as well as skill in working on a team. Its usefulness is based on the premise that the social worker alone cannot meet all the needs of one family—child abuse and neglect require shared responsibility and the concerted efforts of many people.

12. Multidisciplinary review team. Comprised of other service providers and consultants, this is a check and balance system of reviewing what action has or may be taken on a case. There is a delicate balance between the legal mandate of the Department of Social Services (and the worker) to be responsible for the case, yet accountable to such a review team which often carries certain powers to action. The social worker needs to be able to function autonomously, however, within certain parameters of review or action by others or both. For example, it is unacceptable for a social worker doing an intake evaluation to function under the constraints of having to ask the supervisor or multidisciplinary review team for sanction to initiate removal of a child from his home. He must have the ability and sanction to take this action quickly for the child's protection.

13. Community education. In conducting educational programs for con-

cerned community groups, the worker is sensitized to community awareness and understanding of the phenomenon of abuse and neglect and the
perception of the Department of Social Services, as well as the means of
creating more cooperation within the community.

14. Direct experience. Direct experience characterized by an adequate
knowledge base, flexible supervision, and a gradation of increased responsibility is perhaps the most essential means of skill acquisition. There is a
certain illumination which takes place when one has had direct experience
and can critically look at what has worked and what has not. Reflection is a
means of knowing "where to go from here." A year of direct experience
appears to be an average amount of time for a social worker to go through
the process of reflection, to gain confidence in his abilities, and to assimilate the necessary knowledge and skills.

Encourage Personal Development and Self-Awareness

Inherent to protective services are certain "loaded" issues with which
the social worker must feel comfortable to effectively work with abusing/
neglecting families. We will discuss six key issues, which we see to be
essential in the positive use of self-awareness by the social worker, and
which should be fostered by the supervisor.

1. Appropriate use of power.
2. Ability to make decisions.
3. Objectivity.
4. Limit setting (for self and client).
5. "Refueling" (for example, academically and compensatory time).
6. Personal identity.

1. *Appropriate use of power.* The legal mandate of protective services carries with it an enormous amount of power (for example, initiation of action
to remove a child from the parental home). The social worker is frequently
seen by the parents and the community as an authority figure. The protective service worker must feel comfortable in this position and exercise his
powers sensitively.

2. *Ability to make decisions.* High on the list of key areas facing the protective services worker are a multitude of varied, and often life-threatening
decisions. These decisions include questions regarding: if a court petition
should be filed; if a child, for his well-being, must be removed from his
home; if it is safe for the child to be placed back in the parental home; and if
a case can be closed. The ability to make decisions can be broken down in
the following way:

(a) Gathering all the relevant data. (Poor decisions are often the result of
an insufficient data base.)
(b) Assimilating and organizing the data.
(c) Arriving at the decision.
(d) Being prepared to state the rationale for the decision.

Agency guidelines regarding the above identified areas concerning the child and his family are extremely helpful. They should be available in writing to workers to assist in thinking through case decisions. These can be especially helpful to a worker during a crisis (see Appendix D-1).

3. *Objectivity.* Maintaining the perspective of neutrality is often very difficult, though critically necessary. The protective services worker should be aware of the "three camps"—the community camp, the parent camp, and the child camp (C. Pollock, *personal communication,* Feb. 1974). Over-identification with any one of these three camps blocks the worker from effective intervention with the family. As a result the stage is set for a lack of clarity in viewing the composite picture. For example, if the social worker over-identifies with the parent this could prevent a lack of awareness regarding the child's safety. Concomitantly, in over-identifying with the child, the social worker could become very angry with the parents, thus, lacking empathy for their situation and problems. Over-identification with the community may cloud seeing both the parents' and the child's situation and, therefore, responding out of frustration to the community demand (for example, agencies being set up against each other or unnecessary removal of a child from his natural home).

4. *Limit setting.* The needs of the abusive/neglecting family are vast, and one of the functions of the social worker is to help the family look to other adults, rather than their children, to have those needs met.[4] The worker is thrust into the position of being one of the first people the parent looks to for need fulfillment. (The dependency on the worker in the beginning and middle stages of working together are enormous.) Judgement must be keen both in timing and in discriminating areas which would require limit-setting (e.g., availability to the parents, saying "no" when necessary, and knowing how much to do for the family). This limit-setting is necessary to help the parents grow, and, for most parents, it is the first opportunity they have had to learn how to negotiate in a give-and-take relationship.

5. *"Refueling."* Due to the draining nature of this work, it is essential that the protective services worker have the ability to emotionally "get away" from work regularly. This can be accomplished in two ways: (1) academically, theoretical ideas assist in putting into perspective the daily demands of a caseload, as well as in developing better services to families, and (2) a flexible compensatory time policy by which the worker is encouraged to take time off for past periods of overwork. For this physical and emotional time off to succeed, agency sanction is imperative. Additionally, the worker who has interests outside of work is better equipped to maintain a constant "refueling" and, thus, a better perspective of the job.

6. *Personal Identity.* Finally, there are personal characteristics of protective service workers which enhance performance. A strong sense of personal identity is an important characteristic, since the worker is regularly faced with people who are frightened and angry. The protective services

worker must be sensitive to these feelings, yet not internalize them. The parents are usually angry with many people and often these feelings are directed at the worker. If the social worker needs to be liked or appreciated by his clients, he will quickly become immobilized. A person with a tenuous self-image will be faced with increased self-doubts, which could preclude taking decisive action on a case when necessary. Other manifestations of self-doubts in protective service workers may result in over-identification with one of the "camps" (for example, inappropriate anger directed at the parents leads to thoughts of becoming the child's "savior" and rescuing the child from "bad" parents).

Complementing a strong self-identity is the ability to communicate to the parent that he, the worker, is "feeling with" them and is sincerely interested in them as individuals. Client movement can begin once the parent begins to trust the social worker and believes that this person cares. This stage of treatment usually takes time and testing, but it is unquestionably the foundation of all else in protective service social work. This process of moving beyond the initial angry, demanding feelings of the parents is the first step to a trusting, mutual arrangement.

Being aware of one's own feelings and situation is essential, so that one does not project onto the parents what are truly feelings related to self (for example, having a flat tire on the way to work and then displacing these feelings to the parents). This is a process of identifying and compartmentalizing those feelings related to the family and those related to oneself.

Finally, a sense of humor serves to maintain one's own equilibrium, as well as to lighten the morale of other staff. An entire unit of depressed protective service workers produces only more depression, lack of energy, and poor productivity.

Specific Supervision for Different Levels of Worker Functioning

For each level of worker functioning, specific types of supervision are more appropriate than for other levels. Three general levels of worker functioning have been identified.

LEVEL OF WORKER FUNCTIONING

1. *Beginning Functioning.* This level is usually characterized by inexperience and limited knowledge in regard to abuse and neglect, although not necessarily to social work. There is a desire to effectively and humanely

provide services, uncertainty about expectations of performance, and an expectation that a certain creativity or ingenuity will be needed to transcend the gravity of a "welfare bureaucracy."

2. *Seasoned Functioning.* This worker has come to grips with those areas discussed pertaining to personal development and self-awareness and has skill in a variety of treatment experiences. The competent protective services worker makes decisions on both an academic and a "gut level" basis, and he communicates with confidence to clients and the community.

3. *Burnt-Out Functioning.* This is the worker who may be overwhelmed by caseload size, is emotionally drained, and cannot cope adequately. Such a worker manifests symptoms in a variety of ways: He becomes immobilized by even the slightest crisis in the caseload, denies or glosses over the severity of a case or important details, or may be insensitive to feelings of the parents or child.

THE SUPERVISORY PROCESS: THE BEGINNING WORKER

In discussing the process of taking a social worker from an inexperienced to competent level of functioning, it is with the assumption that the beginning worker is a reasonably emotionally healthy person and has the capacity to handle the multiple and serious dimensions of the job. Hence, he is a potentially competent person. He must have the ability to grow professionally and personally in relation to the job.

The beginning, inexperienced worker requires a good period of inservice training prior to assuming the responsibilities of the caseload. Minimally, we suggest two weeks of intensive training, using a variety of approaches which will be discussed. Ironically, agencies often provide a more comprehensive inservice orientation period to volunteers and paraprofessionals than to the social work staff. Unless a new worker has had prior protective service experience, it behooves the supervisor to refrain from assigning the "waiting caseload" until the new worker has first had some opportunity for education and training.

The supervisory process with the beginning worker should be a fluid one whereby, initially, the supervisor is involved in most case decisions, moves to a moderate degree of involvement in case planning, and, finally, within a period of a year, moves to a consultative role with the worker. Certainly all the means of skill acquisition identified in this chapter are useful in moving an inexperienced worker to a competent level of functioning. For the new worker, however, the key is utilizing these skills by gradation. Of all the skills necessary to a protective service worker, two of the most essential are knowledge of abuse and neglect theory and self-awareness. The first is a cognitive, didactic process, the latter, an emotional, introspective process. (The other thirteen skills are also important; however, they can be mastered more easily with a good foundation in the two areas just identified.)

Facilitating Understanding of Abuse and Neglect Dynamics

Knowledge about abuse and neglect can be gained through such means as one-to-one teaching by the supervisor and reading pertinent to the subject. Additionally, observation through viewing video material or going to a court hearing with another worker is helpful. Group discussion, either on an organized basis (unit meeting) or informally, with other protective service workers, is extremely relevant during this period of learning. Participant-observation could be the next step used, whereby the worker goes out with a seasoned worker on an intake and participates in the interview and subsequent decision making with the family.

Facilitating Self-awareness of the Worker

A beginning worker in protective services experiences a multitude of mixed feelings ranging from uncertainty, fear, and anger, to the initial stage of feeling comfortable in handling the job responsibilities. In looking at personal development, as well as a better knowledge base, we identify a variety of methods to facilitate growth.

1. Unit meetings. Mutual discussion of difficult case situations in a sharing way is helpful to the worker in identifying his own feelings regarding a family and gaining a better understanding of the family.
2. Use of psychiatric consultant and supervisor. Consultation may be useful in sorting out the worker's feelings which may be getting in the way of moving ahead with the family. Consultation is also helpful in understanding therapeutic plateaus with a family and blockages to treatment.
3. Interagency team treatment. Sharing a case is an excellent way of gaining immediate feedback as to how one is relating positively or negatively to a family.
4. Direct experience. This is, in our opinion, one of the most elucidating methods of coming to a realization of the best use of self with families. This process requires time, the ability to reflect critically, and the ability to recognize where one has succeeded and where one has failed. Insight is gained through introspection, as well as information from peers and clients. It is unlikely that one ever feels entirely comfortable in "going out on their next child abuse intake," since that situation seems to be charged with anxiety. However, we do believe one learns much through personal experience. Only through direct experience does one really gain the appreciation of how the theory of child abuse and neglect fits within the family constellation.

THE SUPERVISORY PROCESS: RESTORING A BURNT-OUT WORKER

With the current fiscal constraints and lack of adequate staff, some may say the task of restoring a burnt-out worker is heroic, impossible, or even ludicrous. Skilled protective service workers are leaving the field daily because of the ever increasing pressures related to high caseloads. Recognizing that this is a formidable task, we would like to underscore a previous point, that is, one of the main responsibilities of the supervisor is to help in making the situation in protective services more manageable for the social worker.

One of the conflicts we continually see with protective service workers is that of trying to make changes in nontreatable families. Historically, Departments of Social Services or Public Welfare have been expected by the community to work with anyone and everyone. This, of course, cannot be done; and social service departments have for far too long been carrying this burden too silently. One of the issues, then, for the burnt-out worker is the need to identify *realistic* treatment goals based on a sound psychosocial diagnosis of the family. If the family is not treatable, this must be recognized and steps taken to move to some resolution of the problem as quickly as possible, for example, court action. The worker's time must be freed to be spent on those families who will benefit. The task and skill at hand for the supervisor and the burnt-out worker is most often that of good caseload management, because the worker has become overwhelmed and drained by the demands of the workload. (Refer to chapter 19 regarding more discussion of caseload management.)

Helping a burnt-out worker set priorities within and among families, complete the minimum necessary paperwork, and perform the other tasks of case management requires the supervisor to be especially sensitive to the quality of the worker's dormant skills and knowledge, as well as his burnt-out feelings. A worker who has gone from seasoned-competent to burnt-out should be supervised vis-a-vis the means of competency. This emphasizes the abilities which are there and the supervisor's confidence in those abilities. This is not to say that feelings and attitudes should not be addressed. A burnt-out, competent worker usually wants to vent these feelings, and it certainly is useful in order to identify the causative factors. Venting feelings can help, because sometimes some of the causative factors can be eliminated or ameliorated through: (1) transferring a case, (2) taking time off, or (3) striking a better balance between the energy-draining tasks and the positive ones. However, it is equally important to supervise using means which help the worker regain, maintain, or reintegrate skills and knowledge. Therefore, the means utilized are highlighted more by what is not utilized, than by what is utilized.

One-to-one supervisory conferences should be characterized by type and purpose, as well as by language, as consultative, not teaching. If the topic is a problem of case management, that topic should be adhered to. Use of self and self-awareness are almost always related to the worker-depletion syndrome, and it should be addressed at some point. But consultation on case management should deal with identifying the issues and problem solving of those issues.

Means by which the worker can become refueled are taking time off and academic stimulation. Other useful means may include the unit meeting, in which common issues of case management may be addressed; workshops on the issue; and informal discussions with peers.

Tandem and team supervision may be quite useful, if the worker has skills and knowledge, however dormant. At Adams County Department of Social Services, Colorado, we explored both of these possibilities but decided that the high caseloads mitigated against the usefulness of either method, at least in terms of the responsibility for cases inherent to public welfare agency supervision. We, therefore, employed these methods only in consultative terms.

Prevention of Burnt-Out Workers

In the larger arena, to prevent burnt-out workers, we must all work toward a system of protective services whereby:

1. Many community agencies share responsibility for treatment of abusive, neglecting families.

2. A variety of treatment options are available from which to choose (for example, day care, crisis nurseries, lay therapy and treatment for each family member).

3. A maximum workload standard for a social worker exists (for example, Colorado is proposing to the legislature a maximum workload standard of 22 families per protective service social worker).[a]

4. A variety of protective service experiences are available to workers (e.g., treatment with families, supervision of a student, lay therapists, or community aid; involvement in groups; and participation in public speaking). This ameliorates such feelings as frustration and incompletion that result if any of these is the worker's exclusive task.

5. Preventive programs are developed, rather than total emphasis on after the fact, "keeping your finger in the dike," crisis intervention. Such preventive programs could include: family life education in grade and high schools, greater availability of good day care, prenatal education and supportive services, "health visitors," and the like. Dr. Karl Menninger has said, "It is easier, more logical, and more efficacious to help a child grow up with love and courage, than it is to instill hope in a despondent lost soul."

Note

[a]Kawamura, G. and Carroll, C. (1976): Managerial and Financial Aspects of Social Service Programs. In: *Child Abuse and Neglect, The Family and the Community*, edited by R. E. Helfer and C. H. Kempe. Ballinger Publishing Co., Cambridge, Mass.

References

Alexander, H. (1972): The social worker and the family. In: *Helping the Battered Child and His Family*, edited by C. H. Kempe and R. E. Helfer, p. 28. J. B. Lippincott Co., Philadelphia.

Amatai, E. (1969): *The Semi-Professions and Their Organizations*. Free Press, New York.

Eisenberg, S. S. and Finch, W. A. (1972): Supervision in a public welfare agency. In: *Issues in Human Services*, edited by F. W. Kaslow, p. 231. Jossey-Bass, Inc., San Francisco.

Hawthorne, L. (1975): Games supervisors play. *Social Work,* 20(3).

Kadushin, A. (1975): Games supervisees play. *Social Work,* 20(3).

21

The Physician's Role in Treatment

Jane D. Gray

In addition to the physician's role in the evaluation phase and his contribution to the decisions of the multidisciplinary, problem-oriented team, the doctor is frequently a part of the treatment program. The physician follows the child not only for signs of aberrant parenting (physical abuse, failure to thrive, slow development, or behavioral difficulties), but also to maintain comprehensive health supervision of the entire family, to offer any guidance or counseling that is appropriate, and to anticipate which problems could best be alleviated with the help of other professionals. Therefore, the physician's role is essentially the same, whether he is following a family that has been thought to have a high potential for abnormal parenting practices, or he is following a family in which there has been previously documented abuse. In addition, this role is also appropriate for office or clinic-based pediatric nurse practitioners or child health associates.

One maxim for the physician is that he not attempt to manage a family by himself. Abusive families, and those thought to have a potential for abuse, are notoriously multiproblem families. No one person and no single specialty can be expected to possess all the expertise necessary to benefit this family. Thus, in order to provide the best services, the physician should view himself as part of a group effort, rather than as the sole caretaker responsible for this family. In this role, the doctor, or if he is a member of a child protection team, the coordinator (see chapter 25), should see that all medical/developmental/behavioral assessments and recommendations are provided to all other professionals involved in treatment.

251

This may include the public health nurse, the protective service worker, the school system (including Head Start and preschools), and some medical consultants (for example, orthopedists, neurologists, and dentists).

Medical Follow-Up of High-Risk Families

Close medical supervision and supportive rapport with a family have been very beneficial in decreasing the incidence of serious physical abuse. The following aspects are essential in the medical follow-up of high-risk families.

COMPREHENSIVE MEDICAL CARE

The physician's primary role is to offer the family comprehensive health supervision, including updating immunizations, plotting growth curves, developmental screening tests, routine laboratory testing, and referrals to subspecialists as necessary. Also, in a broader sense, it should include referrals for total health care, including dental care and routine vision and hearing testing. The parents are also often in need of health care and may need referrals for their own health problems. The most common referral seems to be for obstetrical-gynecologic care for the mother, either for family planning or for subsequent pregnancy.

The physician should plan to see not only the abused child, but also his siblings. Since all of the children in the family have theoretically been exposed to the same abusive/neglectful environment, even those who have not received physical abuse may also show developmental lags, behavioral maladjustments, and lack of general health care.

ONGOING ASSESSMENTS FOR SIGNS OF TRAUMA

In addition to comprehensive well-child care, the physician must be especially alert to signs of physical trauma. Even minor lesions should be questioned, the physician remaining alert to a history that is discrepant with the degree or type of injury. It seems to "go without saying" that the children be completely undressed during a physical exam. One should not be hesitant to retake X-rays, either as (1) follow-up to what was seen in the hospital, (2) for reevaluation of a suspected injury (periosteal elevations may be seen two to three weeks after a normal X-ray), or (3) if reabuse occurs. Skeletal surveys are also important in the total evaluation of failure-to-thrive infants, since a certain percentage of these children will have previously unsuspected injuries.

ONGOING DEVELOPMENTAL INTERACTIONAL ASSESSMENTS

A frequent reassessment of a child's developmental status and progress is necessary in order to help ascertain the amount of stimulation he is receiving. In addition, throughout the interview and examination, the physician should be alert to the child's behaviors, the mother's reactions to them, and the interaction between the parents and the child(ren). In our experience, observations during the DDST are often very revealing, possibly because it is a performance test that reflects on the mother's self-esteem.

ASSESSING PARENTAL FEELINGS

After assessment of a child's health and developmental status, it is wise to direct the evaluation to the mother or father, asking how they are doing and some nonthreatening questions about the status of their present social situation. An understanding of how the parents are functioning, what the present living conditions are, and how the parents feel about their situation can be gleaned. This is worthwhile, because it permits the physician to determine the direction and tone of his counseling to the parents.

ACUTE ILLNESS COUNSELING

What to anticipate with acute minor illness and when to call a physician are important areas to cover. Symptoms and signs to be watched for should be outlined in detail—both signs that are a natural consequence of the disease and any signs that might cause undue concern. Reassurance that the physician will be available to answer additional questions will help alleviate their concerns. Medication or special diets should be gone over in detail with the parents. Writing out directions is often reassuring to the parents and avoids confusion. Parents are often eager to know "how long it will last," and an overestimate of the duration of the disease is usually better than an underestimate.

Two diseases which seemed to be hardest for parents to handle are otitis media and gastroenteritis. Otitis is difficult because the child is often fussy and may be wakeful at night, without many overt signs of illness. Also, vomiting and diarrhea, because of its general messiness, is a difficult disease for parents to cope with. During these illnesses, the parents will be grateful for support from medical personnel. The physician, by his availability (office and home phone numbers), may prevent parents from getting beyond their ability to cope and, thus, resorting to physical abuse.

GROWTH AND DEVELOPMENT

A detailed history of a child's development should be explored with the parents. This is done for several reasons. First, all counseling can then be appropriate to the child's developmental level and projected ahead only until the next visit. Projecting too far ahead may only confuse the parent. Second, if parents know the next stages of development, they can be shown ways to stimulate and reinforce the child in a skill. Third, additional guidance can be given about any related aspects, for instance, counseling with regard to safety measures as a child's gross motor skills increase.

ANTICIPATORY GUIDANCE FOR PROVOCATIVE STAGES

Anticipatory guidance can also be given for certain stages of development that are apt to be provocative for the parents. In any of the following areas, advice must be given in a nonjudgmental tone. Explanations as to why certain rearrangements are necessary, and even beneficial, usually meet with more success. In many childrearing practices, there is more than one acceptable manner of proceeding. Explaining this to the parents with the pros and cons of the alternatives, and allowing the parents to choose which method is most feasible for the family, will permit them to feel that they have some say in their child's care. This usually leads to a more satisfactory outcome for both the child and the doctor-parent relationship.

Feeding

In the neonatal period, parents are particularly concerned about feeding patterns. They are worried about over- or under-feeding the baby, the timing and methods for introducing solid foods, the need for vitamins and iron supplements, the introduction of finger foods, and, then, self-feeding skills. During the newborn period, mothers are very unsure about feeding because of the lack of feedback from the baby. Later, the messiness of self-feeding becomes hard for some parents to tolerate. Nutritional facts, some very specific techniques of feeding, and reasons why certain foods are necessary for the child are important in alleviating the parents' anxieties.

Sleep/wakeful patterns

Another area which is often difficult for parents to adjust to is the baby's sleeping/waking patterns, which are often quite unreliable in the first months of life. Babies who are frequently awake at night are a physical drain on parents, as well as being disruptive of parental life-styles. Even when babies sleep well, there are times when the sleep schedules change (two naps to one nap), and this can be difficult for some rigid parents to tolerate. Suggestions to the parents regarding changing sleep patterns must be done with an effort to make them compatible with the parents' life-style. Attempting to change the whole family's method of functioning usually meets with frustration and eventual defeat. On very rare occasions, a mother will express the fear that if "that baby doesn't get to sleep, I'll hit him." This is certainly the time to consider medicating the child (for example, chloral hydrate). This requires close monitoring and probably a daily telephone call. If medication is deemed to be unfeasible for this family (fear of overdose or unreliability in giving medications), foster care, a crisis nursery, or hospitalization must be seriously considered.

Independence/exploratory behaviors

As a child becomes more independent, some mothers have difficulty "letting go." They may see the baby's new found independence as a rejection. Therefore, some mothers need to be prepared for this behavior in advance. She can then realize that independence is a natural part of the child's development. As a child becomes more independent, his exploratory behavior increases. A toddler who is busily exploring his environment is in a difficult stage, and his exploring will often cause messes for the mother to clean up. Also, he is in need of constant supervision for his own safety. This almost constant vigilance by the parent is time consuming and frustrating; and any practical suggestions (for example, a special place for the child's toys, rather than throughout the whole house, removing obvious hazards, and adding safety measures to those hazards which can't be easily removed—locks on cabinets, gates in front of stairs) can be helpful to the parents. Exploratory behavior often occurs at the same time as the independence issue comes to the fore, which makes the situation doubly difficult for some parents.

Toilet training

One especially troublesome area for these parents is the issue of toilet training. It brings many of the conflicts of the parents to the foreground, making this a particularly difficult time. Children are frequently punished for toilet accidents, and counseling in an effort to prevent this must be begun early. Many of these parents begin toilet training before the child is physiologically mature enough to have bladder/bowel control. This only ends in failure and frustration. Counseling the parents to wait until the child is older and begins to show some interest will meet with better success.

SAFETY MEASURES

Often, battering parents lead a chaotic life-style. This can also be reflected in their homes, and, therefore, suggestions for safety measures are appropriate. This is probably more necessary than in the general population, because of the family's disorganization.

HOSPITALIZATION

If a child needs to be hospitalized for an intercurrent, acute illness, it is worthwhile to encourage the parents to visit the child frequently and help take care of the child (for example, feeding). In some hospitals, it is possible for the parents to live in with the child and assume much of his care. This (1) is helpful in fostering the bonding between mother and child, (2) may help educate the parents about certain aspects of child care, and (3) may also alleviate some of the fears and suspicions these parents so commonly manifest.

PUBLIC HEALTH NURSE REFERRALS

Frequently the physician will need to ask that a public health nurse also follow the family. In addition to the help she provides in sharing the burden of caring for a troubled family, she also adds the dimension of an assessment of the family's functioning in their own home setting, where they are often more relaxed and natural (see chapter 22). In the home setting, the public health nurse can easily assess the physical layout and safety of the home. She then is better able to advise what changes, if any, are necessary or even feasible. After she has established some rapport with the family, she will also be in an excellent position to evaluate the parent-child relationship in the natural home setting, rather than in the more formal clinic or office surroundings.

A public health nurse is especially needed to complement the physician's role in the following instances: (1) the young, preschool age child who has been abused but is still in the home; (2) the family where there is a potential for abnormal parenting, and where there is a child less than two years of age; (3) all infants with failure to thrive; and (4) when the parents could benefit from educational measures demonstrated in the home.

When there are several professionals involved with a family, it is important that they communicate frequently. These families can be very manipulative, and sometimes they will try to set one professional against another. Open communication is the only way to deal with the manipulation. When the professionals can provide a united front, the family can then face their problems and begin to deal with them in a more realistic manner.

SCHEDULING OFFICE VISITS

Particularly when the baby is young, these families need especially close supervision and support. Office visits should be scheduled every one to two weeks or more frequently if needed. The first visit should occur by the time the baby is two weeks old. Since the main purpose of these frequent visits is to evaluate the developing mother-child relationship, more than the usual amount of time must be scheduled for well-child visits. An average of 30 to 45 minutes for a well-child visit is not unusual.

TELEPHONE CONTACT

In addition to frequent office contacts, close communication by telephone is important and may serve as this family's lifeline. Mothers should be encouraged to call the doctor for any concerns, which means the physician must be willing to give out his home telephone number. Also, the doctor should initiate an outreach program by telephone, calling parents with the results of laboratory tests, checking on the progress of a disease, or to offer support during a period of crisis.

EXPECTATIONS FOR THE PARENTS

It is somewhat unrealistic to expect these parents to be prompt for an appointment, or even to show up the first time they are scheduled. Some arrive early, stating they had nothing else to do, with the implication that they will use the office or clinic as a social outlet. Others are late owing to a myriad of reasons, such as oversleeping and transportation problems. On occasion, these parents may get the day of their appointment confused and arrive at the right time, but on the wrong day. They frequently forget their clinic or Medicaid cards, necessitating some changes in administrative routine.

If a patient does miss an appointment, it is probably best to wait two or three days before telephoning to ask the mother to reschedule another appointment. A telephone call several days later is not viewed as so threatening as when the family is called on the day of the missed appointment. The delay of a day or two also gives the mother a chance to initiate the rescheduling herself. Usually, a gentle reminder of the need for an appointment is met with appreciation, since it is viewed as evidence of the physician's continued concern.

EDUCATION OF OFFICE STAFF

Because of the above problems, these patients offer limited gratification and, indeed, are often very difficult to handle. Therefore, nurses, secretaries, and clerks need to be advised of the fact that even though these patients can be irritating, demanding, complaining, or even openly hostile, they are the very patients who most need to be seen. Therefore, whether on the telephone or in person, the doctor needs to spend time with the family. The office/clinic staff should not try to protect the doctor from them.

COMMUNITY REFERRALS

These multiproblem families can often benefit from the services of a variety of community agencies. The doctor must be willing to initiate referrals, even if it is not strictly a medical referral. These patients need help in contacting public welfare departments for financial assistance, food stamp programs, job training programs, and school reeducation programs.

NEONATAL ASPECTS OF PREVENTION

Many pediatricians are initiating a policy of seeing a young mother during the last month of her pregnancy. This can be particularly helpful to first-time parents, especially if there seems to be the potential for difficulty interacting with the baby. In these cases, every effort can be made to foster early bonding with the infant. This may include having the father present in the labor and delivery rooms; allowing the mother to see and hold the baby while still in the delivery room; getting the mother, father, and baby together in the recovery room; and encouraging the mother and the baby to room-in. In addition to examining the newborn baby, the physician caring for the infant should also spend time with the mother while she is on the maternity ward in order to answer questions, allay fears, and support attachment behaviors.

Pitfalls

These families are not particularly gratifying to follow. They are a drain on one's emotional resources and give very limited positive reinforcement in return. The first axiom for a physician who finds himself in the role of following abusive families, or families with the potential for severe interactional difficulties, should be that if he finds he cannot tolerate or emotionally handle these patients, he should refer them to someone who can. Another reason to refer a family is if the physician feels he is making no progress with the family and someone else's approach might be more helpful. The overriding objective should be never to allow these people to drop out of the health-care system and to refer them to someone with whom they can work comfortably.

The physician must work to maintain his objectivity. It is surprisingly easy for the physician to become so closely allied with the parents that he wants to believe (1) that a minor injury, such as bruising, won't recur, (2) flimsy excuses account for the injury, or (3) a parent who promises to reform actually will, even without added intervention.

On the other hand, the physician can easily become so closely allied with the child that he considers "taking a child out of the home and working toward severing parental rights" as the only possible solution. This can be termed the "rescue phenomenon." Here, the only alternative considered is to rescue the child, rather than to work toward restoring family functioning.

Other pitfalls relate to the issue of reporting. It is important not to adopt the attitude that, if an injury is reported, the family won't return for health care. If the explanation for the necessity of the report is handled with understanding and empathy, the family may think of the physician as someone who is actually being helpful in trying to protect them and the child. Also, any recurrences, even minor ones, need to be rereported, rather than taking the attitude that all the hassles of reporting and court involvement will not benefit the family. Sometimes, it takes more than one documented injury or period of failure to thrive before the full complement of helping services will be offered to a family.

An easy pitfall to slip into is not taking enough time to hear what the parents are trying to say. The parents may talk at length about extraneous subjects before finally getting to the point of the real issue. Or, what they are saying may need to be interpreted, since the actual problem may never be frankly stated. Therefore, identifying the real problem areas may take extra time, gentle probing, and intuition, none of which can be done easily or rapidly.

The physician should not build his self-esteem on how the family is functioning. Families will notoriously have many high and low points during the physician's time of involvement. These highs and lows for a family can be more profitably shared with others working with the family (for example, public health nurses or social workers), rather than being considered a reflection on one person's value as a therapist.

Summary

Close and comprehensive health supervision, with frequent office/clinic visits and continued telephone/in-person availability, can serve as a lifeline for troubled parents. This can usually only be done safely by sharing the responsibilities with all appropriate, available community services. If a physician is thought of as a helping person and has established rapport with the family, it will be the physician to whom the family turns in times of crisis or at the time of a minor reinjury. By offering health care and anticipatory guidance, and serving as a lifeline, the physician can give the family an opportunity to grow and change their childrearing practices.

22

The Public Health Nurse's Role in Treatment

Sharon L. Cross

Indications for Public Health Nursing

The public health nurse (PHN) involved in health promotion through visits in the community is a valuable resource to parents and team members in dealing with abuse and neglect cases. In many instances, families are initially more receptive to a nurse entering their home than they are to visits by other qualified professionals. Although not all cases of identified child abuse or neglect require or benefit from nursing intervention, there are several roles which can most effectively be assumed by a public health nurse.

The primary indicators to be considered in determining the inclusion of a PHN on the intervention team are:

1. The child's need for follow through of a medical plan.
2. The child's need for developmental and behavioral assessment.
3. Parental need to gain and implement knowledge regarding normal development of children.
4. Parental need for information regarding common childrearing practices.
5. The need for an involved professional to coordinate community resources.

The following are frequently encountered, specific examples of the five primary indicators for nursing involvement:

1. Following a child's discharge from an outpatient setting or hospital, nursing expertise should be employed to assist the natural or foster parent

261

or both and the physician and other professionals to monitor medications, head circumference, and weight changes.

2. To instruct caregivers in physical care procedures and environmental stimulation.

3. To interpret medical terminology to nonmedical persons. In order to continue the hospital-established plan for management of children diagnosed as failure to thrive, the case should also be referred to a public health nurse for ongoing implementation.

Abused or neglected children have typically been found to experience growth or developmental delays. Through the use of age-specific history taking and the administration of a developmental screening tool, the nurse can collect valuable baseline data for use in direct intervention with parents and for team evaluation of the environmental needs of the child.

Abusive parents have typically been found to have unrealistically high performance expectations of children. In response to this parental reaction, the public health nurse can competently demonstrate a child's abilities at a specific age and, thus, assist the parent in understanding and anticipating current and future development. When a parent gains this knowledge, he is better able to understand the rationale for child rearing practices and to implement age appropriate expectations.

Included among the anticipated results of such intervention are the parent's ability to provide a safe environment for an energetic child, to interpret the cues of a nontalking infant, to assess when an ill child requires medical intervention, and to determine when a child is physically and behaviorally ready for new skills such as toilet training.

Finally, because the public health nurse is knowledgeable regarding community resources, she can, as a team member, assist in identifying appropriate programs for families, assist them in securing ongoing medical care, and function as a coordinator for the interagency services being received by the family.

Treatment Approaches

The public health nurse must be acutely aware not only of the child's need for parental change, but also the parent's needs. Throughout the literature on child abuse, authors recommend that all professionals concentrate their attention initially on the parents in order to establish an effective working relationship. The parent must be nurtured as well as the child. Because the content of the PHN's intervention is so often child centered, the nurse must be particularly aware of the need to establish a trusting relationship with the parent, before concentrating on child-directed information. Also, the readiness of the parent to accept assistance in child rearing practices and other stresses which may be operational in the family, such as, financial difficulties or marital discord, needs to be assessed. Initially one may want to discuss something as nonthreatening as the day's activities of the needy parent. Once the relationship has been established, and the nurse has assessed with the parent the priority problems, they need to jointly negotiate a contract which will establish the purpose and the content of future visits as well as the responsibilities of both parties. The contract should also include the nurse's option to observe the child physically.

The primary consideration at this early stage is to establish a safe environment for the child. Therefore, a plan must be developed which can be implemented when the parents experience the frustration which places the child at risk. At such times, parents can separate themselves from the child by placing him in a safe room, or contact someone to stay with him, or call Parents Anonymous, if such a group is available.

In providing follow through of the medical plan, the public health nurse must maintain open lines of communication with the physician so that information given to the parents is consistent. Again, the nurse must review the parents' interpretation of the information received. In a diagnosed failure-to-thrive infant, it will be important to assess the parent's perceptions of the child's growth, expectations for type and quantity of food, frustration level surrounding feeding times, method of feeding, capability for cuddling the infant, and the child's response to feeding. The nurse can then demonstrate to the parent appropriate amounts of food, formula preparation, and activities which make meal times more comfortable and reinforce the positive behaviors demonstrated by the parent. She should monitor the baby by weighing him weekly. Any observation of reabuse must be documented and reported to the physician and child protective services.

When assessing the developmental level of a child, the nurse should observe him in his own environment and determine the parental response to his verbal and behavioral cues. Utilization of the Denver Developmental Screening Test, the Draw-A-Man, the Washington Guide, and school reports provides more specific data regarding the developmental level of the child. Such information assists the nurse in determining performance-appropriate expectations of the child and socialization activities or stimulation programs which may be needed.

An infant program might include utilization of mobiles, jungle gyms, responsive speech, and mirrors. Nurses can teach parents how to use books, paints, stacking toys, homemade instruments, and varied shapes with older children. As parents complete these stimulation assignments, the PHN has another opportunity to positively reinforce changed parental behaviors.

Awareness of the individual child's level of development prepares the PHN to assist the parent in understanding why a child may behave as he does and what methods the parent can appropriately use in dealing with a child's misbehavior. By identifying and describing examples of similar behaviors seen in other children, the nurse helps the parent realize that he and his child are not abnormal or unusual. Instead, an infant's crying or rubbing food in his hair or a child's refusal to go to bed or get dressed, crossing a street when told not to, or persisting in interruptive behaviors can be interpreted as difficult but normal developmental phases. Parents can then recognize that other parents also experience the same frustration and anxiety.

A parent may initially interpret normal two-year-old behavior as totally unmanageable and rebellious. When the nurse describes the child's beginning development of autonomy and discusses ways of directing the child to make his behavior more acceptable, while still encouraging independent development, both the child and the parent benefit. When the parent offers a child the choice between reading a story and coloring a picture, the child experiences control over his environment. When a child whines in order to gain control over his parents and environment, the parent can define the unacceptable behavior and the consequences of its continuation. If the child proceeds, the parent must then enforce the consequences by placing the child in his room.

As the parent and the nurse collaborate in observing and assessing a child's behavior and the parental response to it, they jointly develop methods to effectively deal with the child's behavior. As a result of such intervention, parents learn the basic child rearing principles of consistent follow through and reinforcement of positive behaviors. The parent also learns that problem solving can be satisfying, and that there are alternatives to the harsh discipline techniques they experienced as children.

As parents are guided to gain awareness of how children learn and what they can be expected to learn at a specific age, they no longer are as likely to strap a sixteen-month-old child into a chair for three hours until his plate is clean or to hold a child's hand on a stove in order to teach him not to reach for hot objects. Similarly, as parents become alert to anticipating the inquisitive nature of a toddler, they become more aware of keeping household poisons out of the child's reach.

When the PHN assists the parents in identifying and defining the stress caused by the developmental crisis of pregnancy and the entry of another child into the family unit, he or she encourages a problem-solving approach to family planning. Discussion based upon the parents' understanding of conception and contraceptive methods further fosters implementation of rational utilization of appropriate birth control measures. Again, as in all previously defined areas of intervention, the PHN must recognize the vital significance of establishing mutually-defined goals.

Pitfalls

A frequent pitfall in child abuse cases is uncoordinated treatment efforts. Coordination with child protective services and the medical team is often as significant to the outcome of the case as the direct nursing intervention. Coordination of services requires open channels of communication with other professionals, a negotiated clarification of who will do what, notification regarding case changes, and parental knowledge that information is shared among team members. If the team working with the family is unaware and untrusting of the activities of the other nonteam professionals, the care provided the family is negatively affected. In counties where public health nurses and protective service workers work separately, nurses may inappropriately place themselves in a position of singular therapist for an abusive family they have detected. In so doing, they limit the care given families and jeopardize needed court information.

A second potential pitfall is for the nurse to become so close to the parent that she is lulled into a false sense of security regarding reabuse. Someone must be alert to recurrences of physical abuse. This is not solely the social worker's role, but it is an important responsibility of all medical personnel involved in these cases. On routine home visits, the PHN needn't undress the baby, but she should carefully scrutinize him for symptoms of abuse (for example, crying, not moving one arm, weight loss, and dehydration). If any of these are present, an exam should be done. If the mother tells the PHN that the child is sleeping, this could mean that the mother is hiding something. Babies have experienced undetected and untreated starvation, fractures, and gangrene under such circumstances. If such a story is offered on two successive visits, the PHN must act on the child's behalf, refer to the original contract including physical observation of the child, and proceed to check the child's status.

The third hazard is lack of supervision. Nursing intervention in child abuse cases requires a great deal of knowledge, self-understanding, energy, and time on the part of the public health nurse. Due to the long period of required involvement, progress of the family and positive reinforcement for the nurse often seem immeasureable. Unless the nurse has available a supervisor with whom she can discuss and reevaluate the case and share responsibility for the mutually agreed upon plan of intervention, and from whom she receives appropriate feedback, the nurse will experience discouragement and a sense of hopeless frustration. Effective and ongoing supervision is essential to a positive case outcome.

References

Becker, W. C. (1971): *Parents Are Teachers.* Research Press, Champaign, Illinois.

Brazelton, T. B. (1969): *Infants and Mothers.* Delacorte Press, New York.

Dreikurs, R. (1969): *Children, the Challenge.* Meredith Press, New York.

Fraiberg, S. (1959): *The Magic Years.* Charles Scribner's Sons, New York.

Guillon, M. E. and Patterson, G. R. (1968): *Living with Children.* Research Press, Champaign, Illinois.

Hopkins, J. (1970): The nurse and the abused child. *Nurs Clin North Am,* 5:594.

Savino, A. B. and Sanders, R. W. (1973): Working with abusive parents. *Am J Nurs,* 73:482–484.

23

Modern Treatment Options

Patricia J. Beezley

In many communities, treatment is limited to pediatric services, casework by protective service workers of the child welfare department, and public health nurse services. All three of these treatment options will often be essential to successful case management. However, in the last five years, other treatment modalities have been successfully utilized with abusive and neglectful families.[1] A carefully planned combination of treatment options is the most useful means of intervening with parents and children.

Treatment Principles

The main goal in working with abusive parents is to help them relinquish their abusive, neglectful pattern of child rearing and replace it with a method of caring which is more rewarding to both the parents and the child. This necessitates focusing the treatment initially on the parents and increasing their own growth and development. Therapy for the parents includes helping them build their sense of self-esteem; to develop better basic trust and confidence; to learn how to make contacts with other people in the family, neighborhood, and community; to establish responsive lifelines; and to develop the ability to enjoy life and have rewarding, pleasurable experiences with other adults and with their own children.

To accomplish these goals, treatment for abusive families usually needs to be a two-part process. The first step is a *restitution*—that is, a nurturing or reparenting process. During this phase, a more positive model of parenting than what the parent had as a child is offered. The therapist provides support and interest to the parents for their own needs, regardless of the child's situation. There needs to be a considerable degree of tolerance for dependency which had never adequately been met in the parents' early lives. This process of nurturing on an "as needed" basis is frequently enough to stop the parent from using the child to meet his or her needs and to stop the physical abuse. However, to make such gains more permanent, and to alter the long-term, negative emotional relationships, a *resolution of conflict* through emotional insight and understanding is usually necessary. However, a cognitive, intellectual understanding, without experiential relearning, results in a parent who can explain his or her dynamics but has changed nothing. Other parents will have more difficulty with insight therapy, but still need help in rearranging their lives to lessen the stress-producing situations which get them into difficulty.

It is important to remember that abusive parents are not the only members of the family who are in distress and in need of treatment. The abused child and his siblings have medical and psychological needs and have a right to treatment for themselves, regardless of their parents' prognosis.

The integration of the various separate treatments for the different members of the family is a difficult but necessary task. The timing of the introduction of the various treatment modalities into the overall treatment plan is critical. What is done for one member of the family will have effects on the other members. The professionals involved will need to periodically clarify their roles, openly share information, and jointly share in decision making.

Treatment for Parents

INDIVIDUAL PSYCHOTHERAPY

Individual psychotherapy[1,2] for abusive parents is usually provided by psychiatrists, clinical psychologists, or clinical social workers in an office by appointment. Therapy can be very diversified, depending on the particular patient, the therapist's experience and style, and the many treatment techniques which can be utilized. The one commonality is that the psychotherapist is usually in tune to unconscious material, even though he or she may choose not to use that material directly. Psychotherapy often focuses on more than just here and now reality problems. There is some exploration of the parents' behaviors and feelings with the goal of intellectual and emotional insight. It is frequently most useful in conjunction with some less traditional treatment such as lay therapy which insures that the parents receive adequate support and nurturing. There are drawbacks to individual psychotherapy. First, psychotherapy rarely focuses on parent-child interactions. Therefore, changes in the parents' behaviors toward the child may be too slow to protect the child's psychic development. Second, most abusive parents are too mistrustful and erratic in their behavior to come to an office on time for a 50 minute hour. Few psychotherapists will make extensive phone calls or home visits needed to elicit the trust of a parent. Also, long-term psychotherapy is expensive and generally unavailable in rural areas.

LAY THERAPY

Lay therapy[1,3] is provided by paraprofessionals, also called parent aides, who are parents themselves and have highly satisfactory family relationships. The primary role of these surrogate parents is to provide long-term nurturing to the abusive parents. Most of the work is done through visiting in the home several times a week and providing transportation and social experiences for the mother or father. This modality is extremely useful with most abusive and neglectful parents, because it provides a supportive relationship that the parents have never before experienced. Frequently, lay therapists are much less threatening to these families than a more traditional mental health person. Also, lay therapy is extremely economical and saves valuable social work and psychiatric time. Many hours of high-caliber service can be provided at a very low cost. It is essential that any lay therapy program be organized and supervised by a clinical social worker, psychologist, or psychiatrist.

MARITAL THERAPY

Marital therapy[1,4] is primarily provided by clinical psychologists and clinical social workers in an office setting. The husband and wife are seen together, preferably by cotherapists, with the focus being on marital problems. This modality is especially useful when the parents are aware that anger from their marriage is getting displaced onto their child. With improved communication and increased gratification of needs within the marriage, the child is less at risk. Marital treatment is contraindicated when the parents are so dependent and hungry for attention that they need a one-to-one relationship with a therapist. Such parents in marital treatment often end up competing for the therapists' attention and getting little work done. Occasionally, marital treatment can be successful if the partners are concurrently in individual treatment. Marital treatment is also not indicated if one parent is psychotic or schizophrenic, but the other has much more ego strength. In such cases, it is more useful to work individually with the healthier parent, so that he might unilaterally work out some long-range plans for himself and the child.

GROUP THERAPY

Group therapy[1,5] for abusive parents is usually provided by clinical psychologists, clinical social workers, and psychiatrists, although professionals from other disciplines may be involved. The purposes of groups vary, depending on the types of people involved and on what they have chosen to focus. The advantages of groups are numerous. They give an opportunity to reach more people with fewer professional staff. They provide a means of decreasing the isolation of parents and facilitating mutual support systems. There is also increased confrontation of denial and problems among group members. This usually takes place earlier and more intensely than it would in one-to-one treatment. Parents can also feel through a group experience that they can be helpful to others. Many groups of abusive parents, with the help of co-therapists, can also provide accurate child-rearing and child development information. Group psychotherapy is indicated for those parents who are not extremely threatened by exposing themselves and their feelings to others. For some parents it is safer to approach Parents Anonymous,[6] a self-help group for abusive parents, than a more traditional group. In Parents Anonymous, confidentiality is respected to the utmost, and reports are not made available to agencies. Group psychotherapy is contraindicated if a parent is in a severe crisis situation when one-to-one support is usually needed. The decision to use groups must also be based on an individual diagnosis. Parents who are extremely disturbed will be destructive in groups and may experience further rejection.

CRISIS HOTLINES

Crisis hotlines[7] can be provided by a metropolitan interagency council, a single agency, a Parents Anonymous chapter, a hospital emergency room, or a volunteer organization. Hotlines provide supportive crisis counseling as well as referral services. They become lifelines to abusive and neglectful parents in times of stress. Once an abusive or neglectful family has been identified, that family should additionally have the phone numbers of the primary physician, the public health nurse, the therapist, and the caseworker. This includes home numbers as well as office numbers. These parents never have too many lifelines. The more numbers they have available to them, the more likely it is they will be able to reach someone when they are overwhelmed.

Treatment for Children

THERAPEUTIC PLAYSCHOOLS

Therapeutic playschools[8,9,10,11] are staffed by early childhood education teachers and paraprofessionals, with multidisciplinary consultants available for developmental assessments of children. Playschools provide abused and neglected children with intensive, therapeutic experiences and planned stimulation which would not be available to them in their biologic homes or in foster care. The emphasis is on developmental and emotional growth through positive interaction among peers, children, and adults. Structured learning with specific cognitive tasks is not a critical part of the program as it is in most preschools. Playschools are especially indicated for children between the ages of two and five who have not had other types of preschool experiences, and who are very isolated from peers in their home settings. The parents of these children must be able to tolerate daily separation and personality changes within their children. Therefore, playschools are especially indicated for those families whose parents will involve themselves in parent conferences or parent groups or both. Otherwise, the child may make changes that the parent does not appreciate, and there may be a reinjury. If a therapeutic playschool is not available, a day care center, Head Start, preschool, or summer day camp can suffice if consultation regarding the dynamics of child abuse and the personality of the abused child is made available to the teacher. There are few contraindications for therapeutic playschool experiences for abused and neglected children. An alternate plan should be discussed only if a child is so emotionally disturbed or retarded that he will not be able to keep up with the group activities.

INDIVIDUAL PLAY THERAPY

Individual play therapy[12] for abused and neglected children is usually provided by child psychiatrists, clinical psychologists, and clinical social workers in an office and by appointment. Through the use of play materials, a safe setting, and an understanding therapist, a child can learn to express his conflicts and fears. Most abused children, even as young as three and four years, can greatly benefit from this intensive, one-to-one contact with a skilled play therapist. Because manpower is limited, individual play therapy is usually reserved for those children whose conflicts are so intense that a group experience alone, such as a playschool, will not be enough to resolve their problems. Children who have extremely low self-esteem, are depressed, are extremely aggressive toward other people, or have other severe behavior management problems should be seen in play therapy. The parents of such children are usually ambivalent about their children's treatment and often openly resistant to it. They must be intensely involved in parent conferences to insure that they will continue letting the child be seen. Also, such conferences can help them accept changes in the child's personality. The one contraindication to play therapy is when a child is fairly healthy, yet his parents need to see him in a very distorted fashion. Seeing such a child in individual treatment, often at the urging of the parents, would only reinforce the parents' belief that the child is "sick."

GROUP THERAPY

Group psychotherapy for abused and neglected children and their siblings is a relatively new modality that can be provided by child psychiatrists, clinical psychologists, and clinical social workers. Many of the advantages of group psychotherapy for adults also apply to children's groups. Group treatment is especially appropriate for latency-age children who have interactional problems with their peers. Male and female cotherapists are an important variable, since they can provide alternate parental models for the children. Parent conferences or parent groups or both are necessary to maintain the children in therapy and to help parents facilitate positive changes in the children.

Treatment for Families

CRISIS NURSERIES

Crisis nurseries[1,3,13] for children can be provided through foster homes, extended-care facilities of hospitals, preschools, and day care centers. They usually are staffed by early childhood education teachers, nurses, and paraprofessionals, including foster parents. Crisis nurseries must operate 24 hours a day, seven days a week.

The primary purposes of a crisis nursery are to provide an outlet for parents during crisis situations and safety and therapeutic experiences for children. Also, parents can be helped to feel comfortable about getting away from their children; using a crisis nursery is often the prelude to parents finding acceptable babysitters and day care facilities in the community. Occasionally, a nursery can be a stepping stone to a voluntary foster placement. It can provide short-term care so that the parent has time to sort things out and consider alternatives. It can also be used as a holding facility between the time of hospitalization or initial reporting and foster placement. Occasionally, a short-term placement will be enough to reconstitute a family, so they can be reunited. A nursery can also legitimately be used for child care while parents are having their therapy sessions. In no way should a crisis nursery be considered "babysitting," because it can be a very therapeutic experience for the children. Seeing the children in a nursery can often provide access to getting developmental assessments and perhaps treatment for a particular child. Finally, a nursery can provide a means of acquainting a family with other treatment modalities. When a family visits a nursery and begins to develop some trust, they also learn of other ongoing programs and frequently ask to become involved.

Crisis nurseries are rarely misused or overused by abusive parents. A nursery is contraindicated for children with such severe medical or emotional problems or both that they cannot be handled by a paraprofessional staff. Such a child needs to be hospitalized or placed in a residential treatment facility rather than a nursery.

FAMILY THERAPY

Family therapy[14] has not been used extensively in treating abusive and neglectful families. It can be provided by psychiatrists, clinical psychologists, or clinical social workers. The whole family is seen together with the emphasis being on the communication, verbal and nonverbal, that occurs among them. Family therapy is based on the family as a functioning unit with no single member as the identified patient. This very premise is useful in its lack of corroboration with perceptions of the "battered child" or "failing parent." Instead, a premise of each member's part in the family problem is offered as a working base. Family therapy can be used diagnostically, even if the children are very young, but it is more beneficial if the children are old enough to express their feelings. It is contraindicated if the family members are extremely competitive for the therapist's attention, or if their anger at each other is so intense that other family members would be unable to tolerate it. In those cases, it may be more productive to begin by seeing family members individually and much later utilize family therapy with cotherapists.

FAMILY RESIDENTIAL TREATMENT

Family residential treatment[15,16] for abusive and neglectful families is a very new modality, offered in only a few places in the United States and Europe. The whole family moves into a treatment facility for several months as an alternative to the child's being placed in a foster home. The goals of residential treatment are to provide intensive therapeutic work with parents and children, to prevent the weakening of parent-child bonds that occurs with foster placement, and to correct the distortions that the parents have of their children. Extensive evaluation is needed in order to know if this is a viable treatment modality for other communities.

PARENT-CHILD INTERVENTION

Parent-child intervention includes many types of counseling and can be provided by a wide range of personnel. Child-rearing counseling, including a discussion of discipline and age-appropriate expectations, can be provided by a pediatrician, public health nurse, or protective service caseworker.[17,18] Parent education classes can be provided by private agencies or organizations. The need for basic information cannot be ignored as most abusive parents have serious deficits in their knowledge and understanding of child care and child development. However, it is best if this direct counseling is done by someone other than the parents' primary therapist who is attempting to provide some nurturing and reparenting experiences. Because of the parents' high degree of sensitivity about their parental deficits, any direct counseling may be taken as implied criticism. Such counseling is contraindicated with parents who strongly defend their right to employ harsh physical punishment with their children. These people need progress in psychotherapy before they will be able to grasp the fundamental differences between dangerous-harmful and safe-helpful discipline.

Educational efforts should not be expected to be the primary means of changing the parent-child relationship. At best, it is a supplement to other interventions. Modeling of appropriate child-care methods and adequate parenting may be a more appropriate method of changing parent-child interactions. Parents should have the opportunity to observe others dealing with children. The modeling can be provided by a teacher, day care worker, foster parent, caseworker, or therapist. Modeling is less likely to imply criticism of the parents and goes beyond a mere intellectual understanding of child development.[1] A relatively new means of intervening with parent-child relationships is through the use of planned interactions with a clinician which are recorded on video-tape and played back to the parents with discussion.[15] Parent-child interventions are critical if any permanent changes are to occur in the emotional interactions between parents and children.

The Therapist

Modern treatment modalities can be effectively combined with traditional pediatric services, public health services, and casework to successfully treat abusive parents and their children. It is critical, however, to take a look at the therapists who will be providing these treatment options. Even the most elaborate and best-planned treatment program will not succeed if the therapists do not possess certain qualities. Not everyone can work in the areas of child abuse and neglect, and not everyone should be expected to do so.

The therapist must be able to listen to the expertise of other disciplines without feeling it is a threat to his own identity. The therapist should have confidence in his own skills, while at the same time being able to acknowledge his weaknesses and ask for consultation. To work successfully with abusive parents, the therapist must be able to tolerate a lot of dependency from the parents initially. He must be extremely nonjudgemental, slow, and cautious in his expectations of the parents. He must be able to spend a lot of time with a family and be willing to be on call when necessary. Because the personal changes in abusive families are quite small and take a great deal of time to accomplish, the therapist must be comfortable with such therapeutic progress and receive much of his work satisfaction from collaborating with the multidisciplinary team.

TABLE 1. *Treatment for Parents*

1. Individual psychotherapy
2. Lay therapy
3. Marital therapy
4. Group therapy
5. Crisis hotlines

TABLE 2. *Treatment for Children*

1. Therapeutic playschool
2. Individual play therapy
3. Group therapy

TABLE 3. *Treatment for Families*

1. Crisis nursery
2. Family therapy
3. Family residential treatment
4. Parent-child intervention

References

1. Beezley, P., Martin, H., and Alexander, H. (1976): Comprehensive family-oriented therapy. In *Child Abuse and Neglect: The Family and the Community,* edited by R. E. Helfer and C. H. Kempe. Ballinger, Cambridge, Mass.
2. Steele, B. F. (1975): Working with abusive parents from a psychiatric point of view. D.H.E.W. Publication No. (OHD) 75-70.
3. Kempe, C. H. and Helfer, R. E. (1972): Innovative therapeutic approaches. In *Helping the Battered Child and His Family,* edited by C. H. Kempe and R. E. Helfer. J. B. Lippincott Co., Philadelphia and Toronto.
4. Geist, J. and Gerber, N. M. (1960): Joint interviewing: a treatment technique with marital partners. *Social Casework,* 41:76.
5. Paulson, M. J., Savino, A. B., Chaleff, A. B., and Sanders, R. W.: Group psychiatry: a multi-disciplinary approach in the treatment of abusive parents. Unpublished paper.
6. Starkweather, C. L. and Turner, S. M. (1975): Parents anonymous: reflections on the development of a self-help group. In *Child Abuse: Intervention and treatment,* edited by N. B. Ebeling and D. A. Hill. Publishing Sciences Group, Inc., Acton, Mass.
7. Schmitt, B. D., and Kempe, C. H. (1975): The pediatrician's role in child abuse and neglect. In *Current Problems in Pediatrics, Vol. 5.* Year Book Medical Publishers, Inc., Chicago.
8. Mirandy, J. (1976): Preschool for abused children. In *The Abused Child: A Multi-disciplinary Approach to Developmental Issues and Treatment,* edited by H. P. Martin. Ballinger Press, Cambridge, Mass.
9. Bean, S. L. (1975): The use of specialized day care in preventing child abuse. In *Child Abuse: Intervention and Treatment,* edited by N. B. Ebeling and D. A. Hill. Publishing Sciences Group, Inc., Acton, Mass.
10. Gardner, L. (1975): The Gilday Center: a method of intervention for child abuse. In *Child Abuse: Intervention and Treatment,* edited by N. B. Ebeling and D. A. Hill. Publishing Sciences Group, Inc., Acton, Mass.
11. Ten Broeck, E. (1974): The extended family center: 'a home away from home' for abused children and their parents. *Child Today:* 2.
12. Beezley, P., Martin, H. P., and Kempe, R. (1976): Psychotherapy. In *The Abused Child: A Multi-disciplinary Approach to Developmental Issues and Treatment,* edited by H. P. Martin. Ballinger Press, Cambridge, Mass.
13. McQuiston, M. (1976): Crisis Nurseries. In *The Abused Child: A Multi-disciplinary Approach to Developmental Issues and Treatment,* edited by H. P. Martin. Ballinger, Cambridge, Mass.
14. Group for the Advancement of Psychiatry: The Field of Family Therapy, Vol. 7, Report No. 78, March 1970.
15. Alexander, H., McQuiston, M., and Rodeheffer, M. (1976): Residential Family Therapy. In *The Abused Child: A Multi-disciplinary Approach to Developmental Issues and Treatment,* edited by H. P. Martin. Ballinger, Cambridge, Mass.
16. Lynch, M., Steinberg, D., and Ounsted, C. (1975): Family unit in a children's psychiatric hospital. *Br Med J,* 19:127–129.

17. Chamberlin, R. W. (1974): Authoritarian and accommodative child-rearing styles: their relationships with the behavior patterns of 2-year-old children and with other variables. *J Pediatr,* 84(2):287.
18. Sumpter, E. A. (1975): Behavior Problems in Early Childhood. *Pediatr Clins North Am,* 22:663.

24

Treatment Review

Candace A. Grosz and Patricia J. Beezley

Treatment Review Defined

The most critical diagnostic and legal issues pertaining to a specific abusive or neglectful family, such as, suggestions to the court regarding removal or return of a child to his biologic home or termination of parental rights, will be made at the multidisciplinary team conference (see chapters 14 to 17). However, in the ongoing clinical treatment of the family members, many other decisions will need to be made. Treatment review provides for the meeting of a group of primary therapists and selected consultants to review the progress in treatment of specific families and to consider special aspects of the treatment progress. In the past, this process was called "staffing."

The treatment review team is generally a subgroup of the multidisciplinary team for child abuse and neglect and clinicians from the various community agencies who are working with a particular family. Treatment review can be based at a particular community agency (for example, mental health center, hospital, or protective services). The treatment review team members are usually selected by the nature of their discipline: social work, psychology, and psychiatry. However, personal and professional ideologies must be considered. Some nurses, teachers, and physicians may share the psychotherapeutic model and be invested in the processes of counseling and personal rehabilitation.[1] If so, they should be included in the treatment review.

Another type of treatment review team consists of paraprofessionals in specific therapeutic programs, such as lay therapists, child care workers, foster parents, day care parents, or homemakers. Such review teams would also include the professional consultants for those programs.

Purposes of Treatment Review

Treatment review provides continuing education to the therapists and improved services to the families. Initially, a treatment review team may have only one or two purposes, but, as time goes on, the functions of the team will multiply and may include the following purposes:

1. To provide an overview of the total treatment picture for an individual family. This helps promote a more integrated, efficient approach, since these families frequently require the services of many agencies.

2. To coordinate therapies for the individual family members, and to consider the effects of the treatment for one family member on other members.

3. To provide consultation around clinical issues, such as what types of therapy should be used for which family members, when to start and stop various treatments to the best advantage, and when to increase or decrease different types of treatment.

4. To provide an in-depth look at selected aspects of the treatment, such as resistance to the therapy, transference issues, and parent-child interactions.

5. To improve and upgrade the clinical skills of the therapists.

6. To provide an objective perspective for the primary therapists through discussion with each other and consultants, and to balance either an overly pessimistic or optimistic perception regarding the progress of treatment.

7. To balance the interests of the parents and the children and maintain a family perspective in the total treatment plan, and provide more objectivity to individual therapists who may have become aligned with one family member to the detriment of other family members.

8. To provide emotional support and shared decision making regarding frustrating and emotionally-draining treatment cases.[2]

9. To identify the key issues that need to be reviewed at the full multidisciplinary team conference, including evaluating if the current treatment plan is appropriate and making tentative legal recommendations that can be reviewed at the multidisciplinary team meeting.

10. To provide an addition or an alternative to the one-to-one supervision traditionally used in social service agencies, and to provide more effective and efficient consultation for the primary therapist through

shared learning with other treatment review team members. One-to-one consultation and support should still be readily available from other professionals to help manage crisis situations.

Structure and Ground Rules

Once the team members have agreed on purposes for the treatment review, the structure and ground rules for the meetings will need to be determined.

1. *Establish treatment review teams to reflect different levels of expertise.* For example, there could be separate treatment review teams for lay, beginning, and advanced therapists.

2. *Establish mechanisms to interconnect these various levels of treatment reviews.* For example, the director of a lay therapy program may supervise the lay therapy treatment review and, then, carry on to the advanced therapist treatment review, the lay therapists' major concerns and current status of the family's treatment.

3. *Hold regular treatment reviews.* These should be scheduled weekly, at least.

4. *Have mandatory participation of therapists.* Even if a particular therapist is not presenting a family at a particular treatment review, he can learn from the review and upgrade his skills.

5. *Limit the people in treatment review to a group of six to eight individuals.* Have the same people attend the same treatment review consistently. This will facilitate discussion and provide continuity within the group.

6. *Identify a treatment review leader.* It is extremely helpful if this person is skilled and in tune with group process. In many situations this would not follow the tradition of being the team psychiatrist, since a social worker or psychologist may be better qualified in this regard.

7. *Arrange psychiatric consultation.* The availability of psychiatric consultation is crucial. If psychiatric time is limited, the choice should be made to use a psychiatrist or psychologist in treatment review rather than with the full multidisciplinary team. Since the primary role of a psychiatrist at treatment review is to help put the psychiatric material into perspective, to form the best treatment plan, and to determine the need for further referrals, it is imperative that the psychiatrist have recent experience with abusive families and that he continue to evaluate and treat abusive families.

8. *Invite clinicians from community agencies working with a particular family.* It is critical that coordination of treatment be community-wide, and that independent reviews for a family at each agency providing service are

avoided. This would be a duplication of efforts and could result in a treatment plan that is not unified.

9. *Review all families.* Criteria for reviewing cases should be set by the group, not left to the discretion of the individual therapists. Initially, individual therapists may find it more comfortable to go it alone, although these advantages are often short-lived and devastating when treatment fails.

10. *Use a written problem-oriented approach.* Current treatment issues should be clearly identified by the primary therapists, prior to treatment review, and outlined on a written sheet (Tables 1 and 2). This can be supplemented by a sheet of identifying information to help the team recall the specific characteristics of the family and to prevent lengthy introductions.

11. *Inform clinicians that they must present materials succinctly.* The written outline will help with this. Also, therapists should be reminded not to go into lengthy anecdotes which consume a great deal of time and are not particularly helpful. The therapist should be encouraged to present a summary of his ideas. Persons who do not attend regularly but are invited for a particular family should be prepared in advance regarding the format and preliminary information, such as family history, so that they are ready to move ahead with the discussion.

12. *Keep reviews limited to no more than two hours with maximum discussion of four families.* When the maximum level is reached, a second treatment review team should be formed to help manage the caseload. The families should be reviewed by the same team each time to help provide continuity.

13. *Begin and end reviews on time.* Frequently, discussion is expedited by answering easier questions first such as case management issues (scheduling assessments and arranging transportation). This leaves the majority of the time for discussion of complex treatment issues. With the short time period allotted, it will not be possible to review material for a member who arrives late. The typed problem sheets and identifying information sheets can help with this. The group leader will need to encourage the group to be specific in their recommendations and reach a consensus at the close of the discussion.

14. *Limit numbers and types of visitors.* Visitors that come sporadically may be destructive to the ability of the group to get the work done, especially if they are spectators and not a part of the consultation process. Therapists may be hesitant to express some of their negative feelings regarding the family and their mistakes in front of visitors they do not know.

15. *Use some consultant selectively.* It can be helpful from time to time to bring a specific consultant to treatment review who does not regularly attend to help sharpen the focus of the group and its skill. The format of the meeting should be carefully explained to the consultant to help him prepare. The group should be informed of his attendance in advance and have some willingness to use the consultation.

16. *Record summary of discussion and recommendations in the family's chart.* This need not be a detailed, typed report, but rather a brief summary of the main points discussed and recommendations. This could be the current problem sheet with additional comments (Table 3). Either the primary therapist or group recorder can assume responsibility for this record.

Pitfalls

An effective treatment review team is difficult to establish and maintain. A great deal of work over an extended period of time will be needed before the team will feel comfortable in expressing difficulties in treatment and in fully utilizing the group's recommendations. At times, the group dynamics can impede useful consultation in treatment review. The following are some common pitfalls that all treatment review teams experience.

Initially, all team members will be reluctant to make suggestions when they feel those suggestions will not be valued. Other members will feel hesitant in asking questions or giving constructive criticism because they know at some point they will need to present families to the group, and they may fear that others will retaliate with harsh criticism. This can mean that members leave treatment review feeling angry or that they have not received any help. To overcome these problems, the team needs to develop an atmosphere of mutual support and constructive consultation. Only then will therapists be able to be completely honest at treatment review sessions, including the reporting of no progress in therapy when such is the case.

The pitfalls of a treatment review team can be accentuated in many ways: briefing late-comers to the meeting; relating numerous anecdotes with no summation; expecting a psychiatrist to have all the answers; being unwilling to make specific recommendations to the primary therapists; deferring decisions to the judge or multidisciplinary team rather than making tentative recommendations that can be reviewed; deferring discussion by saying there is an incomplete data base; and drifting into other subject material such as staff issues, taking phone calls in meetings, leaving early or missing meetings. If the treatment review team leader or other members can point out some of these difficulties in a noncritical manner, the group may be able to look at their resistance, make some agreements about their participation, and move on to a more useful level of participation. As the group becomes more secure, there will be an increasing ability to look at the clinician's role in the treatment process, that is, the clinician's feelings and behaviors, rather than the patient's feelings and behaviors. Also, in time, there will be more members actively participating and they will challenge any member who tries to become authoritative, including the psychiatrist. Once the group is well established and experienced, they will protect its existence and come fully prepared for the presentations.

As with any group, there are stages in development, and a treatment review team must consider group process issues.[3] One issue relates to changes in group composition, such as the introduction of a new member or loss of a member, either temporarily or permanently. The effect of a new member usually results in making the group revert back to a previous level of functioning. This is not sustained and the group learns to regain its prior level of functioning. Each time the group goes through these process steps, the integration of new members or adjustment to a loss is easier and accomplished more quickly.

Although these pitfalls are common in any treatment review team, they can be overcome. When they are overcome, the treatment review team can be much more effective than one-to-one supervision in providing consultation and support to therapists. This will result in improved services to families, including better coordinated treatment with therapists who have a higher level of expertise.

TABLE 1. *Treatment Review—Master Problem List*

A. Date
B. Name of family
C. Therapists currently involved with family
D. Problem
   1. Emotional problems of the mother
   2. Emotional problems of the father
   3. Marital problems
   4. Emotional and developmental problems of the child
   5. Emotional and developmental problems of the siblings
   6. Parent-child interaction
   7. Environmental problems
   8. Safety of the home

TABLE 2. *Pre-Meeting Summary*
Treatment Review—Current Problem Sheet[a]

Date: 2/27/76
Smith family
Currently Involved with Family:
Lay therapist
Mental health worker (individual therapy for mother)
Social service worker (therapy for father)
Playschool
Public health nurse

1. Mother—depressed, missing therapy appointments
2. Father—manipulative, therapist frustrated with father's intellectualization and lack of behavior changes
3. Marriage—father leaves home whenever mother gets enough strength to confront him about his behavior
4. Identified child—Jeff, age 3, has serious gross motor and speech delays, but he is less withdrawn and depressed since beginning playschool
5. Siblings—Susan, age 7 months, public health nurse to report at meeting
6. Parent-child interaction—public health nurse to report at meeting
7. Environmental problems—father has new job as a salesman but is already having problems with his boss, hospital bill now quite large
8. Safety of the home—no new injuries, but concern for emotional neglect

[a]This sheet is prepared prior to the meetings by the primary therapist and distributed to those attending for discussion.

TABLE 3. *Post-Meeting Summary*
Treatment Review—Current Problem Sheet[a]

Date: 2/27/76
Smith family
Currently Involved with Family:
Lay therapist
Mental health worker (individual therapy for mother)
Social service worker (therapy for father)
Playschool
Public health nurse

1. Mother—depressed, missing therapy appointments.
   Depression appears chronic, needs transportation and emotional support from lay therapist to get to individual psychotherapy appointments.

2. Father—manipulative, therapist frustrated with father's intellectualization and lack of changes in behavior.
   Father appears sociopathic. Little progress with insight-oriented therapy. Try reality-oriented therapy with increased limit-setting.

3. Marriage—father leaves home whenever mother gets enough strength to confront him about his behavior.
   Too soon for marital treatment; both parents become overwhelmed when it is raised as possibility.

4. Identified Child—Jeff, age 3, has serious gross motor and speech delays, but he is less withdrawn and depressed since beginning playschool.
   Continue playschool with physical therapy and speech therapy. Reevaluate delays in three months.

5. Siblings—Susan, age 7 months, public health nurse to report at meeting.
   Shows some developmental delays. Full evaluation scheduled with possible need for stimulation program by public health nurse.

6. Parent-child interaction—public health nurse to report at meeting.
   Child seems to reflect mother's depression. Mother seems able to take some suggestions about parenting skills. Father has superficial relationship with children and can relate to them for only brief periods of time. Plan to continue suggestions for child development and behavioral management from public health nurse. Involve father when possible.

7. Environmental problems—father has new job as salesman but is already having problems with his boss. Hospital bill now quite large.
   Father's therapist to encourage discussion of relationship with authority figures. Lay therapist to take parent to the hospital to negotiate payment of bill.

8. Safety of the home—no new injuries, but concern for emotional neglect.
   Physical abuse is less likely to recur, but the emotional neglect of both children continues. Juvenile court supervision will continue.

[a]This sheet with additional comments recorded at treatment review is filed in family's chart.

References

1. Carter, J. (1974): *The Maltreated Child.* Priory Press, London, Chapter 5.
2. Ebeling, N. B. and Hill, D. A. (1975): *Child Abuse: Intervention and Treatment.* Publishing Sciences Group, Inc., Acton, Mass.
3. Yalom, I. D. (1970): *The Theory and Practice of Group Psychotherapy.* Basic Books, Inc., New York.

25

The Coordinator's Role in Treatment

Marilyn R. Lenherr and Candace A. Grosz

Functions of the Coordinator

The coordinator's role in case follow-up includes the following four major functions listed in order of priority: (1) implementation of team recommendations for families, (2) assistance to direct service providers, (3) feedback to diagnostic and evaluation team, and (4) collection of data for routine statistics and program planning. (See Table 1.)

IMPLEMENTATION OF TEAM RECOMMENDATIONS FOR FAMILIES

1. *Share team's decisions and evaluation information.* Following the dispositional conference, the coordinator revises the problem-oriented team report. He or she distributes it and the evaluation reports to persons providing ongoing service, which usually includes county social service workers, visiting nurses, private physicians, and mental health workers. If the juvenile court is involved, it is also advisable to send information to the county attorney for the Department of Social Services and the guardian *ad litem.* Confidentiality does not have to be a major concern, since many state laws provide for easy sharing of information in child abuse and neglect cases. While consideration is needed for the privacy of the family, the main focus should remain on providing protection for the child and integrated treatment services for the family. This requires the sharing of team diagnosis and recommendations for treatment. The coordinator should inform

the professionals providing the data for the report (for example, pediatricians, psychiatrists, and social workers) of its distribution.

2. *Determine status of services to family.* A follow-up call is made to direct service providers within four weeks of the dispositional conference to determine if services are being provided as recommended. Where services are not being provided, it is important to elicit the reasons for nonimplementation—for example: the family refuses, current demands on the worker prohibit providing the services, the resource is not available either temporarily or in a particular community, the recommendations are not appropriate, the service has failed, or the recommendations were not properly communicated to the primary worker.

3. *Restate team recommendations.* When critical aspects of a case are overlooked or ignored, it becomes crucial for the coordinator to restate the team's recommendations and try to facilitate services that are not being provided for the family. This should be done tactfully and diplomatically, yet assertively.

4. *Ascertain legal status of the case.* The coordinator inquires about the legal status on each follow-up contact with the following questions: Has a petition been filed in juvenile court? Has temporary custody or court supervision been granted? Who are the attorneys involved for the county department, parents, and child? What are the stipulations of the current court order? What is the date of the next review, adjudicatory, or dispositional hearing? What are the anticipated recommendations at the next court action?

5. *Negotiate witnesses and testimony.* The coordinator contacts the protective service worker and the attorney for the Department of Social Services to discern if a stipulation is possible. If the case will proceed to a hearing, it is necessary to find out what information is needed, who is needed to provide the testimony, if subpoenas are required for witnesses or records, and the date, place, and time of the hearing.

These contacts include: negotiation for the possible use of written reports in lieu of testimony, arrangements for witnesses to be on call (available within a short period of time), or to make appointments for witnesses to testify and, therefore, avoid prolonged waiting in court for professionals. Subsequent contacts will probably be necessary to arrange availability of witnesses. In some instances, the coordinator may need to request continuation of the hearing date and rescheduling.

6. *Evaluate the need for team review.* In calls to the direct service providers, the coordinator suggests the scheduling of a team review if some of the following circumstances are present: recommendations or testimony are needed for an upcoming court hearing; the service plan seems ineffective and treatment for the family is failing; or the team needs to reconsider progress in treatment, modify the service plan, or review decisions, such as returning the child home after foster placement (see chapter 16).

7. *Decide the frequency of subsequent follow-up.* With an increasing volume

of cases, it has been necessary to develop criteria for ongoing follow-up. The following criteria are being implemented by a hospital-based child protection team, and modifications may be needed for their application to county-based operations. Differentiations are made according to the severity of the case.

The coordinator makes a follow-up call on all cases within one month of initial contact to determine if services have been initiated and to elicit other data for routine statistics. Most outpatient cases, where hospital team involvement has been limited to medical evaluation or consultation, will not be followed further by the hospital team if services have been initiated successfully. Obviously, any case being reviewed by another community team does not require close follow-up by both teams.

Moderately severe cases will require variable follow-up which can last from three to eighteen months. This will include the following types of cases:

(1) A family not receiving or not accepting services.

(2) A diagnostic dilemma; for example, an unexplained injury with low-risk parents. This will require a second check in approximately six months to determine the appropriateness of the team's diagnosis.

(3) Mild cases with a special aspect for educational review (for example, a true accident, but in a chaotic family).

(4) Failure-to-thrive cases, to check for adequate weight gain over at least three months.

(5) Cases at risk for poor case management owing to change of worker within the agency, inexperienced service providers, deficiency in community resources, or a family that is moving frequently.

(6) A family where there is a strong potential for abuse; or a child reports past abuse, but no abuse has been documented. This situation needs a minimum of six months follow-up.

The most severe cases require long-term, indefinite follow-up with checks every three to six months. These include families with a team recommendation for termination of parental rights, voluntary relinquishment, or long-term foster placement. Follow-up contacts are usually scheduled two to three weeks prior to court hearings to allow arrangements for testimony or team review as needed.

8. *Record case management follow-up data.* Current status of services and legal action are recorded in short narrative notes or using the problem-oriented format. The problem-oriented format is used primarily for more severe cases and as a means of helping organize the information prior to a team review (Table 2 contains an example of such a report). Copies of follow-up information are distributed to hospital charts, the child protection team file, and the direct-service providers. Most importantly, the coordinator should develop an easy and efficient way to record this information and share it with other team members.

Follow-up data should be clearly marked with the type of follow-up and include the next review date. The case is also entered into the follow-up recall system to help assure that the next check is not missed. This can be a card file divided by months to show the cases that need to be reviewed currently. Each case has a separate index card. When the current review is completed, the date for the next review is noted on the card, and it is placed into the appropriate section.

ASSISTANCE TO DIRECT SERVICE PROVIDERS

1. *Provide support and consultation.* This involves helping the worker sort out the case, allowing ventilation, and reconfirming his or her reading that a family is difficult and scary. In some cases, all the appropriate services may already be in effect. The coordinator may need to listen, share the worry about these situations, and offer encouragement to the community worker.

2. *Explore alternative resources.* Frequently, there are problems in locating needed services for either evaluation or treatment of a family. The coordinator can help the community workers by contacting other agencies or eliciting the help of other team members for a specific service such as developmental testing, play therapy, or psychiatric evaluation or treatment.

3. *Promote a more unified approach to family treatment.* Direct service providers (that is, social workers, visiting nurses, and physicians) may not be able to maintain frequent communication with each other on a particular case, even though each is seeing the family. The coordinator can collect and share among these professionals changes in status and progress and help assure a more consistent, unified treatment plan.

FEEDBACK TO DIAGNOSTIC AND EVALUATION TEAM

The main purpose of this follow-up is an educational one that helps the team maintain a good reality base.

1. *Appropriateness.* Follow-up information can help the team assess if the diagnosis was correct, if all major problems were identified, if any significant factors were overlooked, and if the recommendations were appropriate.

2. *Attainability.* Follow-up also looks at if services recommended were available, effective, and properly implemented without great delay. A diagnostic and evaluation team needs this type of follow-up to sharpen their skills and to maintain an integrated position within a community. A diagnostic team is not effective if recommendations are made from a detached position, are idealistic, or cannot be implemented.

3. *Review.* Usually, the multidisciplinary team is also a review team; the serious cases will be reassessed by them prior to court hearing or when treatment plans need to be modified. The volume of cases prohibits consultative follow-up of all cases. Certain cases will be reviewed only briefly. These would be educational rather than decision-making or consultative reviews allowing five to ten minutes for each presentation. Usually, the coordinator gathers case information from many sources prior to the meeting and presents it herself for educational reviews.

A speaker-phone may also be utilized to contact county workers or others involved in a case. Another approach is to design a checklist outlining the major services implemented for a family and the current status of each. This checklist can be circulated among all team members for discussion. No matter how the data is presented, after the meeting it should be shared with those who are involved with a case, but not present at the meeting.

COLLECTION OF DATA FOR ROUTINE STATISTICS AND RESEARCH

1. *Routine statistics.* The coordinator records information related to case management, length of foster placement, type of intervention and services provided, number of cases recommended for termination, types of evaluations completed, and age and nature of injury. If this data base is recorded rigorously, it may be important for current or retrospective clinical research studies. This information is also tabulated for an annual report (see Table 3).

2. *Program planning.* The annual report can be used by groups involved in evaluating current services, implementing new services, requesting funding, or recommending changes in policy legislation. Follow-up statistics collected can be modified according to the specific goals of a community.

FOLLOW UP—PRIORITIES AND FRUSTRATIONS

Priorities for follow-up are required, since there are many obstacles to adequate follow-up. On the practical level, it can be difficult to reach the appropriate person because the family has moved, the case has been transferred to another worker within that agency, busy schedules, and large case volume. These factors may require placing phone calls four to five times and persistence.

Most important, follow-up can be difficult on an emotional level. The coordinator frequently learns that things are not going well in a case, and this creates aversion to soliciting more bad news. New cases which demand immediate attention during the crisis phase may seem to demand priority, and it is difficult to keep in mind the crucial value of follow-up to a child's ongoing safety.

These obstacles often result in the inability to complete follow-up on schedule. Ways to decrease these frustrations are to have more than one person involved in collecting follow-up information, set priorities for which cases can be delayed when the coordinator becomes exceedingly busy, and develop manageable criteria that will allow one to feel comfortable with closing some cases. Developing good rapport and trust with persons providing ongoing services can certainly aid this task.

TABLE 1. *Treatment Tasks of Coordinator*

Implementation of Team Recommendations for Families
1. Share team's decisions and evaluation information
2. Determine status of services to families
3. Re-state team's recommendations
4. Ascertain legal status of the case
5. Negotiate witnesses and testimony
6. Evaluate the need for team review
7. Decide frequency of subsequent follow-up
8. Record case management follow-up data

Assistance to Direct Service Providers
1. Provide support and consultation
2. Explore alternative resources
3. Promote a more unified approach to families in treatment

Feedback to Diagnostic and Evaluation Team
1. Help determine appropriateness and attainability of recommendations by team
2. Arrange consultative and educational reviews by team

Collection of Data for Routine Statistics and Research
1. Routine statistics for annual report
2. Information to aid program planning

TABLE 2. *Problem-oriented Follow-up Information and Team Review on Case from Chapter 14.*

Child Protection Team Review Conference 7/6/75
DOB: 7/12/73
CGH#
County: Sedgwick
23-month-old boy
Currently involved:
Suzanne Higgins (SW-Sedg.Co.SS)
Elaine Kaiser (Sup.-Sedg. Co.SS)
Ted Fremont (Psychologist-Sedg. Co. Mental Health Ctr.)
Paul Lindstrom (MD- Private Practice)
David Hershey (MD-Sedg. Peds Clinic)
Randolph Daily (Psychiatrist-CGH)

Problems and Recommendations
1. Physical abuse (33 bruises, harsh discipline from father)
   Recommendation 1/6/75: Report to CPS, medical followup at CGH Peds Clinic.
   Results 7/6/75: No further injuries known. Medical follow-up continued at CGH until present.
   Recommendation 7/6/75: Medical care now at Sedgwick County Peds Clinic to be checked every two weeks for first 3 months at home.
2. Question of failure to thrive
   —Resolved as familial short stature.
3. Siblings emotional problems (two girls, ages 3 and 4, take care of mother and fearful of father)
   Recommendation 1-6-75: Day care for both siblings.
   Results 7/6/75: Day care arranged for both siblings 3 times a week—paid for by Department of Social Service. Day care continues in Sedgwick County. No new information available.
   Recommendation 7/6/75: Continue day care for both girls.
4. Father's physical problems (severe headaches and blurred vision for six years)
   Recommendation 1/6/75: Thorough neurologic and physical work-up at CGH Neurology Clinic.
   Results 7/6/75: Neurological exam completed 2/18/75—symptoms are psychosomatic.
   Recommendation 7/6/75: Continue follow-up and symptomatic treatment by private physician.
5. Father's emotional problems (acutely depressed, possible thought disorder)
   Recommendation 1/6/75: Full psychiatric evaluation and urgent intensive psychotherapy at CGH adult psychiatry clinic, consider hold and treat order for psychiatric hospitalization.
   Results 1/13/75: Psychiatric evaluation in progress, goes twice weekly.
   Results 7/6/75: Psychiatric evaluation completed 2/5/75. Hospitalized 3 weeks from 2/1/75–2/21/75. Diagnosis: severe depression, no schizophrenia. Intensive psychotherapy at CGH adult psychiatry clinic until 5/18/75.

continued

TABLE 2 *(continued)*

Transferred to Sedgwick County MHC for ongoing treatment. Currently free of depression and can use alternatives to physical punishment.
Recommendation 7/6/75: Continue psychotherapy on weekly basis.
6. Mother's emotional problems (pervasive denial, does not protect children, high expectations)
Recommendation 1/6/75: Treatment at Family Center or Adams MHC, CPS counseling and follow-up, give 3 phone numbers for crisis or suggestion of suicide in husband.
Results 7/6/75: Seen in joint sessions during husband's hospitalization with CGH adult psychiatric clinic, supportive counseling with social services. The mother has more realistic expectations of herself, her children, and her husband. Able to protect children.
Recommendation 7/6/75: Continue supportive counseling—Sedgwick Co. Department of Social Service. Consider lay therapist.
7. Environmental problems/crisis (Mother returned to work, father babysitting)
Recommendation 1/6/75: Father must not babysit, mother work days or other sitting arrangement.
Results 7/6/75: Day-care services for children arranged, mother terminated work on 5/18/75 with relocation, remains in home, father not babysitting.
8. Safety of the home (repeated severe abuse to young child, emotional problems of father)
Recommendation 1/6/75: Temporary foster care for at least 3 months—court enforced.
Results 7/6/75: Adjudicated 3/9/75. Frequent visits with parents have gone satisfactorily.
Recommendation 7/6/75: Continue court supervision in Sedgwick County. Change of venue in process, as family moved 5/18/75. Child to return to parents' care.
Review 6 months

TABLE 3. *Follow-up Data*

CHILD PROTECTION TEAM
Colorado General Hospital

NAME	AGE	TYPE OF FOLLOWUP:	#1—1 check	#2—short-term	#3—long-term	PLACEMENT:	Remained at home	Less than 2 weeks	2 weeks–3 months	3 to 6 months	6 months–1 year	More than 1 year	Previously placed	Voluntary placement	COURT ACTION:	Not filed

Temporary Custody	Court Supervision	Adjudicated	Not Adjudicated	Dismissed	Termination	Relinquished	SERVICES:	Visiting nurse: 0–3 months	Visiting nurse: 3 months plus	Day Care	Mental Health Service	Homemaker	Lay Therapist	CASE CLOSED IN:	3 months	6 months	12 months	12 months plus	REASON FOR CLOSURE	Services completed	Services refused	Family moved	Referred to another county DSS

APPENDIX A

CHILD ABUSE AND NEGLECT

Intake Data Checklist

NAME:_____ CGH#_____

BIRTHDATE:_____ COUNTY:_____

PLEASE RECORD THE DATE COMPLETED OR MARK "NOT APPLICABLE" (N.A.).
ALSO RECORD THE RESULTS WHERE THEY ARE REQUESTED.

A. MEDICAL DATA (CPT Pediatrician)

1. Child abuse and neglect,
    diagnostic category   a) _____
                                  b) _____

2. History of injury

    a. Detailed injury history from mother____   Results_____
    b. Detailed injury history from father____   _____
    c. Brief injury history from child ____
    d. Other   ____

3. Physical exam of patient   ____   Results_____

4. Trauma X-ray survey   ____   Results_____

5. Bleeding disorder screen   ____   Results_____

6. Sub-specialty consults that may
    be needed in court   a) _____
                                      b) _____

7. Color photographs   ____

8. Physical exam of siblings by name
    (within 12 hours)   a) ____   Results_____
                                      b) ____   _____
                                      c) ____   _____

9. Behavioral assessment of patient ____   Results_____

10. Developmental assessment of patient ____   Results_____

11. Submit an official, typed medical
    report to Child Welfare (within 48
    hours). (Medical problem list to
    be taken from this.)_____

Intake Data Checklist

    12. Inform parents that injury will
        be reported   _____

    13. Give handouts to appropriate
        house staff   _____

B. PSYCHO-SOCIAL DATA (CPT Social Worker)

    1. Interview mother   _____ Impressions_____
       Interview father   _____ Impressions_____
       Interview boyfriend   _____ Impressions_____
       Interview babysitter   _____ Impressions_____
       Interview other   _____ Impressions_____

    2. Observe mother-child interaction
       (by CPT or Ward R.N.)   _____ Results_____

    3. Take parent on brief tour of
       the hospital   _____

    4. Write brief evaluation in CGH
       chart   _____

    5. Complete high-risk checklist
       (prior to mini-conference)

       Mother   _____ Score_____
       Father   _____ Score_____

    6. Arrange psychiatric consult

       Mother   _____ Diagnosis_____
       Father   _____ Diagnosis_____

    7. Arrange for home evaluations
       (CPT or CW)   _____ Results _____

    8. Prepare psycho-social problem
       list including recommendations
       (first draft prior to mini-
       conference)   _____

    9. Arrange interpretive hour with
       both parents after dispositional
       conference   _____

    10. Dictate complete evaluation   _____

Intake Data Checklist

Use date to designate actions completed.

C. CPT COORDINATOR'S TASKS

    1. Prepare:

        a. File
        b. Face sheet   _____
        c. CGH registry cards   _____
        d. Statistical sheet   _____

    2. Check previous medical resource
                            a) _____ Results_____
                            b) _____ Results_____

    3. Check State Central Registry   _____ Results_____
        County Department of Social
          Services   _____ Results_____

    4. Report to Department of Social
        Services by phone (within 24 hours)_____

    5. Obtain, type, and mail CWS-59
        forms   _____

    6. Keep ward physician and ward
        nurse informed of any change in
        status (e.g., police hold,
        projected date for foster
        placement, etc.). Make chart
        notes accordingly.   _____

    7. Schedule other consultations
        or special tests   a) _____
                                b) _____
                                c) _____

    8. Schedule Tuesday dispositional
        conference and contact all
        participants

        a. House staff
        b. Ward nurse   _____
        c. _____   _____
        d. _____   _____
        e. _____   _____

Intake Data Checklist

9. Type tentative team report (POR)
   before Tuesday dispositional
   conference, preferably following
   mini-conference _____

10. Retype revised team report after
    dispositional conference _____

11. Distribute final team report with
    recommendations to:

    a. CGH and CPT charts _____
    b. Child Welfare _____
    c. Primary physician _____
    d. PHN _____
    e. County attorney _____
    f. Guardian ad litem _____
    g. Parents' attorney only if
       attended CPT conference _____
    h. Coordinator of county CPT _____

12. Distribute additional copies of
    CWS 59 medical statement to:

    a. Primary physician or medical
       care facility _____
    b. PHN _____
    c. GAL _____
    d. Parents' attorney, even if
       didn't attend CPT conference _____

13. Distribute typed social work
    evaluation to:

    a. CGH and CPT charts _____
    b. Child Welfare _____
    c. Primary physician _____
    d. PHN _____
    e. Guardian ad litem _____
    f. Psychiatrist, if one is
       involved _____

14. Distribute typed psychiatric
    evaluation report to:

    a. Psychiatrist who submits _____
    b. CGH and CPT charts _____
    c. Child Welfare _____
    d. Guardian ad litem _____

Appendix A-1 (5)

Intake Data Checklist

15. Notify billing department if child
    becomes temporary ward of the state   _____

16. Arrange discharge with county worker
    if foster placement planned   _____

17. Initiate team follow-up as follows:

	To be done	Completed
Education review	_____	_____
Consultation review	_____	_____
Indefinite reviews	_____	_____

Developed by Schmitt, Grosz, Gray, & Carroll, Child Protection Team
at The University of Colorado Medical Center, 4200 East Ninth Avenue,
Denver, Colorado 80262

May be utilized in direct service settings without authors' permission
but not for publication. Comments will be appreciated and may be sent
to the Child Protection Team. (4th revision, July, 1976)

Appendix A-2

CPT CONSULTATIONS

TO: Pediatric House Staff and Faculty
FROM: CGH-Child Protection Team
SUBJECT: Consultations on Child Abuse or Neglect Cases

A. Weekdays

On weekdays from 9:00 A.M. to 5:00 P.M. call the CPT office
(x. 8269 or x. 7533). Consultations will be initiated by the
Coordinator (Candy Grosz or Marilyn Lenherr). If no answer, try
general page (x. 8111) or the National Center (321-3963).

B. Weekends or Evenings

If the CPT office is closed, specific consultations can be obtained as follows: (A pediatrician on the Team is usually the
best person to contact first--especially if the diagnosis is uncertain.)

1. Pediatric Consultations: Office   Home

   Dr. Barton Schmitt   7961   298-7277
   Dr. Jane Gray   8269   255-0173
   Dr. C. Henry Kempe   7576   277-6563
   Dr. Pamela Boggess   321-3963   255-2998
   Dr. Richard Krugman   7963   258-2807

2. Coordinators (for help with routine reporting, emergency foster
   placement, police holds, etc.)

   Candy Grosz   8269   233-7361
   Marilyn Lenherr   321-3963   255-6244

3. Social Work Consultations:

   Claudia Carroll   8269   270-5398
   Bob Schrant   321-3963   258-0697
   Patricia Beezley   321-3963   221-1028
   Helen Alexander   321-3963   277-1357

4. Psychiatric Consultations:

   Child Psychiatry Fellow   7412 or 7431
   (on-call)   If no response: Bellboy 105 days
                                                   Bellboy 149 nights

   Dr. Lloyd Eckhart   7737   222-7867
   Dr. Brandt Steele   8483   288-3177
   Dr. Ruth Kempe   321-3963   277-6563

Appendix A-3

UNIVERSITY OF COLORADO MEDICAL CENTER

Inter-office Communication

TO _____Pediatric Clinic and Wards_____ Date_____

FROM _____CPT-CGH_____

SUBJECT: POLICE HOLDS - Procedures for obtaining a 48-hour police hold

Indications for a police hold are:

1. The parents refuse to admit an abused child to the hospital.
2. The parents threaten to take an abused child out of the hospital.
3. The parents make threats of physical violence against hospital staff.

Consultation with a member of the Child Protection Team should be made for assistance in obtaining the police hold, unless it is considered an emergency. Team members can be reached at the CPT office (x. 8269 or x. 7533) or through the individual home telephone numbers listed on the consultation sheets in the clinics and wards. The physician can also ask the administrator on call (x. 8446) to obtain the police hold.

For obtaining a police hold on your own, directly contact the police department in the area where the child resides. Usually, the police will give you a verbal police hold by phone and then come to Colorado General Hospital to provide an official written police hold for the patient's hospital record. An officer's request form that can be utilized in all counties is attached. The hospital security guard (x. 7689) can be called if the parents actually try to remove their child by force. If the parents succeed in removing their child, the police in the child's area of residence should be called so that they can try to locate the child and return him to the hospital.

The numbers for the law enforcement agencies within the Denver Metropolitan area are listed below. If you are not sure of the exact locality of the child's residence, call the sheriff's department in that county.

Boulder	422-2020	Greenwood Village	798-8381
Denver	297-2011	Littleton	794-1551
Lakewood	234-8536	Northglenn	452-1946
Arvada	424-5556	Sheridan	761-7410
Aurora	366-1511	Thornton	287-5544
Cherry Hills	798-8381	Westminster	429-1546
Commerce City	287-2844	Broomfield	466-2345
Edgewater	279-2571	Castle Rock	688-3121
Englewood	761-7410	Edgewater Zone	279-2571
Federal Heights	428-8538	Golden Zone	279-2557

Police Holds

Glendale.........	759-1511	Lafayette	665-5571
Golden	279-2557	Louisville	666-6565
		Thornton Zone ..	287-5544

Sheriffs:

Adams County 659-2422
Arapahoe County 798-8381
Douglas County Castle Rock . 688-3133

Jefferson County 279-2571
Northglenn 452-1946

Appendix A-4

AUTHORIZATION TO HOLD

AND TREAT A CHILD

SUSPECTED OF SUFFERING

NONACCIDENTAL TRAUMA

DATE: _____

MINOR'S NAME: _____

_____

WARD: _____

HOSPITAL NO.: _____

I hereby certify that I have reasonable grounds to suspect that
_____ is suffering from nonaccidental
(Name of Minor)
trauma, and I, therefore, confirm authorization of a 48-hour police
hold. As the temporary legal guardian of the subject child, I
authorize the staff of Colorado General Hospital to hold and to treat
this child for a period of 48 hours.

_____
(Signature of the Officer)   (Badge No.)

_____   _____ AM/PM
(Witness)   (Date)   (Time)

311

COURT ORDER TO TREAT WHEN PARENTS REFUSE TO CONSENT

TO: Pediatric Clinic and Wards
FROM: \ Child Protection Team - Colorado General Hospital
SUBJECT: Court Order to Treat (Administrative Consent)

Indications for a court order to treat (administrative consent) are situations where the parent refuses to give consent for a specific diagnostic procedure or treatment in a life-threatening situation. Examples are: (1) a spinal tap in suspected meningitis confirmed by two physicians, (2) a blood transfusion for severe bleeding, and (3) an infectious disease that threatens the public safety if it goes untreated (e.g., diphtheria).

Mechanism:

1. If the physician is extremely busy, he can turn this problem over to the administrator on call. (Phone - 8446)
2. If the physician has time, he can call the judge on call in the Denver county. He should also request that written consent be forwarded to the hospital. The physician should record the date, time, judge's name, and judge's orders precisely into the patient's chart. Please note that a police officer cannot provide consent to treat in a nonchild abuse case. The following number can be called to reach a probation officer who will contact the judge on call, 892-3661.

Note: Cases requiring a court order to treat do not need to go through a court in the child's county of residence. In Colorado, they go through the hospital's county.

A letter of clarification to the parents
in an administrative consent case:

Dear Mr. and Mrs. Smith:

I am writing to you on behalf of our Pediatric Clinic. As you
know, last Friday we had to obtain a court order to do a spinal tap
on your baby. The spinal tap was needed to make sure your baby did
not have meningitis. The only way to diagnose meningitis for certain
is with a spinal tap. If we had missed meningitis, your baby could
have died or have been seriously brain damaged. Fortunately, your
baby had a normal spinal tap. We are sorry you had been led to believe that the spinal tap was a dangerous procedure. On the contrary,
it is a very safe test and has saved many lives.

We wanted you to be aware of the fact that we don't like to be
in disagreement with parents; in fact, this rarely happens. We want
to also be sure that it is clear that we are not in disagreement with
you about anything else. For the record, we found your baby to be
well fed, well loved, and well cared for. We hope by this time your
boy's ear infection is improved, and we also hope that we can forget
the past and look forward to seeing you and your family for any future
health needs that you may require.

Sincerely,

C. D. Jones, M.D.

Appendix A-7

REPORTING CHILD ABUSE/NEGLECT (CA/N) BY PHONE
AND OBTAINING EMERGENCY CHILD WELFARE SERVICES

TO: Pediatric Clinics
FROM: CPT-CGH
SUBJECT: Reporting, Emergency Evaluation or Foster Placement
         on Weekends and Evenings

In Colorado, all cases of suspected CA/N by law must be reported by
phone immediately to the Child Welfare Department in the child's county
of residence (see the telephone list below). On weekdays during normal
working hours, this can be done by the CPT coordinator. Most hospitalized cases can also wait until the next working day for reporting because the children are in a safe setting.

In the OPD, many hospitalizations of children with CA/N who don't require hospitalization for medical reasons can be prevented by contacting the on-call Child Welfare social worker. In some cases, their
evaluation in our OPD may determine that the family setting is safe
with ongoing treatment services. In other cases, they may determine
that the home is unsafe and that the child can be placed in an emergency receiving home. Sometimes, because of the unavailability of an
emergency foster home, hospitalization will still be necessary.

A county protective service worker can be contacted to help you with
such situations by calling the following numbers after hours and on
weekends.

        *Denver County-Family Crisis Center   893-6111
         Adams County-Answering Service   427-5013
         Arapahoe County-in care of Sheriff's Office   798-8381
         Jefferson County-Answering Service   234-9062
         Boulder County-in care of Sheriff's Office   441-3630
         El Paso County-days   471-5951
                        nights   475-9593

_____

*This agency will take referrals for Metro Denver area residents
 and help in locating the appropriate service agency.

Physical Abuse - OPD

GUIDELINES FOR PEDIATRIC EVALUATION OF OUTPATIENT CASES OF
PHYSICAL ABUSE AT COLORADO GENERAL HOSPITAL

When a Child Welfare social worker or police officer brings a child to
our Outpatient Department, they usually only want a pediatric evaluation to document the medical evidence for physical abuse. Children
who have been abandoned, left unsupervised, or live in other adverse
environments may also be brought in for physical checkups. In cases
where the home is unsafe, Child Welfare will take the child to a foster
home after the medical evaluation is completed. By contrast, when a
parent or guardian brings a child with suspected nonaccidental trauma
to the Emergency Room or the Child Care Clinic, the child should
usually be hospitalized so that he will be in a protective environment
until Child Welfare can become involved and complete their evaluation
of the safety of the home. The following guidelines are recommended
for the physician on outpatient cases:

1. See These Patients Immediately. Patients who are brought in by
    other professionals (nurses, social workers, police, etc.) will
    be seen in the Child Care Clinic before other walk-in patients.
    Other patients on the log sheet should be skipped when these
    patients are present. The reason for this policy is that a pro-
    fessional who is on duty should not have to spend long periods
    of time waiting to see another professional. The only cases of
    higher priority are suspected emergencies.

2. Maintain a Helping Approach Toward These Parents. This is the
    hardest step. Feeling angry with these parents is natural, but
    expressing this anger is very damaging to parent cooperation.
    Repeated interrogation, confrontation, and accusation must be
    avoided. Keep in mind that most of these people are lonely,
    frustrated, unloved, needy people who actually love their child
    but have lashed out at him in anger.

3. Elicit a Detailed History of the Injury. A complete history should
    be obtained by one physician as to how the injury allegedly
    happened (the informant, date, exact time, place, sequence of
    events, people present, time lag before medical attention sought,
    etc.). The parent can be pressed for exact details when neces-
    sary. No other professional should have to repeat this detailed,
    probing interview. If the parents are not present, the physician
    can request that the person who brought the child to the clinic
    (e.g., police or social worker) also bring the parents to the
    hospital for a brief interview. It is important for the physician
    to talk with the parents directly so that his history is not
    looked upon as hearsay evidence (second-hand information) in
    court. If the child is old enough to give a complete history
    (usually over age 6) the parents may not need to be brought in.

Physical Abuse - OPD

4. **Perform a Thorough Physical Exam.** All bruises should be listed by site and have recorded their size, shape, and color. If they resemble strap marks, grab marks, slap marks, bite marks, loop marks, tie marks, choke marks, cigarette burns, a blunt instrument, or any identifiable object, this should be recorded. Special attention should be paid to the retina, eardrums, oral cavity, and the genitals for signs of occult trauma. All bones should be palpated for tenderness and joints tested for full range of motion. The height and weight should be plotted and, if the child appears malnourished, he should be given a return appointment for a weight check after two weeks either in the foster home with ad lib meals, or in his natural home with specific feeding advice.

5. **Order Bone Survey X-rays on Selected Cases.** Every suspected case under 5 years of age should receive a radiologic bone survey (termed "trauma survey" at CGH). Over age 5, X-rays should be obtained only if there is any bone tenderness or limited ROM on physical exam. If films of a tender site are initially negative, they should be repeated in 2 weeks to pick up calcification of any subperiosteal bleeding or nondisplaced epiphyseal separations that may have been present.

6. **Order a Bleeding Disorder Screen on Selected Cases.** If there are bruises and the parents deny inflicting them or claim the child has "easy bruising," a bleeding disorder screen (platelet count, bleeding time, partial thromboplastin time, thrombin time, and prothrombin time) should be ordered (Extension 8471). During nights or weekends, such patients should be scheduled to return for these tests during the morning of the next working day.

7. **Request a CPT Pediatric Consultation on Difficult Cases.** Some cases are obvious; others are confusing. Try to observe the following guidelines:

    (a) Weekdays - call Dr. Schmitt (Extension 7961) or the CPT office (Extension 8269 or 7533) on all cases for consultation. Usually wait until your evaluation is completed and any diagnostic studies are back.

    (b) Evenings and weekends - call the CCC attending on all cases. If the CCC attending feels that the diagnosis is definitely confirmed and won't need an expert witness in court, CPT consultation is unnecessary. If the attending feels the diagnosis is uncertain or the case is complex and may require an expert witness in court, let the clerk at the front desk locate Drs. Schmitt, Gray, Kempe, Boggess, or Krugman for you by calling them at the home numbers posted on the CPT consultation list.

Appendix A-8 (3)

Physical Abuse - OPD

    (c) Always <u>SAVE</u> the chart for Dr. Schmitt or the CPT, so that a typed report can go in within 48 hours.

8. <u>Request a CPT Social Worker Consultation on Selected Cases.</u> In general, the psycho-social evaluations in these cases will be done by Child Welfare. However, if you feel the need for another opinion, call our CPT social worker (Extension 8269 or 7533). An example might be where the police are going to return the child home but you feel that temporary foster care is necessary for the child's safety. On weekends and evenings if you need a social worker, phone the on-call child welfare worker in the county of residence (see that list).

9. <u>Complete an Official Written Report of the Physical Abuse Within 48 Hours.</u> The case should be reported to Child Welfare by phone immediately, and this will be done as soon as you notify the CPT coordinator (Extension 7533). The official medical report is required by law within 48 hours and should be written by the examining physician. As long as the medical record of the Clinic visit contains the following data, the official typed medical report can be extracted from it. (Example attached.) After completing your chart note, give the chart to Dr. Schmitt or the CPT Coordinator immediately. On weekends or evenings, save the chart until the next working day as we have no facility for typing these reports during these hours. <u>To prepare an adequate report, your chart notes must include</u>:

    (a) History:
- the date and time the patient is brought into CCC
- name of professional(s) who accompany the patient
- the informant (parent, child, or both)
- the date, time and place of the abuse incident
- how the abuse occurred
- who allegedly abused the child
- any history of past abuse

    (b) Physical exam (description of the injury or injuries):
- list the injuries by site (e.g., head, arms, legs, back, buttocks, chest, abdomen, genitalia)
- describe each injury by <u>size</u>, shape, color, etc.
- if the injury identifies the object that caused it, always say so (e.g., strap mark, cigarette burn)
- use nontechnical terms like "cheek" instead of "zygoma", "bruise" instead of "ecchymosis"
- use inches instead of centimeters, where possible

Note: A diagram of the body surface findings is helpful, but is <u>not</u> as important as the verbal description of the same (<u>see</u> <u>sample report</u>).

317

Appendix A-8 (4)

Physical Abuse - OPD

    (c) Lab tests: X-rays, bleeding tests, etc.

    (d) Conclusion: Concluding statement on reasons why this represents nonaccidental trauma.

10. Provide Follow-up Appointment. A child with physical abuse who is not placed in a foster home needs close follow-up of his physical condition. The first appointment is usually made at a 1 - 2 week interval. If the child has a primary physician, he should be reappointed to him. If he has no prior health care resource, he should return to our clinic. In addition, the child may need to return to have some immunizations or routine screening tests brought up to date.

Prepared by B.D. Schmitt, et al., Child Protection Team, at the University of Colorado Medical Center, 4200 East 9th Avenue, Denver, Colorado 80262.

May be utilized in direct service settings without author's permission, but not for publication.

August/1976

Physical Abuse - OPD   Sample

PHYSICAL ABUSE - MEDICAL REPORT

S.D.
BD: 12/7/68
CGH # 222333

History: On 7/12/76, at 3:20 P.M., this 7½-year-old boy was brought
to the Colorado General Hospital/Child Care Clinic by R. Smith of the
Adams County Child Welfare Department for medical evaluation of suspected child abuse. The patient states that his mother struck him
numerous times last evening (about 7:30 P.M.) with a strap. She also
shook him. He claims the punishment was for refusing to take out the
garbage. His older sister witnessed the beating. He reported the
incident to his teacher today who then notified Child Welfare. Prior
to last evening, the patient states he has been struck with fan belts,
bicycle tires, straps, and various wooden paddles. He states this has
left bruises on at least two other occasions, but only on his buttocks.

During a brief phone conversation with the mother, she admits to hitting the patient with a belt, but claims he bruises easily.

Physical Exam: The patient was at the 60th percentile for hgt. and
the 70th for wgt. The exam was normal except for the following:

1. Head: (R) ear - linear bruise 1" x 2", running across top portion
       and including adjacent scalp (resembles strap mark).
       Posterior scalp - tender swelling, 2" x 2", no bruise.

2. Arms: (R) upper arm - 3 oval-shaped bruises, dime size. (Resemble
       grab marks.)

3. Back: 2 linear bruises, on (R) side below shoulder blade, 1" x 3"
       and 1" x 4". (Resemble strap marks.)

4. Buttocks: at least 8 bruises; most are linear, a few circular,
       (R) more than (L); length 2" to 6". (Resemble strap marks, tongue
       of belt visible at 2 sites.)

5. Legs: (R) upper lateral thigh - 1 linear bruise, 1" x 3".

Note: All the above bruises are purple-red and are recent.

Lab Tests:

    Bleeding screen - normal.
    Trauma X-rays - not indicated.

Conclusion: This 7½-year-old boy has at least 12 strap mark bruises
inflicted by his mother with a belt. The one on the head points to
serious loss of control. The history of past similar incidents increases the risk for this child.
                    July 12, 1976 - Barton Schmitt, M.D.

Physical Abuse - Hospitalized

GUIDELINES FOR PEDIATRIC MANAGEMENT OF HOSPITALIZED CASES
OF PHYSICAL ABUSE AT COLORADO GENERAL HOSPITAL

When a parent or guardian brings a child to the Emergency Room or
Child Care Clinic and the physician suspects that the child has sustained nonaccidental injuries or serious medical neglect, the following guidelines are recommended:

1. Hospitalize the Suspected Case. The purpose of hospitalization
   is to protect the child until family evaluations regarding the
   safety of the home are complete. The extent of injuries is not
   relevant to this requirement. The reason given to the parents for
   hospitalization can be that "his injuries need to be watched" or
   "further studies are needed." It is not helpful to mention the
   possibility of nonaccidental trauma in the E.R. The outpatient
   physician should keep incriminating questions to a minimum. If
   it becomes difficult to persuade the parents of the need for admission, contact Drs. Barton Schmitt or Jane Gray (Extension 7961
   or 8269) for assistance. If the parents refuse hospitalization,
   a police hold can be obtained (see that protocol). This is rarely
   needed and should not be a routine procedure.

   The case can be safely evaluated without hospitalization in some
   instances such as where Child Welfare is already involved and will
   be placing the child in a temporary foster home or where the
   offender no longer has access to the child (i.e., a boyfriend who
   is in jail or a babysitter who is no longer employed). Serious
   homicidal threats (e.g., "If I have to spend another minute with
   that kid, something bad is going to happen.") also require admission and psychiatric consultation.

   When a baby with suspected abuse needs to be transported from a
   private physician's office to the hospital, an office nurse or
   aide should try to accompany the parents. The name of a specific
   admitting physician at Colorado General Hospital should also be
   given to the parents. This prevents the parents from running away
   with the child.

2. Treat the Child's Injuries. Once the child is in the hospital,
   the medical and surgical problems should be cared for in the
   appropriate manner. An orthopedic consultation is commonly needed.
   Opthalmologists, neurologists, neuro-surgeons, and plastic surgeons are occasionally consulted. The parents can be reassured
   that good medical care for their child is our first priority.

3. Elicit a Detailed History of the Injury. A complete history should
   be obtained by one physician as to how the injury allegedly
   happened (the informant, date, exact time, place, sequence of
   events, people present, time lag before medical attention sought,

Physical Abuse - Hospitalized

etc.). If possible, the parents should be interviewed separately.
The parents can be pressed for exact details when necessary. No
other professional should have to repeat this detailed, probing
interview. This history should be obtained as soon after admission
as possible, before the parents have had time to change the story.
It is important for the physician to talk with the parents directly
so that his history is not looked upon as hearsay evidence (second-
hand information) in court. Any child over age 3 should also be
interviewed regarding what happened to him.

4. Perform a Thorough Physical Exam. All bruises should be listed by
site and have recorded their size, shape, and color. If they
resemble strap marks, grab marks, slap marks, bite marks, loop
marks, tie marks, choke marks, cigarette burns, a blunt instrument,
or any identifiable object, this should be recorded. Special
attention should be paid to the retina, eardrums, oral cavity, and
the genitals for signs of occult trauma. All bones should be palpated for tenderness and joints tested for full range of motion.

5. Order Bone Survey X-rays on Selected Cases. Every suspected case
under 5 years of age should receive a radiologic bone survey
(termed "trauma survey" at CGH). Over age 5, X-rays should be
obtained only if there is any bone tenderness or limited ROM on
physical exam. If films of a tender site are initially negative,
they should be repeated in 2 weeks to pick up calcification of any
subperiosteal bleeding or nondisplaced epiphyseal separations that
may have been present. If there are visible physical findings,
color photographs should be obtained before they fade. These may
be needed in court in addition to the X-rays. (The CPT Coordinator
at Extension 8269 can arrange for these.)

6. Order a Bleeding Disorder Screen on Selected Cases. If there are
bruises and the parents deny inflicting them or claim the child has
"easy bruising," a bleeding disorder screen (platelet count,
bleeding time, partial thromboplastin time, thrombin time, and prothrombin time) should be ordered (Extension 8471). During nights
or weekends, such patients should be scheduled to return for these
tests during the morning of the next working day.

7. Request CPT-Pediatric Consultation to Help Confirm Your Diagnosis
on All Cases Within 24 Hours of Admission. Some cases are obvious;
others are confusing. The stakes are high; physical abuse is a
life-threatening disease. Diagnosis is the pediatrician's job--
not the psychiatrist's or social worker's. It is based on medical
judgement. If there is any doubt about the diagnosis, the Child
Protection Team pediatrician should be called during the initial
admission since these parents sometimes don't visit. In most cases,
however, wait until you have completed your own evaluation and any
needed diagnostic studies are back. For pediatric consultation

Physical Abuse - Hospitalized

call Drs. Gray, Schmitt, or Kempe. Phone numbers are posted on the CPT consultation sheet on the bulletin boards of the clinics and wards. If child abuse has not occurred, steps 8 through 19 need not be taken.

Indications for CPT-Pediatric consultation are:

(a) Physical abuse (i.e., unexplained or inadequately explained bruises, swellings, fractures, or burns. This should also include any bruises which are inflicted in the name of discipline).

(b) Failure to thrive, secondary to under-feeding (as documented by having the infant gain at over 1.5 ozs. per day while in the hospital on a regular diet or suspected on admission because of the mother's behavior). (See special protocol.)

(c) Sexual abuse--molestation or incest. (See special protocol.)

(d) Medical care neglect (i.e., not seeking medical care or not administering therapy when the omission is life-threatening).

(e) Intentional drugging or poisoning (i.e., caretakers who give children dangerous drugs without a physician's orders).

8. Tell Parents the Diagnosis and the Need to Report It. Tell the parents the diagnosis and the need to report it before doing so. One can state: "Your explanation for the injury is insufficient. Even though it wasn't intentional, someone injured this child. I am obligated by Colorado Law to report all suspicious injuries to children." The physician should do this since the case is reported on the basis of his medical findings. In fact, after all diagnostic studies are completed, the physician should review in a kind way the actual cause of each specific injury. This convinces the parents that we know what actually happened and permits them to turn their attention to therapy. He should be willing to discuss the general content of the medical report. The overall outlook should be positive and emphasize that this problem is treatable, Child Welfare will be involved (not the police), that the matter will be shared only with professionals (not appear in the newspapers), and that everyone's goal is to help them find better ways of dealing with their child (not to punish the parents). If the parents become argumentative, they can be advised to seek legal counsel.

9. Examine All Siblings Within 12 Hours. Although it is unusual to have multiple children abused in the same family at the same time, it does occur. For the safety of any siblings, they should be brought in for a full examination within 12 hours of reporting a

Physical Abuse - Hospitalized

case. Parents can be told this is "hospital policy." If the parents say they can't bring them in because of transportation problems, the protective service agency can accomplish this. If the parents refuse to have their other children seen, a court order can be obtained and the police sent out.

10. **Maintain a Helping Approach Toward These Parents.** This is the hardest step. Feeling angry with these parents is natural, but expressing this anger is very damaging to parent cooperation. Repeated interrogation, confrontation, and accusation must be avoided. During visits, the ward staff must go out of their way to be courteous to these parents. The primary physician must see or phone them daily. They become suspicious quite easily if communication is not optimal. If the child is brought in with multiple life-threatening injuries or DOA, the parent requires an emergency psychiatric evaluation because he may be psychotic or suicidal.

11. **Involve the Mother in the Child's Hospital Care.** The ultimate goal is to have the mother care for her baby adequately. The mother should be encouraged to visit frequently and to take over the care of her baby during these times. Since the appropriate disposition may depend on the mother's involvement with the child on the ward, an exact record should be kept of the number of visits, the duration of the visits, and what the mother does during the visits. If the mother does not visit or visits rarely, the hospital should attempt to provide the nurturing environment these children need. A foster grandmother and/or selected ward nurse can attempt to be mother surrogates for these children.

12. **Report to Child Welfare by Phone Within 24 Hours.** The call goes to the agency charged with children's protective services in the patient's county of residence. The CPT Coordinator (Mrs. Candace Grosz or Ms. Marilyn Lenherr) will place this call if the physician wishes her to do so.

13. **Complete an Official Written Report of the Physical Abuse Incident Within 48 Hours.** The official medical report is required by law, and should be written by a physician and contain the following brief but accurate data:

(a) History:
- the date and time the patient is brought into CCC
- name of professional(s) who accompany the patient
- the informant (parent, child, or both)
- the date, time, and place of the abuse incident.
- how the abuse occurred
- who allegedly abused the child
- any history of past abuse

Physical Abuse - Hospitalized

    (b) Physical exam (description of the injury or injuries):
- list the injuries by site (e.g., head, arms, legs, back, buttocks, chest, abdomen, genitalia)
- describe each injury by size, shape, color, etc.
- if the injury identifies the object that caused it, always say so (e.g., strap mark, cigarette burn)
- use nontechnical terms like "cheek" instead of "zygoma", "bruise" instead of "ecchymosis"
- use inches instead of centimeters, where possible

Note: A diagram of the body surface findings is helpful, but is not as important as the verbal description of the same. (See sample report.)

    (c) Lab tests: X-rays, bleeding tests, etc.

    (d) Conclusion: Concluding statement on reasons why this represents nonaccidental trauma.

This report should be hand-written on ordinary paper by the pediatric intern in charge of the case. It should be taken to the CPT Coordinator, Room 3203, for typing on the official CWS59 form. She will also have it critiqued and co-signed by the CPT pediatrician.

14. Request CPT Social Worker Consultation Within 48 Hours. This referral can be explained as "hospital policy." The CPT Coordinator will schedule these appointments. The social worker does the indepth psychosocial interview to determine overall family problems, environmental problems, the safety of the home, the state of the marriage, how disturbed the parents are, and how likely they are to accept therapy. In severe or complex cases, or when the initial social history information is inconclusive, the CPT social worker may request a psychiatric evaluation. (This helps to uncover the 10% of parents that are very dangerous because they are sociopathic or psychotic.) Child Welfare services carry out their own home evaluation concurrently. The pediatrician is not usually able to provide these three types of evaluations.

15. Refer Parents Who Need Crisis Psychotherapy. After diagnosis, some of these parents will experience anger and other strong emotions that require ventilation. Also some of them have strong dependency needs. The pediatric intern or resident may desire to personally help these parents. Usually, however, you will not have the time. Those parents who obviously need a long talk with someone about subjects other than their child's medical status can be referred to the CPT Coordinator or social worker. If a psychiatric crisis develops on nights or weekends and the CPT social worker can't be reached, contact the child psychiatry fellow on call. (See that consultation list.) If the parents threaten to take the child

Physical Abuse - Hospitalized

out of the hospital against medical advice, a police hold should
be obtained. (See police hold protocol.) Any member of the CPT
or the hospital administration can help with this.

16. Attend CPT Dispositional Conference. The social worker, pediatric
consultant, house staff, Child Welfare worker, police representative, psychiatrist, CPT Coordinator, and any other community
agencies involved with this family should meet within 1 week of
admission. All evaluations should have been completed. All possible suspects (including babysitters, neighbors, siblings, boy-
friends) should have been interviewed. When decisions are urgent,
the physician, CPT social worker, and Child Welfare social worker
involved on the case will meet on a nonscheduled basis and make
the necessary decisions. Their actions will later be reviewed by
the full team.

The regular CPT dispositional meetings with consultants present
take place on Tuesdays from 11 to 12. An attempt is made to list
all the family's problems in the case being reviewed. Then a
joint decision is reached regarding the best immediate and long-
range plans for each problem. Based on the assessed safety of the
home, a decision must be made on whether to have the child followed voluntarily or to go to court for temporary foster-home
placement or court-enforced supervision. In severe cases, the
Team may decide to urge the court to terminate parental rights
and place the child for adoption. The CPT Coordinator will convey these recommendations immediately by phone to Child Welfare
if they have not been able to attend the meeting. The composite
recommendations of this meeting are typed and copies distributed
to all involved individuals or agencies. (See example of Team
report.)

17. Provide Medical Testimony for Cases Which Go to Court. Usually
these cases are heard in juvenile court rather than criminal court.
Petitions are sustained on the basis of a "preponderance of evidence." The physician's statement that it is highly unlikely that
the injury was due to an accident puts the burden on the parents
to prove that they did not cause the injury in question. If the
physician keeps precise medical records, reviews them before the
hearing, and confers with the protective agency's lawyer about the
points he wishes to stress, the court hearing can have a favorable
outcome. The physician should bring a copy of his typed medical
report to court with him. An extra copy should be available to
submit into evidence. Extra copies of particularly graphic photographs should be brought to court and used as evidence. X-rays
are not needed in the courtroom in Colorado.

When the house staff are subpoened for court, one of the CPT
pediatricians will accompany them. Only after seeing a CPT

Physical Abuse - Hospitalized

physician testify will they be requested to assume this role.
The CPT pediatrician and/or lawyer are very willing to review
with the house staff members in advance the questions they will
probably be asked during cross-examination.

18. Provide Follow-up Appointment to Monitor the Child's Physical
Status. The pediatrician is responsible for coordinating health
care. The battered child needs more frequent well-child care than
the average child. He should be seen weekly for a while. He
needs follow-up to detect any recurrence of physical abuse. If
he has sustained head injury, he needs follow-up for mental re-
tardation, spasticity, and subdural hematoma. These return
visits can be provided by the pediatric resident who was initially
involved on the ward, if he belongs to a Pediatric Group Practice.
Another option is to have Dr. Gray, Dr. Schmitt, or a pediatric
group practice provide follow-up care. When these children are
followed at CGH, their charts are marked with the letters "CPT."
If the parents come from a great distance, the pediatric follow-up
should be assigned to a physician in that community. He should
receive telephone notification prior to discharge.

19. Child Welfare Will Provide Psycho-social Follow-up and Treatment.
The pediatrician should not feel responsible for restoration of
these families to emotional health. Child Welfare is primarily
responsible for coordination of the family's therapy. This
therapy should begin while the child is still in the hospital.
Some innovative types of therapy that have been successful when
designed for individual cases are Lay Therapists or Mothering
Aides, Homemakers, Parents Anonymous groups, telephone hotlines,
day care centers, environmental crisis therapy, marital counseling, vocational rehabilitation, etc. Child Welfare also makes
home visits and attempts to locate any families who become lost to
follow-up. A pediatrician can contribute to the therapeutic process by giving the parent his telephone number to call if things
get rough. It is best if the parent has several people available
as life-lines. After the parent calls, Child Welfare should be
notified if the parent is in a crisis and needs nonmedical help.

Prepared by B.D. Schmitt et al., Child Protection Team, at the University of Colorado Medical Center, 4200 East 9th Avenue, Denver,
Colorado 80262.

May be utilized in direct service settings without authors' permission, but not for publication.

August/1976.

Nutritional Deprivation-
Hospitalized

GUIDELINES FOR PEDIATRIC MANAGEMENT OF HOSPITALIZED
CASES OF FAILURE TO THRIVE SECONDARY TO NUTRITIONAL
DEPRIVATION AT COLORADO GENERAL HOSPITAL

Failure to thrive can be defined as an underweight and malnourished
condition. These children are usually below the 3rd percentile for
weight and above the 3rd percentile for height and head circumference.
Although there are numerous causes of failure to thrive, these guidelines pertain to the child who is failing to thrive because of underfeeding or nutritional deprivation. This diagnosis is confirmed when
the failure to thrive child who has not been able to gain weight at
home easily gains weight in the hospital setting. The following steps
will help in management of these children.

1. Hospitalize these babies. Any baby with failure to thrive who does
   not respond to a one-month trial of increased calories and public
   health nurse visits in the home should be hospitalized. Any case
   where maternal deprivation is suspected should be hospitalized
   immediately, as these children are hard to follow as outpatients.

2. Elicit a detailed diet history and feeding history. In most cases
   the mother will claim that the child is receiving more than adequate calories. In a few cases the baby will be reported to be on
   a very bizarre diet, and this will help to uncover a psychotic
   parent. In some cases the mother will report that the child has
   significant vomiting and diarrhea. The child's subsequent course
   in the hospital will prove most of these diet and feeding histories
   to be false. However, it is important to initially document these
   misleading histories in the medical record so that they can later
   be contrasted with the child's actual behavior in the hospital
   setting. The previous attempts by the parents to seek medical
   care for the child's failure to thrive should be noted (i.e.,
   sometimes no physician has been consulted). A history of any
   preceding acute medical illness such as severe diarrhea or pneumonia that is well documented by a previous physician should also
   be recorded. The parents obviously should not be held accountable
   for a transient debilitating illness that caused weight loss and
   that is followed by a rapid weight gain in the hospital.

3. Perform a thorough physical exam. The physical examination in
   children with failure to thrive due to nutritional deprivation
   should reveal a healthy but underweight child. The only abnormal
   physical findings should relate to malnutrition. The physician
   should obtain all available past heights and weights on the patient and carefully plot them. The growth chart in this disorder
   should reveal a fall off or plateauing of weight that greatly
   exceeds the plateauing of height. Head circumference plateauing
   only occurs with severe malnutrition. Signs of associated

Nutritional Deprivation -
Hospitalized

hygiene neglect or inflicted injuries should also be looked for.

4. Order limited laboratory tests. A child showing failure to thrive
   in an otherwise normal physical examination requires very few
   base-line laboratory tests unless an attempt at caloric rehabilitation fails. A complete blood count, erythrocyte sedimentation
   rate, urine analysis, urine culture, stool pH, stool Clinitest,
   stool hematest, stool culture, serum electrolytes, BUN, and tuberculin test are adequate. Elaborate endocrine tests, malabsorption
   tests, and gastrointestinal X-rays could be deferred unless the
   baby fails to gain weight during a one-week period of adequate
   feeding. Diagnostic tests that require fasting are especially
   contraindicated. Special tests for alleged vomiting or diarrhea
   should not be ordered unless these symptoms are verified in the
   hospital setting.

5. Order bone survey X-rays in selected patients. A radiologic bone
   survey is indicated in any child once the nutritional deprivation
   is documented. In 5% to 10% of these children fractures will be
   detected and confirm that they also are suffering from physical
   abuse. Obviously these X-rays should be ordered initially in any
   children who have associated limited range of motion or other bone
   or joint findings. A before-and-after photograph of the child
   with failure to thrive can vividly demonstrate the malnutrition
   and may be helpful in court.

6. Evaluate the infant's psychosocial development on the day of
   admission. Over 90% of the children who have failure to thrive
   on a maternal deprivation basis will also manifest delays in development as well as deprivational behavior. A DDST should be
   obtained on the day of admission so that it can be compared to a
   later DDST after the child has received adequate stimulation.
   Any bizarre behavior that the child has on admission should also
   be carefully recorded in the physician and nursing notes.

7. Refer to CPT for consultation as soon as nutritional deprivation
   becomes a likely diagnosis for the failure to thrive. Certain
   cases of failure to thrive should be referred to the CPT on the
   day of admission so that a social evaluation can be obtained. The
   indications for this early referral depend on the presence of
   specific psycho-social findings. These findings will usually be
   elicited by the ward nurse or physician.

   (a) The child who is referred in by Child Welfare or the police
       should have immediate CPT involvement.

   (b) Certain findings in the baby point to the need for early
       referral, such as:

Nutritional Deprivation -
Hospitalized

- a severe degree of malnutrition (for example, minimal weight gain in the previous 2 months)
- a baby who has not received any medical attention despite failure to thrive
- the child whose parents are not at all concerned about his weight problem
- associated nonaccidental trauma
- gross hygiene neglect
- lack of supervision
- inadequate past medical care
- previously documented physical abuse or failure to thrive in a sibling.

(c) Early referral is indicated when the mother (on admission) is depressed, suicidal, overwhelmed with crises, retarded, psychotic, or bizarre.

(d) Early referral is indicated when the mother/child interaction on the ward reveals a lack of interest by the mother or open hostility toward the child. Also, a history of the child being unwanted/rejected requires the same course of action.

In the above cases the CPT social worker will evaluate the mother before she leaves the hospital on the day of admission. This is important because she may need immediate services such as psychiatric hospitalization in a suicidal mother. In addition, the early interview tends to elicit a history that is more valid and prevents the problem of having difficulty with getting the mother in for the history at a later date. The children with failure to thrive who are not referred to the CPT on the day of admission should be referred after they demonstrate a rapid weight gain for 2 or 3 days in the hospital.

8. Involve the mother in the child's hospital care. The ultimate goal is to have the mother care for her baby adequately. The mother should be encouraged to visit frequently and to take over the care of her baby during these times. Since failure to thrive evaluations may require one to two weeks of hospitalization, the mother should be encouraged to room-in with her baby. At a minimum this rooming in will be required during the last two or three days of hospitalization. During this time the ward medical and nursing staff should offer help, remain supportive, compliment the mother on her efforts, and generally build her confidence in herself as a mother. Criticism should be avoided, and if advice must be given, it should focus on the aspect that "he's a somewhat difficult child to feed."

Nutritional Deprivation -
Hospitalized

Since the appropriate disposition may depend on the mother's involvement with the child on the ward, an exact record should be
kept of the number of visits, the duration of the visits, and what
the mother does during these visits. If the mother does not visit
or visits rarely, the hospital should try to provide the nurturing
environment these children need. A foster grandmother and/or
selected nurse can attempt to be mother surrogates for these children. These babies also need extra cuddling and verbal stimulation
during their hospitalization from all the ward doctors, nurses,
and clerks.

9. Treat the baby's failure to thrive with unlimited feedings of a
regular diet for age. This step is essential at reaching a definitive diagnosis. The formula should be identical to the one
reportedly provided at home. Rapid weight gain on a special formula free of cow's milk protein or lactose would not prove that
the child was underfed in the home setting. The daily intake
should approach 150-200 calories per kilogram per day (ideal
weight). The baby should also be provided with supplemental
vitamins. A nutritionist should be consulted to document the
daily hospital intake and calories per kilo per day attained.
This diagnostic trial of feeding should be carried out for a minimum of one week and in some cases extended to two weeks.

10. Confirm the diagnosis of nutritional deprivation by documentation
of a rapid weight gain. While in the hospital, the baby should
be weighed on a daily basis on the same scale. Babies with failure
to thrive on a nutritional deprivation basis will gain rapidly and
easily in the hospital and also will demonstrate a ravenous appetite in most cases. A rapid weight gain can be defined as a gain
of over 2 oz. per day sustained for a one-week period, a gain of
greater than 1.5 oz. per day sustained for 2 weeks, or a gain that
is strikingly greater than seen during a similar interval at home.
Average weight gains for normal children vary according to age:
0.9 oz. per day in the first three months of life, 0.8 oz. per day
from three to six months, 0.6 oz. per day from six to nine months,
and 0.4 oz. per day from nine to twelve months of age.

11. Report all confirmed cases to Child Welfare by phone and in
writing. By law all cases of failure to thrive due to underfeeding
should be reported to the Child Welfare Department in the patient's
county of residence. The only exception is where the underfeeding
was due to ignorance on the parent's part and was easily remedied
by office advice. The CPT coordinator will be glad to place this
call if the physician requests it. Within 48 hours the phone reporting should be followed by an official medical report written
by the pediatric intern in charge of the case. It can be hand
written on ordinary paper and taken to the CPT coordinator, room

Nutritional Deprivation -
Hospitalized

3203, for typing on the official CWS 59 form. She will also have
the report critiqued and cosigned by the CPT pediatrician. A
sample of a well documented report is included at the end of this
protocol.

12. Initiate an organic workup for the babies who fail to gain ade-
    quately in the hospital setting. The babies with organic failure
    to thrive will fail to gain rapidly with unlimited feedings. Some
    of them will gain 1 oz. per day with great effort on the part of
    the nursing staff but will then level off after the initial week
    (e.g., those with dysphagia or cardiochalasia). Most of them will
    not gain anything substantial. These babies have an organic basis
    for their failure to thrive and in general fall into four groups.
    The first group has associated vomiting and will be recognized early
    in their hospital course (e.g., hiatal hernia). The second group
    will have inadequate caloric intake due to anorexia but without
    vomiting. The poor feeders seem disinterested in food and in some
    cases have a poor sucking reflex. The underlying cause is often
    a central nervous system defect as evidenced by associated micro-
    cephaly, developmental delays, floppiness, or seizures. A third
    group will have an adequate caloric intake in the hospital but
    will not have an adequate weight gain. Most of these babies have
    associated diarrhea and their underlying cause will be determined
    by a full malabsorption workup (e.g., celiac disease). A fourth
    group of babies will have an adequate caloric intake without any
    adequate weight gain but will have no diarrhea (e.g., diencephalic
    syndrome or hyperthyroidism). There will usually be adequate
    diagnostic clues to suggest a selective laboratory approach to
    these patients who fail to gain weight in the hospital. Consul-
    tation is often in order at this point.

13. Provide follow-up appointments. Full nutritional catch-up to ideal
    weight may require 4 to 6 weeks. During this time the child should
    be seen weekly for weight checks. In addition, the natural mother
    or foster mother needs careful dietary counseling by the physician
    on discharge. His recommendations should not be misinterpreted as
    forced feedings which could lead to secondary food refusal. If
    the child has a feeding problem, the ward nurse and nutritionist
    should be involved in this discharge counseling.

                                                        August/1976

Nutritional Deprivation -
Hospitalized

NUTRITIONAL DEPRIVATION - MEDICAL REPORT

Name: D.L.
B.D.:   1/22/73
CGH #:   333444
County: Fairfax

History: This 7 1/2 month-old girl was admitted on August 2, 1973, for the second time for severe failure to thrive. The mother states that the child has frequent vomiting and is a picky eater.

Physical Exam: Scrawny child with little fat tissue. No other findings.

Hospital course: The child had a ravenous appetite. There was no vomiting. On a regular diet the following weights were recorded:

1. Birth, 6 lb. 13 oz. to adm. #1 (gained < 1 oz./wk)

2. Admission #1 (May 29) 7 lb., 14 oz.
   Discharge (June 11), 9 lb., 3 oz. (gained > 2 oz./day)

3. Two months at home - no weight gain

4. Admission #2 (August 2) 9 lb., 3 oz.
   Discharge (August 9), 10 lb., 2 oz. (gained > 2 oz./day)

Trauma X-rays: Normal.

Conclusion: This child has been seriously underfed at home as documented by rapid weight gain in the hospital on two occasions. Treatment in the home has failed.

Benjamin Taylor, M.D.

Appendix A-11 (1)

GUIDELINES FOR PEDIATRIC EVALUATION OF INCEST AND
OTHER FAMILY-RELATED SEXUAL ABUSE CASES AT COLORADO GENERAL HOSPITAL

Sexual abuse of children by parents or caretakers includes incest
(sexual intercourse), sodomy (anal intercourse), oral-genital contact,
and molestation (fondling, masturbation, etc.).

Most of these incidents occur without force. By contrast, rape is
usually defined as sexual intercourse forced upon a victim using violence or threats of harm (usually by a stranger). All family-related
cases of incest and all molestation cases should be evaluated by the
pediatric house staff. Rape cases (except in emancipated minors) should
also receive a brief workup by the pediatric house staff before requesting gyn-consultation. They should be seen promptly, since the
family usually looks upon the situation as an emergency. The following
guidelines are recommended for the pediatrician.

1. Elicit a detailed history of the incident. If the problem is known
   in advance, a woman intern or resident should be assigned to the
   case if possible. Documentation of sexual abuse is usually totally
   dependent on the history. Therefore, the interview needs to be
   long, relaxed, and tactful. The patient should be encouraged to
   reveal all details concerning the incident(s). No other professional should have to repeat this interview. If the patient describes symptoms that could be related to sexual abuse, the story
   must sometimes be drawn out by a question such as, "I have a feeling that maybe somebody has done something to your body that has
   frightened you. Why don't you tell me about it?" In addition to
   facts regarding date, time, place, and person, the physician must
   document sites of sexual abuse (e.g., mouth, breasts, genitals,
   anus). Also, information on menstrual history, whether or not
   force was involved, the patient's concept of intercourse, and whether or not ejaculation took place should be sought and recorded.
   In children under age 6, this information will usually have to
   come from the mother. Older children should be encouraged to tell
   their own story in a private setting. (Note: on true rape cases,
   the gyn. resident will elicit this history.)

2. Perform a general physical examination. The patient needs a general physical exam to look for any signs of body injury or infection. The mouth, anus, and external genitals should receive
   special scrutiny for signs of trauma. The hymenal ring should be
   inspected for intactness. If the throat is inflamed, a throat
   culture for gonorrhea should be plated on Thayer-Martin media.

3. Refer selected cases to gynecology for a forensic vaginal exam.
   The gynecology resident on call to the E.R. has the expertise to
   perform a forensic vaginal exam that can stand up in court. Evidence (e.g., hair specimens, fingernail scrapings, acid phosphatase, sperm tests, etc.) is collected, transported, and analyzed
   utilizing a patient identification system that fulfills legal

333

Sexual Abuse - OPD or
Hospitalized

requirements. All rape cases (post-pubertal or pre-pubertal) should
be referred to gynecology for this procedure. Incest cases should
be referred only if intercourse has taken place in the last 48 hours
(evidence for sperm rarely persists beyond this time period). Obviously, molestation cases do not need a gynecology referral. The
first pelvic exam in a girl should be preceded by careful explanation and preparation from the clinic nurse. Cases at risk for
pregnancy should receive prophylactic stilbesterol, 25 mg. b.i.d.
for 5 days, assuming evidence exists that the patient is not pregnant. Cases at risk for venereal disease should receive 1.0 mg.
of probenicid plus 4.8 million units of procaine penicillin IM.
The gynecology resident will usually attend to these matters.

4. Hospitalize selected cases. The immediate objective in sexual
    abuse cases is to prevent continued sexual exploitation of the
    child. This usually requires placing the child in a foster home
    and getting the parents into therapy. In cases where Child Wel-
    fare accompanies the family, the above actions can usually be ar-
    ranged quickly. In cases where the parents or girl present
    themselves initially to the hospital without any prior agency in-
    volvement, the best course of action is usually to hospitalize the
    girl until Child Welfare can become involved.

5. Request a CPT pediatric consultation on difficult cases. Some cases
    are obvious; others are confusing. Try to observe the following
    guidelines:

    (a) Weekdays -- Call Dr. Schmitt (Extension 7961) or the CPT of-
        fice (Extension 8269 or 7533) on all cases for consultation.

    (b) Evenings and weekends -- Call the CCC attending on all cases.
        If the CCC attending feels that the diagnosis is definitely
        confirmed and won't need an expert witness in court, CPT con-
        sultation is unnecessary. If the attending feels the diag-
        nosis is uncertain or the case is complex and may require an
        expert witness in court, let the clerk at the front desk
        locate Drs. Schmitt, Gray, Kempe, Boggess, or Krugman for
        you by calling them at the home numbers posted on the CPT
        consultation list.

    (c) Always SAVE the chart for Dr. Schmitt or the CPT, so that a
        typed report can go in within 48 hours.

6. Request a CPT Social Worker consultation on selected cases. In
    general, the psycho-social evaluations in these cases will be done
    by a Child Welfare worker. However, if they do not accompany the
    patient, call our CPT social worker (Extension 8269 or 7533).
    Another reason for consultation might be where the police and child

---

Sexual Abuse - OPD or
Hospitalized
_____

welfare social worker are going to return the child home but you feel that temporary foster care is necessary for the child's safety. On weekends and evenings, if you need a social worker, phone the on-call child welfare worker in the county of residence (see that list).

7. Complete an official written report of the sexual abuse incident. The case should be reported to Child Welfare by phone immediately and this will be done as soon as you notify the CPT coordinator (x. 7533). The official medical report is required by law within 48 hours and should be written by the examining physician. As long as the medical record of the clinic visit contains the following data, the official typed medical report can be extracted from it (example attached). After completing your chart note, give the chart to Dr. Schmitt or the CPT coordinator immediately. On the weekends or evenings, save the chart until the next working day. We have no facility for typing these reports during evening hours. The report should include:

 (a) History - the alleged sexual abuse incident (with dates, times, places, sites involved, people involved, etc.).

 (b) Physical exam - description of any positive findings or pertinent negative findings (use nontechnical terms as much as possible).

 (c) Vaginal exam by gynecology consultant - if done, list his name here.

 (d) Conclusion - concluding statement on reasons why this represents sexual abuse.

8. Provide follow-up appointments. The hospital Child Protection Team will become involved as soon as notified and arrange to have all female siblings interviewed to rule out the possibility of any similar incidents with them. The victim herself should have an evaluation for emotional problems. This is best done as soon as possible by contacting the CPT social worker or the Adolescent Clinic social worker. For nights or weekends, if the victim is visibly upset, the child psychiatry fellow on-call should be notified so that he can provide immediate crisis counseling. If the patient is post-pubertal and runs any risk of becoming pregnant, she should have a one-month follow-up appointment in the Adolescent Clinic to see a physician.

Prepared by B. Schmitt et al., Child Protection Team, University of Colorado Medical Center, Department of Pediatrics, Box C218, Denver, Colorado 80262.

Sexual Abuse - OPD or
Hospitalized

SEXUAL ABUSE - MEDICAL REPORT

Name: T. L.
BD: 6/12/67
CGH # 222333

History: This seven-year-old child was brought to Colorado General Hospital 8/20/74 by her mother because of concern about sexual molestation of the girl by her husband (girl's stepfather). The mother is worried this has been going on for 6 months and quite frequently. The following history is directly from the mother. In the past 2 weeks since the mother quit work, Tracy has been coming to her to say such things as "Daddy tickles my bottom with his tongue, then he potties on me" (interpretation: oral-genital contact and ejaculation). The mother states that she has found the stepfather and daughter lying together on their bed and both have jumped when she walks in. The mother came in today because last night Tracy told her that her father "tickled my bottom with his finger" while the mother was at the laundromat. She says she wants her husband and/or daughter to get help and she has confronted her husband with this. He denies molesting Tracy, but says he will go to get help for himself. The girl is unwilling to talk to the examiner. However, she says "yes" when questioned about her mother's story. She denies that her father has ever put his penis in her bottom.

Physical exam: No signs of physical abuse. No signs of genital trauma. Hymenal opening intact and virginal.

Conclusion: This seven-year-old girl has been repeatedly sexually abused by her stepfather. This includes oral-genital contact and other forms of molestation. Urgent intervention is needed.

Thomas Johnson, M.D.

GUIDELINES FOR TRIAGING SEXUAL COMPLAINTS IN CHILDREN AND ADOLESCENTS

October 1976

The following five situations are apt to present in the Pediatric Clinic or the Emergency Room. The appropriate role and responsibilities of pediatric and ob-gyn house staff are outlined below. In those cases which do not fit the situations listed below, the physician should use his clinical judgement to decide what is best for the patient.

Type of Alleged Sexual Assault	Complete Eval. & Rx by GYN Res. in ER(4)	Eval. & Rx by Ped. in Adol. Clinic or CCC (5)	GYN consult for forensic pelvic exam (6)	Report to Child Welfare(7)	Stat Psychosocial Eval.	Psychosocial Follow-up Appointment	Call Rape Counseling Service
1. Rape--over 18 yrs./plus under 18 if married or an emancipated minor(1)	X		All	None	Most, E.R. Psychiatrist	As needed, Adult Psych.	Most (11)
2. Rape--17 and under, unless married or emancipated minor (1)		X	All	None	Most, Adolescent Clinic SW (8)	Most, Adolescent Clinic SW (10)	Most (11)
3. Concern by parents regarding recent alleged sexual relations in their teenager (but no rape or desire to prosecute).		X	None	None	Some, Adolescent Clinic SW (8)	As needed, Adolescent Clinic SW (10)	None
4. Incest (2) (Family-related)		X	All with intercourse within 48 hrs	All	All, CPT-SW (9)	Child Welfare SW	None
5. Child molestation (3) (both family related and non-family related)		X	None	All	All, CPT-SW (9)	Child Welfare SW	None

Items (1)-(11) are explained on the next page. For additional information, call Dr. Barton Schmitt (x. 7961) or Dr. James Delaney (x. 7554).

Sexual Abuse - OPD or
Hospitalized

(1) Emancipated minor: by Colorado law, any person 16 years of age
     or older who lives separate from parents and makes his/her own
     financial decisions.

(2) Incest: sexual intercourse between family-related adult and
     child. Anal intercourse and oral intercourse should also be
     evaluated according to these guidelines.

(3) Child molestation: sexual contact other than sexual intercourse
     (e.g., fondling, masturbation, exposure).

(4) See GYN Protocol: "The Management of Patients Who Have Been
     Sexually Assaulted."

(5) See Ped. Protocol: "Guidelines for Pediatric Evaluation of In-
     cest and Other Family-Related Sexual Abuse Cases at CGH." Girls
     under 12, evaluated in CCC. Girls 12 and over, evaluation in
     Adolescent Clinic if at all possible.

(6) Page the GYN resident (1-276) to come to the Pediatric Clinic.

(7) Weekdays: The CPT Coordinator will do this (x. 8269 or 7533).
     Evenings or Weekends: Call the Child Welfare Social Worker on
     call in county of residence, posted on bulletin board. SAVE
     chart for Dr. Schmitt or CPT Coordinator.

(8) Days - Adolescent Clinic Social Worker for all.   .
     Nights and Weekends - if distraught, child psychiatrist on call.
                         - if stable, reappoint to Adolescent Clinic.

(9) Days - CPT Social Worker for all. (Exception: Child Welfare
     Social Worker accompanies the patient.)
     Nights and Weekends - Call Child Welfare Social Worker in county
     of residence or get a consult from someone on CPT.

(10) Leave name and phone number for Gloria Zakus, Adolescent Clinic
     Social Worker (Room 2131). She will set up an appointment.

(11) a) E.R. Rape Counsellors. Call the charge nurse in the CGH-ER
        for the name and phone number for the on-call person. They
        will come in and provide crisis counseling; or

     b) York Street Center - Call 321-8191. Free crisis counseling
        is available 24 hours/day, 7 days per week. This agency will
        also help with transportation, a safe place to stay, and legal
        problems.

APPENDIX B

A CHART AUDIT ON CHILD ABUSE AND NEGLECT CASES
INVESTIGATED IN MAY AND JANUARY OF 1974 BY THE
CHILD PROTECTIVE SERVICES UNIT IN HONOLULU, HAWAII

Prepared by Barton D. Schmitt, M.D. and Gail F. Breakey, M.P.H.*

Purpose: The following Chart Audit examines the quality of care in cases of suspected child abuse and neglect accepted for investigation by the Children's Protective Service Center (CPSC) of Honolulu, Hawaii. The audit focused upon case investigation, the data base, decision-making processes, development and implementation of treatment plans.

Method: A total of 59 records were reviewed. This included all cases that were reported and investigated in January and May of 1974. The actual Chart Audit Protocol used to abstract each chart is found in Appendix B-3. Each record was analyzed in terms of the following:

1. Time lapse from report of child abuse/neglect incident to first telephone contact, first visit, development of a treatment plan, and case termination or transfer by CPSC social worker.

2. The data base: the complete data base required to substantiate each type of case was determined in advance or by a consultant. The data actually compiled for each individual case were determined and expressed as a decimal. A score of 0 indicates that none of the complete data base is present, and a score of 1.0 indicates that all data are present.

3. The number of problems uncovered: the average number of family problems found in the University of Colorado Medical Center program in cases of child abuse/neglect was 5.2 in early 1975. This average was utilized as a norm to compare with the number of family problems uncovered by the CPSC investigation and recorded in their charts.

4. Recommendations made with regard to treating the above problems were noted as (A) Adequate, (I) Inadequate, or (N) No recommendations made. Follow-up of the above recommendations, where noted, was rated in the same way.

5. Legal intervention: the analysis of the adequacy of legal intervention and placement outside the home was analyzed as described within that section.

Findings: Table 1 shows the spectrum of child abuse/neglect cases reviewed. Clearly, two-thirds of the cases involved physical abuse. Approximately one-third of all cases were unconfirmed by CPSC social worker.

*The data were abstracted from the records for analysis by Suzanne Kashiwaeda, Arlene Fujimoto, Amy Suzuki, and Virginia Ching.

Chart Audit on CA/N
Cases - Honolulu

Table 1. Types of Cases

	CPS Confirmed	CPS unconfirmed but probable	Unconfirmed
Physical abuse	21	5	13
Sexual abuse	2	2	2
Emotional abuse	-	1	1
Failure to thrive	1	-	-
Medical care neglect	2	-	1
Drugging, poisoning	-	-	-
Abandonment	-	-	-
Lack of supervision	3	-	2
Other (physical neglect)	2	-	-
Parents deceased	1	-	-
TOTAL	32	8	19

Table 2 lists the eight cases that were regarded as unconfirmed by CPSC social workers but with which the Chart Audit disagrees. The reasons for disagreement are noted along with recommendations for better management.

Two cases of physical abuse were unconfirmed as a result of either the parent or the child changing his or her explanation of how the abuse incident occurred. Two other cases of physical abuse were unconfirmed in spite of histories of repeated beatings and past bruises because no current bruises existed. The fact that professionals (for example, public health nurse or teacher) confirmed the existence of bruises in the two cases was apparently ignored. These four cases of suspected physical abuse were labeled unconfirmed and closed. A more precise manner of handling these cases would have involved following the case for six months to see if further beatings occurred.

Two sexual abuse cases were unconfirmed as a result of a lack of physical evidence. In such cases, confirmation by history alone is the rule rather than the exception. If the history remains questionable, an early interview by a child psychologist or psychiatrist should be obtained to clarify the situation.

Chart Audit on CA/N
Cases - Honolulu

Table 2. Unconfirmed But Probable Cases

Type of Abuse	Criteria for Diagnosis Present	Reason CPS Didn't Confirm	Management & Follow-up
Physical	Bruises 4 months ago	Current bruises only to mother	OK, divorced father
	Unexplained burn and bruise; father violent	Parent later provided explanation	Case closed; needed long follow-up
	Child reported mother caused bruised lip; unexplained bruises in past	Girl later retracted story	Case closed; needed long follow-up
	Monthly unexplained bruises; child blamed some on grandmother; some bruises seen by public health nurse	Conflicting stories	Case closed; needed long follow-up; also needed physical exam
	Repeated physical abuse by history; parents both dangerous	Unexplained bruises and burns when seen by physician; later explanation	Case closed; needed long follow-up. Probably needed foster placement
Sexual	Girl reported incest twice plus handcuffs and cord around neck	No physical evidence	Referred home after only 1 month with relative; no treatment of father
	Girl reported repeated molestation by stepfather	No physical evidence	Good intervention
Emotional	Very disturbed child; parents refused therapy	Didn't feel it fell into any specific category of child abuse/neglect	No therapy for child

Chart Audit on CA/N
Cases - Honolulu

The unconfirmed case of emotional abuse contained enough findings to
possibly confirm it. However, emotional abuse is a relatively new
concept in the field of child abuse/neglect, which may have hindered
the social worker from pursuing the case.

Table 3 is a chart of the time intervals between the initial report of
the child abuse/neglect incident and four different types of CPSC response: (1) first telephone contact with the family or involved party
of the child abuse/neglect by the CPSC worker, (2) first visit with the
family of the child abuse/neglect or involved party by CPSC worker,
(3) the date the treatment plan for the case was determined, and (4)
the date the case was closed or transferred. The critical time lag is
from the time of the report of the incident to the time the CPSC social
worker, in person, first contacts the persons involved in the incident.

In cases where suspected physical or sexual abuse are reported, the
CPSC social worker's first contact with the involved persons should be
within the first 24 hours, so as to acquire good confirmation on physical findings. The Chart Audit indicates that in exactly one-third
of the cases of suspected physical abuse, first visits were made by
the CPSC workers in the first 24 hours. In one-sixth of the cases,
first visits were made within the first 72 hours; and in one-third of
the cases, first visits were made after two weeks or more. In cases
involving suspected sexual abuse, first visits were made within 48 to
72 hours in 50% of the cases and within one week for the remaining 50%.

For all other cases of child abuse/neglect, first contacts were made
within the first 72 hours in 20% of the cases, from one to two weeks
in 50% of the cases, and after one month in 30% of the cases.

Table 4 contains the findings for completeness of data base (that is,
data acquired). A maximum score of 1.0 would indicate that as many
data as were required regarding items such as physical exams and interviews with the abused/neglected child and the parents were obtained
directly or indirectly by the social worker.

Overall, data collected in cases tended to be incomplete. In some
cases, existing data were grossly inadequate (13 cases scored less
than 0.50). In ten cases, data acquired were excellent (greater
than 0.90).

Table 5 contains four items considered to be critical data base after
an examination of the caseworker's traditional evaluation has been
completed. These four items include physical exams, trauma survey,
psychological/psychiatric evaluations, and a check for high-risk
characteristics.

Table 3

Time Interval Between Report and CPSC Action

	First Phone Call			First Visit			Plan			Terminated or Transferred		
	Physical Abuse	Sexual Abuse	Other	Physical Abuse	Sexual Abuse	Other	Physical Abuse	Sexual Abuse	Other	Physical Abuse	Sexual Abuse	Other
24 hours	11	-	2	10	-	4	-	-	1	-	-	-
48 hours	4	1	-	4	1	-	1	-	-	-	-	-
72 hours	2	2	-	-	2	2	-	-	1	1	-	-
1 week	4	2	4	8	3	5	4	2	1	-	-	-
2 weeks	4	-	-	7	-	2	4	-	1	3	-	1
3 weeks	1	-	-	3	-	-	3	-	2	4	1	-
1 month	-	-	-	-	-	-	2	2	-	6	-	5
2 months	1	-	-	-	-	-	1	1	-	8	2	3
3 months	1	-	-	1	-	1	-	-	1	6	-	2
4 months	-	-	-	-	-	-	1	-	-	3	2	1
Longer	-	-	-	-	-	-	3	-	-	5	1	2
Not Recorded	11	1	8	6	-	-	20	1	7	3	-	-
Total	39	6	14	39	6	14	39	6	14	39	6	14

Table 4

Data Base Collected

Physical Abuse Confirmed	0.68
Physical Abuse Unconfirmed	0.67
Physical Abuse Unconfirmed but Probable	0.64
Sex Abuse Confirmed	0.46
Sex Abuse Unconfirmed	0.55
Sex Abuse Unconfirmed but Probable	0.70
Other Confirmed[a]	0.66
Other Unconfirmed	0.78
Other Unconfirmed but Probable	0.40

---

[a]Other includes: abuse/neglect such as emotional abuse, medical neglect, physical neglect, failure to thrive, and lack of supervision.

Table 5

Critical Data Base Collected

Type of Abuse	Physical Exams	Trauma X-rays	Psychiatric Evaluation	High-Risk Check
Unconfirmed Physical Abuse (13)	0.54	$0.50^{(6)*}$	1.0	0.31
Unconfirmed but Probable Physical Abuse (5)	0.40	0.00(3)	0.00(3)	0.20
Confirmed Physical Abuse (21)	0.62	$0.50^{(6)*}$	0.92	0.43
Sexual Abuse Confirmed and Unconfirmed (6)	0.00(3)	0.00	0.00(2)	0.00
Emotional Abuse, Medical Care Neglect, Failure to Thrive (6)	0.25	0.00(1)	0.00(1)	0.33
Physical Neglect, Lack of Supervision (6)	0.66	0.00	0.00(2)	0.00
Overall Critical Data Base	0.50	0.33	0.68	0.29

*( ) indicates number of children from total group who required this test or evaluation.

Physical exams are indicated (that is, necessary) in any alleged physical abuse case unless a non-physician has examined the child's entire body surface with all clothing removed and has found no marks or bruises whatsoever. In all cases where serious injuries may have occurred, physical exams are indicated to rule out internal injuries. The Chart Audit indicates that physical exams were completed in only 50% of the suspected physical abuse cases.

Alleged sexual abuse cases require physical exams, including external genital or pelvic exams, under all circumstances and even if the alleged incident occurred in the past. For example, the finding of an intact hymen would make the report of vaginal intercourse highly questionable. Of the suspected sexual abuse cases audited, none of the alleged victims received physical exams. It may be that exams were not conducted in many of the cases because initial findings were gone. Unlike bruises and other signs of skin trauma which last from three to five days, evidence of sexual abuse (semen) lasts only one to two days. Investigation in suspected cases of sexual abuse must be initiated as quickly as possible.

Trauma surveys (that is, complete skeletal X-rays) are indicated only in cases involving children under age five where there are other findings indicative of child abuse/neglect (for example, a past history of abuse/neglect). Trauma surveys were obtained in only 33% of the cases in which trauma survey was indicated. Their absence in cases where they should have been conducted is largely the result of not taking the involved children to physicians.

The High-Risk Checklist examined the caseworker's recording of particular comments about the parents that indicated whether or not they were at risk of abusing their children. For example, if the parent(s) was beaten as a child or is living in isolation, he or she may be at high risk of abusive behavior. It was felt that such psycho-social data should be recorded for all parents as further evidence for confirming or not confirming child abuse/neglect. This predictive data were evident in only 20% of the cases.

The most disturbing findings are located in the second row in Table 5, unconfirmed but probable physical abuse. Of all categories of child abuse/neglect, this received the most incomplete critical data base. Only 40% of these cases received physical exams, whereas 100% required them. Where X-rays were indicated in 60% of the cases, none received them. And, only 20% had a high-risk assessment, whereas all these cases needed this assessment.

Table 6 summarized the data regarding the number of problems identified, the adequacy of the recommendations made with regard to resolving the identified problems, and the adequacy of the follow-up carried out on each recommendation.

The average number of problems identified by the Child Protection Team

Table 6

Adequacy of Recommendations and Follow-up

	Average Number of Problems	Recommendations % A, I, N	Follow-up
Physical Abuse			
Confirmed	3.2	A- 71% I- 7% N- 22%	A- 41% I- 10% N - 37% DK- 10%
Unconfirmed	2.0	A- 92% I- 4% N- 4%	A- 46% N- 25% DK- 29%
Unconfirmed but Probable	3.8	A- 21% I- 16% N- 63%	None tabulated
Sexual Abuse			
Confirmed	5.0	A- 50% N- 50%	A- 50% I- 25% N- 25%
Unconfirmed	3.5	A-100%	A- 20% N- 10% DK- 70%
Unconfirmed but Probable	2.5	A- 57% I- 29% N- 14%	A- 43% I- 43% N- 14%
Other[a]			
Confirmed	2.67	A- 71% I- 8% N- 10%	A- 38% I- 17% N- 21% DK- 24%
Unconfirmed	1.25	A- 80% N- 20%	A- 40% I- 40% DK- 20%
Unconfirmed but Probable (1 Case)	5.0	A-100%	I-100%

[a]Other--emotional abuse, medical neglect, physical neglect, failure to thrive, lack of supervision

[b]A - Adequate   N - Not adequate
I - Inadequate DK - Don't know

at the University of Colorado Medical Center is 5.2 per case of physical or sexual abuse. CPSC averaged 3.0 problems per case. By enlarging the data base and looking at total family problems (for example, siblings, parents, marital, and environmental problems), the CPSC might uncover more problems, thus enabling them to deal with the primary physical or sexual abuse problem in a more comprehensive manner.

The second column in Table 6 contains data on the adequacy of recommendations prescribed, and the third column reveals the adequacy of follow-up. In cases of physical abuse, the greater the number of problems, the less adequate were recommendations made to alleviate the identified problems. In unconfirmed cases of physical abuse, 92% of the recommendations were considered adequate, whereas, in the unconfirmed but probable cases, only 21% of the recommendations were adequate. Follow-up on both unconfirmed and confirmed cases of physical abuse was generally inadequate, with only 41% to 46% of the prescribed recommendations actually carried out. The follow-up on unconfirmed but probable cases was minimal, since these cases were closed due to their unconfirmed status. Why the unconfirmed cases of physical abuse received better follow-up than the unconfirmed but probable cases is highly questionable and largely indefensible.

As expected, in cases of sexual abuse, more problems were identified in confirmed cases than in unconfirmed cases. In the confirmed cases, recommendations for resolving problems were less adequate than were recommendations for resolving problems in confirmed cases of physical abuse (50% versus 71%). This discrepancy perhaps reflects the difficulty in handling cases of sexual abuse, which tend to be more complex than other cases and with which workers have had less experience. Follow-up on the unconfirmed but probable cases of sexual abuse was far better than follow-up in the unconfirmed but probable cases of physical abuse.

Overall, cases other than physical or sexual abuse had fewer family problems identified. Furthermore, recommendations and follow-up were far superior to cases of physical and sexual abuse, suggesting that these "other" cases have guidelines for resolving problems.

Again, the data base on the five unconfirmed physical abuse cases was very poor. While an average number of 3.8 problems were found, only 20% of the recommendations were rated adequate, 16% were inadequate, and no recommendations were made for 63% of problems found. This was the only category for which information on the follow-up of recommendations was not available.

Table 6 also contains the summary of data on the number of problems detected. The overall average is 3.0 problems per case for physical and sexual abuse. The comparable figure for 1975 for cases seen by the Child Protection Team at University of Colorado Medical Center is 5.2. More problems would probably be uncovered in Honolulu if the data base was enlarged to look at total family problems.

Table 7 reviews the distribution of 26 cases of confirmed physical abuse, including five probable cases, in terms of allowing the child to remain at home or removing the child from the home temporarily and placing him or her in foster placement or elsewhere. Of the 26 cases, 11, or 42%, received temporary placement outside of the home. This seems to be an adequate rate of placement, insofar as the safety of the children involved is concerned. Of the 14 confirmed and unconfirmed but probable cases outside of the physical abuse category, only four children were placed.

Table 7

Home Versus Foster Placement Data

For physical abuse only (total cases--26)

Remained in home	15
Removed from home temporarily	11
Permanent severence of parental rights	1
Criminal prosecution	0
Foster care NOT recommended, despite indication	3 (possibly 5)

Table 8 contains further details on the 15 children (all categories of child abuse/neglect) who were temporarily removed from their homes. Of the 15 children, 13% were placed in emergency shelter, 26% with relatives or neighbors, and 61% with foster homes. With the exception of cases placed in emergency shelter, duration of placement ranged from 12 days to an indefinite period of time. Excluding indefinite placements, the average duration was 72 days.

Sound indications for removal from home were present in all but two cases, where indications were questionable. However, the indications for returning the child to his home were less well documented. Only 33% (5 cases) were returned to their homes with good indications (e.g., abusive parent was receiving counseling); 33% (5 cases) were returned to their homes without adequate indications; and reabuse definitely occurred in one of these cases. In another case, a young infant, who had been severely abused, was returned to his parents, and the case was followed for only six months before it was closed. Parents of a child who had suffered incest and sadism simply decided, without consulting the follow-up agency, to bring their child home. The remaining 33% of the children had placements in foster homes of indefinite duration, or they were returned to a family other than the abusive one (e.g., relative's home).

Table 8

Data on Children Removed from Home Temporarily

	Record No.	Place	Duration	Indication for Removal	Indication for Return
Sexual Abuse	43	Relative	1 month	Incest and sadism by father	None, parent decided unilaterally
	44	Foster home	Indefinite, probably until emancipated	Incest X 4 years	Child not being returned
Lack of Supervision	56	Relative	3 months	Lack of supervision; mother on drugs	Mother could not tolerate living with relative, so she and children moved out; Situation remains unresolved
	57	Foster home	Indefinite, mother on mainland	Lack of supervision; mother schizophrenic	Child not being returned
Physical Abuse	20	Foster home	22 days	Homicidal threat by schizophrenic mother	Yes, mother stable and previously a good mother
	18	Foster home	Indefinite	Repeated abuse and rejection by mother	Child not being returned
	17	Neighbor	12 days	Reabuse and run-away	None; father unimproved; in fact, he twice abused the boy with fists following return to home

Table 8 continued

16	Neighbor	10 months	Repeated abuse	Yes, adopted by another family
15	Neighbor	3 months	Father requested placement	Yes, sent to mother to live in Houston
14	Neighbor	13 months	Severe abuse in 6-month old	Pending; no improvement in parents to date
13	Emergency shelter	4 days	15-year-old girl's request	Sent to safe aunt
9	Relative	4 months	Severe injury in young baby	Vague; plus case closed 6 months later
7	Foster home	8 months	Reabuse	No; father on hard drugs and had received no therapy
3	Foster home	1 month	Possible poor impulse control in mother	Yes, since need for foster care was not great
5	Emergency shelter	1 month	Repeated beating with a belt	Yes, since need for foster care was not great

Table 9 lists five cases, three of which should have been placed in foster care, because they suffered repeated physical abuse and ongoing rejection from the entire family. In the two other cases, the involved children should have been placed outside the new home while it was being determined whether or not repeated beatings had actually taken place.

Table 9

Foster Care Not Recommended Despite Indications

1. Indication: Repeated physical abuse, reabuse, runaway, and emotional abuse.

2. Indication: Father hit boy while inebriated; may be dangerous. Father at least needs psychological evaluation.

3. Indication: Repeated physical and emotional abuse from mother, father, and brother.

4. Indication: Needed long-term follow-up to clarify whether or not repeated beating was taking place and, hence, need for foster care.

5. Indication: Needed long-term follow-up to clarify whether or not repeated beating was taking place and, hence, need for foster care.

CHART AUDIT: CONCLUSIONS AND RECOMMENDATIONS

A major difficulty in auditing the charts is in finding critical data which were often dispersed among much irrelevant and extraneous data. At times, it was difficult to determine what or who the caseworker was writing about, and, often times, dates of incidents and interviews were absent. It is essential that some kind of consistent recordkeeping, which is clear and succinct, be adopted by all units related to children's protective service.

The following recommendations refer to the section on findings:

1. All cases of suspected physical or sexual abuse should have complete physical exams (including external genital or pelvic exams in the case of sexual abuse), except in those cases where the physician deems it unnecessary.

2. The "unconfirmed but probable" cases indicate the need to accept past history of abuse as reliable evidence in confirming the suspected cases. Past injuries witnessed by another person are also valid in confirming these cases. Of greater importance, suspicious cases such as these should not be closed so quickly. Instead, they should be followed for six months for surveillance of evidence of alleged repeated beatings.

3. In questionable cases of sexual abuse, an early interview by a psychiatrist or psychologist should be obtained to clarify the situation.

4. The first personal contact (that is, visit) with a child involved in a suspected case of child abuse/neglect should occur before certain time deadlines: see all homicidal threats immediately; see all physical and sexual abuse cases within 24 hours; see all other cases within 72 hours.

5. A more complete data base is recommended. Consider collecting the data utilized in the Chart Audit Protocol.

6. Obtain psychiatric/psychological consultations as recommended in new CPS guidelines. Also, keep in mind the concept of a dangerous parent.

7. High-risk assessment of parents should be undertaken in all cases as a means of screening for their abusive potential.

8. Recommendations in general were quite good where the data base was complete. Where the data base was poor, recommendations tended to be inadequate.

9. Recommendations are of little value unless they are implemented, reassessed, and followed.

Chart Audit: Conclusions
and Recommendations

10. There is need for guidelines indicating appropriate circumstances under which a child can be returned to the natural home. They should be adhered to by the follow-up units. (Note: 33% of patients were returned without indication.)

11. There is a need for court-enforced placements of severely abused children. (See guidelines for when to go to court.)

12. There is a need for a minimum of one year follow-up of severely abused children following their return home.

13. Repeated frequent physical abuse, even when not life threatening (for example, recurrent bruises), requires removal from the family, so that the child doesn't become socially and emotionally incapacitated.

CHART AUDIT PROTOCOL

I. General Background Information   Child's Last Name: _____

Category of abuse/neglect: Case Record No.: _____

Physical abuse (Check if applies) Describe reported problem below:

    Subdural hematoma, brain trauma
    Intra-abdominal injury   _____
    Fractures, dislocations   _____
    Burns   _____
    Soft tissue injury (bruises, etc.)   _____
    Death   _____
    Other_____   _____
                                    _____

Sexual abuse   _____

Emotional abuse   _____

Failure to thrive   _____

Medical care neglect   _____

Dangerous drug exposure   _____

Abandonment   _____

Lack of adequate supervision   _____

Other _____   _____

Referral by: _____

Date of Report:_____ Date, 1st telephone contact:_____

Date first personal visit: _____Date treatment plan determined:_____

Date case closed or transferred:_____ Worker I.D.: _____

Age: _____ Sex: _____ Number, age of siblings:_____

Relation of perpetrator to child:_____

II. Investigative Activities (Check if activity conducted)

  1. Medical Exam (check if done)

     Physical exam   (___)
     Trauma X-ray survey   (___)
     Bleeding disorder screen(___)
     Hospitalization   (___)

Chart Audit Protocol

Detailed injury Hx   (___)
   from mother
Detailed injury Hx   (___)
   from father
Detailed injury Hx   (___)
   from others:
   Identify a _____
         b _____
Brief Hx injury from   (___)
   child
Check medical resources (___)
Physical exam of
   siblings   (___)
Developmental status
   screening exam   (___)

2. Social History (check if done)   CA/N high-risk characteristics

		Present	Absent	Not Explored
Interviews with:				
mother	(___)	(___)	(___)	(___)
father	(___)	(___)	(___)	(___)
perpetrater (if other)	(___)	(___)	(___)	(___)
patient	(___)			
siblings	(___)			
caretakers	(___)			
others (identify)	(___)			
a.				
b.				

Marital status comments (___)
Discipline technique
   comments   (___)   Main type: verbal, isolation,
                                      hand, instrument

Home visit evaluation   (___)

Check central registry (___); check CPSC perpetrater file (___).
Either positive? _____ If so, discuss: _____
Number of face-to-face contacts with family members during
investigation: _____ .

3. Psychiatric or Psychological Evaluation

Child   (___)
Mother   (___)
Father   (___)
Other (identify)   (___)

4. Legal Consultation   (___)

Chart Audit Protocol

III. Problems (uncovered)

1. Describe physical abuse, emotional abuse, sexual abuse, etc.

2. Patient's emotional problems or developmental lags:

3. Mother's emotional status:

4. Father's emotional status:

5. Perpetrator's emotional status:(if not parent)

6. Marital problems:

7. Siblings' significant problems:

8. Personal current crisis:

9. Environmental current crisis:

IV. Recommendations Regarding Problems Above

1. Abuse or neglect:

2. Patient's emotional problems:

3. Mother's emotional problems:

4. Father's emotional problems:

5. Perpetrator's emotional status:

6. Marital problems:

Chart Audit Protocol

   7. Siblings' significant problems:

   8. Personal crisis:

   9. Environmental crisis:

V. Follow-up Services Related to Recommendations Above
(3-month and 9-month check)

Services (include frequency)   3 month   9 month

   1. Abuse or neglect:

   2. Patient's emotional problems:

   3. Mother's emotional problems

   4. Father's emotional problems:

   5. Perpetrator's emotional problems

   6. Marital problems:

   7. Siblings' significant problems:

   8. Personal crisis:

   9. Environmental crisis:

VI. Legal Intervention

   1. Child allowed to remain at home (that is, home considered safe)

      Criteria for this decision: a. close supervision accepted _____
                          b. perpetrator removed _____
                          c. perpetrator lives elsewhere _____
                          d. court-ordered supervision _____
                          e. Other (define)_____

Chart Audit Protocol

2. a. Child temporarily removed from home:_____

   Type of placement: Relative   _____
                      Emergency shelter _____
                      Voluntary foster
                        care   _____
                      Court enforced
                        foster care   _____

   b. Duration of placement:_____Planned duration:_____

       Discuss discrepancies: _____
       _____

   c. What rehabilitation services were provided to parents during
       foster care placement? _____
       _____

       How often was the child seen by worker during this period?___

3. Child returns to natural home:

   What were the criteria for returning the child? (i.e., what
   changes took place, was a psychological evaluation done on
   perpetrator?) _____

   Was there a meeting around this decision? Yes_____ No _____

   Who was present? _____

4. Follow-up

   What rehabilitation services were provided to the parents after
   the child was returned to the natural home? _____
   _____

   What services were provided to child after being returned home?
   _____

   How often was the child seen by the worker after return?_____

5. Child permanently removed from the home:

   a. Voluntary relinquishment for adoption? _____
   b. Were parental rights terminated? Yes _____ No _____

6. Was criminal prosecution sought against the offender?

Chart Audit Protocol

VII. Record Summary (what data present in record)

1. Medical statement _____
2. Caseworker's initial evaluation _____
3. Psychologist's or psychiatrist's
    initial evaluation _____
4. Dispositional conference summary _____

Protocol designed by Barton Schmitt, M.D.; Gail Breakey, M.P.H.; Lei
Lee Loy, M.S.W.; and Suzanne Kashiwaeda of the Hawaii Family Stress
Center. (June 1975)

APPENDIX C

COMPREHENSIVE QUESTIONNAIRE ON
BEHAVIOR AND DEVELOPMENT

<u>Under 2 Years Old</u>
Name _____
Birthdate _____
Today's Date _____

To be completed by a parent.
This medical information is confidential.

A. Speech and Self-Care

Yes ✓ No___ 1. Did he feed himself a cracker by 9 months?
Yes___ No___ 2. Did he walk alone across the room by 18 months?
Yes___ No___ 3. Did he hold a cup and drink from it alone by 18 months?
Yes___ No___ 4. Did he use three words besides "mama" and "dada" by 20 months?
Yes___ No___ 5. Is he learning new things as quickly as his brothers and sisters?
Yes ✓ No___ 6. Do you ever leave him with a babysitter while he's awake?
No___ Yes ✓ 7. Does he object to being left with a sitter?
No___ Yes___ 8. Is there any aspect of sex education or behavior you would like to discuss?

B. Discipline

No ✓ Yes___ 1. Is he a difficult child? Does he often break the rules?
No___ Yes___ 2. Is he impossible to deal with?
Yes___ No___ 3. Does he have many good points?
No___ Yes___ 4. Does he need to be spanked frequently?
Yes___ No___ 5. Does he care whether he's spanked?
No___ Yes___ 6. Do you ever use a paddle or belt on him?
_____ 7. How many times a day does he need to be corrected?
_____ 8. What type of discipline works best with him?

C. Behavior -- Circle any of the following behaviors that are present in your child

Hyperactive
Bangs head
Drinks over 1½ quarts milk per day
Other eating problems
Cries easily
Repeated accidents
Colic
Uncuddly baby
Holds his breath
Very shy

Rocks
Sleep problem
Very stubborn
Temper tantrums
Usually unhappy
Sleeps with parents
Wanders off
Eats dirt or paint
Doesn't like meat
Toilet training problem

Has fears
Sucks thumb
Won't come off the bottle
Poisoned self more than once

(Please complete reverse side.)

Behavior and Development
Questionnaire--Under 2

D. Family Difficulties: The following questions are about the parents rather than the child. You do not have to answer them if you do not wish to. However, difficulties in any of these areas probably have an effect on your child.

No ✓ Yes ___ 1. Are there lots of stresses on your family?
No ___ Yes ___ 2. Any serious disagreements in the marriage?
No ___ Yes ___ 3. Any recent separations between the parents?
No ✓ Yes ___ 4. Does either parent have a violent temper?
No ___ Yes ___ 5. Was either parent ever hospitalized for psychiatric difficulties?
No ___ Yes ___ 6. Is either parent currently receiving counseling?
No ✓ Yes ___ 7. Is either parent currently having difficulty with drugs or alcohol?
No ___ Yes ✓ 8. Any recent deaths or serious illnesses in the family?

Developed by Barton Schmitt, M.D., Department of Pediatrics, University of Colorado Medical Center. (Revised November 1975)

COMPREHENSIVE QUESTIONNAIRE ON
BEHAVIOR AND DEVELOPMENT

__2-5 Years Old__

Name _____

Birthdate _____

Today's Date _____

To be completed by a parent.
This medical information is confidential.

A. Speech and Self-Care

Yes___ No___ 1. Did he walk alone across the room by 18 months?

Yes___ No___ 2. Did he use three words besides "mama" and "dada" by 20 months?

Yes___ No___ 3. Did he feed himself with a spoon by age 2?

Yes___ No___ 4. Did he name a picture in a book by age 2½?

Yes___ No___ 5. Could he stay with one type of play for over a half hour straight by age 3?

Yes___ No___ 6. Did he speak in sentences by age 3?

Yes___ No___ 7. Did he dress himself without supervision by age 5?

Yes___ No___ 8. Is he learning new things as quickly as his brothers and sisters?

Yes___ No___ 9. Was his speech understandable to neighbors by age 5?

No___ Yes___ 10. Does he stutter?

Yes___ No___ 11. Do you ever leave him with a babysitter while he's awake?

No___ Yes___ 12. Does he object to being left with a sitter?

Yes___ No___ 13. Does he like to play at other children's homes?

Yes___ No___ 14. Is he included in simple jobs around the home and yard?

B. Mood

No___ Yes___ 1. Is he often tense?

No___ Yes___ 2. Does he worry a lot?

Yes___ No___ 3. Can he talk about what's bothering him?

No___ Yes___ 4. Is he often unhappy?

No___ Yes___ 5. Is he often angry?

C. Playmates

Yes___ No___ 1. Does he get along well with children his age?

No___ Yes___ 2. Does he have trouble keeping friends?

No___ Yes___ 3. Does he fight a lot with his age group?

No___ Yes___ 4. Has he ever hurt anyone while fighting?

No___ Yes___ 5. Does he prefer to play alone?

No___ Yes___ 6. Is there any aspect of sex education or behavior you would like to discuss?

(Please complete reverse side).

Behavior and Development
Questionnaire - 2-5 Years

D. Discipline

No____ Yes____   1. Is he a difficult child? Does he often break
                    the rules?
No____ Yes____   2. Is he impossible to deal with?
Yes____ No____   3. Does he have many good points?
No____ Yes____   4. Does he need to be spanked frequently?
Yes____ No____   5. Does he care whether he's spanked?
No____ Yes____   6. Do you ever use a paddle or belt on him?
_____   7. How many times a day does he need to be corrected?
_____   8. What type of discipline works best with him?

E. Behavior -- Circle any of the following behaviors that are present
   in your child.

Bangs head	Rocks	Runs away
Eats dirt or paint	Still uses bottle	Holds his breath
Very shy	Gets teased	Has tics
Sexual problems	Sets fires	Destructive, damages
Eating problem	Sleep problem	property
Cries excessively	Very stubborn	Toilet training problem
Has temper tantrums	Hyperactive	Defiant
Bites nails	Has fears	Sucks thumb
Swears	Masturbates	Bites
Lies	Steals	Hurts animals
Has repeated accidents	Sleeps with parents	Has nightmares
BM's in underwear	Daytime wetting	Has frequent pains
(soiling)		Poisoned self more
		than once

F. Family Difficulties: The following questions are about the parents
   rather than the child. You do not have to answer them if you do not
   wish to. However, difficulties in any of these areas probably
   have an effect on your child.

No____ Yes____   1. Are there lots of stresses on your family?
No____ Yes____   2. Any serious disagreements in the marriage?
No____ Yes____   3. Any recent separations between the parents?
No____ Yes____   4. Does either parent have a violent temper?
No____ Yes____   5. Was either parent ever hospitalized for
                    psychiatric difficulties?
No____ Yes____   6. Is either parent currently receiving counseling?
No____ Yes____   7. Is either parent currently having difficulty
                    with drugs or alcohol?
No____ Yes____   8. Any recent deaths or serious illness in the family?

Developed by Barton Schmitt, M.D., Department of Pediatrics, University
of Colorado Medical Center. (Revised November 1975)

COMPREHENSIVE QUESTIONNAIRE ON
BEHAVIOR AND DEVELOPMENT

6-12 Years Old

Name _____
Birthdate _____
Today's Date _____

To be completed by a parent.
This medical information is confidential.

A. Speech and Self-Care

Yes___ No___ 1. Did he walk alone across the room by 18 months?
Yes___ No___ 2. Did he speak in sentences by age 3?
Yes___ No___ 3. Did he tie his shoestrings alone by age 6?
Yes___ No___ 4. Did he develop as quickly as his brothers and sisters?
No___ Yes___ 5. Does he have a problem with pronouncing words?
No___ Yes___ 6. Does he stutter?
Yes___ No___ 7. Does he bathe himself?
Yes___ No___ 8. Does he go over to other children's homes alone?
No___ Yes___ 9. Was there any difficulty separating from his parents when he started school?
Yes___ No___ 10. Does he have some chores?

B. Mood

No___ Yes___ 1. Is he often tense?
No___ Yes___ 2. Does he worry a lot?
Yes___ No___ 3. Can he talk about what's bothering him?
No___ Yes___ 4. Is he often unhappy?
No___ Yes___ 5. Is he often angry?

C. School

1. Name of school _____
   Address _____ Tel. No. _____
   Name of teacher _____ Grade _____
2. How many days has he missed so far this year? _____
   How many total days did he miss last year? _____
3. Circle any of the following that you have been told apply to your child:

Mentally retarded   Slow learner   Perceptual-motor
Brain damaged   Cerebral palsy   problems
Reading problems   Low normal   Other learning
                         intelligence   problems

Yes___ No___ 4. Does he get along well in school?
No___ Yes___ 5. Does he have difficulties with schoolwork?
No___ Yes___ 6. Has he ever repeated a grade? If yes, which one? _____ (Please complete reverse side)

369

Behavior and Development
Questionnaire - 6-12 Years

No___	Yes___	7.	Has he ever been in special classes?
No___	Yes___	8.	Is something upsetting him and interfering with his schoolwork?
No___	Yes___	9.	Does he need pressure to do his homework?
No___	Yes___	10.	Does he seem to have "given up" in school?
Yes___	No___	11.	Is he doing as well in school as his brothers and sisters?
No___	Yes___	12.	Does he get into any trouble with classroom misbehavior?
No___	Yes___	13.	Has he ever been suspended for a while from school?

D. Friends

Yes___	No___	1.	Does he get along well with children his age?
No___	Yes___	2.	Does he have trouble keeping friends?
No___	Yes___	3.	Does he fight a lot with his age group?
No___	Yes___	4.	Has he ever hurt anyone while fighting?
No___	Yes___	5.	Does he prefer to play alone?
Yes___	No___	6.	Does he have a real close friend?
No___	Yes___	7.	Is there any aspect of sex education or behavior you would like to discuss?

E. Discipline

No___	Yes___	1.	Is he a difficult child? Does he often break the rules?
No___	Yes___	2.	Is he impossible to deal with?
Yes___	No___	3.	Does he have many good points?
No___	Yes___	4.	Does he need to be spanked frequently?
Yes___	No___	5.	Does he care whether he's spanked?
No___	Yes___	6.	Do you ever use a paddle or belt on him?
		7.	How many times a day does he need to be corrected?
		8.	What type of discipline works best with him?

F. Behavior -- Circle any of the following behaviors that are present in your child:

Hyperactive	Very shy	Runs away
Has tics	Homesick	Sexual problems
Sets fires	Sleep problem	Eating problem
Tried drugs	Skips school	Masturbates
Suicide attempt	Cries excessively	Very stubborn
Defiant	Temper tantrums	Sucks thumb
Bites nails	Has fears	Bites
Hurts animals	Lies	Steals
Daytime wetting	Bedwetting	Frequent pains (Continued)

Behavior and Development
Questionnaire - 6-12 Years

Gets teased
Destructive,
  damages property
Highly conscientious
Juvenile delinquency

Repeated accidents
Swears
Has nightmares
BM's in underwear

G. Family Difficulties: The following questions are about the parents rather than the child. You do not have to answer them if you do not wish to. However, difficulties in any of these areas probably have an effect on your child.

No___ Yes___ 1. Are there lots of stresses on your family?
No___ Yes___ 2. Any serious disagreements in the marriage?
No___ Yes___ 3. Any recent separations between the parents?
No___ Yes___ 4. Does either parent have a violent temper?
No___ Yes___ 5. Was either parent ever hospitalized for psy-
    chiatric difficulties?
No___ Yes___ 6. Is either parent currently receiving counseling?
No___ Yes___ 7. Is either parent currently having difficulty with
    drugs or alcohol?
No___ Yes___ 8. Any recent deaths or serious illness in the
    family?

Developed by Barton Schmitt, M.D., Department of Pediatrics, University of Colorado Medical Center. (Revised November 1975.)

COMPREHENSIVE QUESTIONNAIRE ON
BEHAVIOR AND DEVELOPMENT

<u>13 Years and Older</u>

Name _____

Birthdate _____

Today's Date _____

To be completed by a parent.
This medical information is confidential.

A. Speech and Self-Care

Yes___ No___ 1. Did he walk alone across the room by 18 months?

Yes___ No___ 2. Did he speak in sentences by age 3?

Yes___ No___ 3. Did he tie his shoestrings alone by age 6?

Yes___ No___ 4. Did he develop as quickly as his brothers and sisters?

No___ Yes___ 5. Does he have a problem with pronouncing words?

No___ Yes___ 6. Does he stutter?

Yes___ No___ 7. Does he have any chores?

Yes___ No___ 8. Does he have career plans?

Yes___ No___ 9. Has he ever had a summer job?

Yes___ No___ 10. Is he starting to loosen his ties to his family somewhat?

Yes___ No___ 11. Does he sometimes challenge your ideas?

B. Mood

No___ Yes___ 1. Is he often tense?

No___ Yes___ 2. Does he worry a lot?

No___ Yes___ 3. Is he often unhappy?

No___ Yes___ 4. Is he often angry?

Yes___ No___ 5. Can he talk about what's bothering him?

No___ Yes___ 6. Does he have many mood swings?

C. School

1. Name of school _____

Address _____

Name of teacher _____ Grade _____

2. How many days has he missed so far this year?_____

How many total days did he miss last year? _____

3. Circle any of the following that you have been told apply to your child:

Mentally retarded   Slow learner   Low normal intelligence

Brain damaged   Cerebral palsy   Perceptual-motor

Reading problems   Other learning   problems
                        problems

Yes___ No___ 4. Does he get along well in school?

(Please complete reverse side.)→

372

Appendix C-4 (2)

Behavior and Development
Questionnaire - 13 Years and Older

No___ Yes___ 5. Has he ever repeated a grade? If yes, which one? _____
No___ Yes___ 6. Has he ever been in special classes?
No___ Yes___ 7. Does he have difficulties with schoolwork?
No___ Yes___ 8. Is something upsetting him and interfering with his schoolwork?
Yes___ No___ 9. Is he doing as well in school as his brothers and sisters?
No___ Yes___ 10. Does he need pressure to do his homework?
No___ Yes___ 11. Does he get into any trouble with classroom misbehavior?
No___ Yes___ 12. Has he ever been suspended for a while from school?
Yes___ No___ 13. Does he take gym?
No___ Yes___ 14. Does he want to drop out of school?

D. Friends

Yes___ No___ 1. Does he get along well with his agemates?
No___ Yes___ 2. Does he have trouble keeping his friends?
No___ Yes___ 3. Does he fight a lot with his age group?
No___ Yes___ 4. Has he ever hurt anyone while fighting?
No___ Yes___ 5. Does he prefer to be alone?
Yes___ No___ 6. Does he have a real close friend?
Yes___ No___ 7. Does he spend most of his free time with other teenagers?
Yes___ No___ 8. Is he up on the latest music?
Yes___ No___ 9. Is he quite conscious of clothes?
Yes___ No___ 10. Is your teenager interested in the opposite sex?
Yes___ No___ 11. Does your teenager date?
No___ Yes___ 12. Is there any aspect of sex education or behavior you would like to discuss?

E. Discipline

No___ Yes___ 1. Is he a difficult teenager? Does he often break the rules?
No___ Yes___ 2. Is he impossible to deal with?
Yes___ No___ 3. Does he have many good points?
No___ Yes___ 4. Do you ever use a paddle or belt on him?
_____ 5. How many times a day does he need to be corrected?
_____ 6. What type of discipline works best with him?
No___ Yes___ 7. Has he been in any trouble with the law?

(Continued)

373

Behavior and Development
Questionnaire - 13 Years and Older

F. Behavior -- Circle any of the following behaviors that are present
    in your teenager.

Hyperactive	Skips school	Swears
Has tics	Very stubborn	Steals
Sets fires	Sucks thumb	Frequent pains
Suicide attempt	Bites	Gets teased
Panics	Lies	Destructive, damages
Temper tantrums	Wets bed	property
Has fears	Runs away	Tried drugs
Hurts animals	Sexual problems	Highly conscientious
Daytime wetting	Sleep problem	Juvenile delinquency
Very shy	Depressed	Repeated accidents
Homesick	Defiant	Cries excessively
Eating problem	Bites nails	Smokes
		BM's in underwear
		(soiling)

G. Family Difficulties: The following questions are about the
    parents rather than the child. You do not have to answer them if
    you do not wish to. However, difficulties in any of these areas
    probably have an effect on your child.

No___ Yes___ 1. Are there lots of stresses on your family?
No___ Yes___ 2. Any serious disagreements in the marriage?
No___ Yes___ 3. Any recent separations between the parents?
No___ Yes___ 4. Does either parent have a violent temper?
No___ Yes___ 5. Was either parent ever hospitalized for
                 psychiatric difficulties?
No___ Yes___ 6. Is either parent currently receiving counseling?
No___ Yes___ 7. Is either parent currently having difficulty
                 with drugs or alcohol?
No___ Yes___ 8. Any recent deaths or serious illness in the
                 family?

Developed by Barton Schmitt, M.D., Department of Pediatrics,
University of Colorado Medical Center. (Revised November 1975.)

374

APPENDIX D

CRITERIA FOR FILING A NEGLECT PETITION

Any one of these points would indicate filing a neglect petition, which should be done in consultation with the supervisor.

1. Severity of injury (i.e., broken bones, head injury, burns, or multiple bruises)
2. Repetitive abuse and neglect
3. Child believed to be in immediate danger
4. Efforts that have been made on a voluntary basis by the Department of Social Service and other agencies with the parents have been nonproductive (i.e., appointments not kept or resistance to involvement).
5. Parents inability to care for or protect the child
6. Parents refuse services, and child is being neglected or abused
7. Long-term planning is needed (i.e., child has been in and out of foster care on voluntary agreement with repeated placements, with no real, long-range plans for the child).
8. Child is hospitalized and "hold order" is needed (i.e., the parents are threatening to remove the child from the hospital and immediate intervention is indicated).
9. Where the police have taken a child into protective custody (48 hours maximum), and placement should continue. (Parents either will not sign voluntary agreement, or court ordered placement appears preferable.)
10. In order for the court to issue a restraining order, they must have jurisdiction. This can be either through a divorce action, neglect petition, or criminal action.

Definition: The "neglected child" as defined in the Children's Code of Colorado is a child:

1. Whose parent, guardian, or legal custodian has abandoned him or has subjected him to mistreatment or abuse; or whose parent, guardian, or legal custodian has suffered or allowed another to mistreat or abuse the child, without taking lawful means to stop such mistreatment or abuse and to prevent it from recurring;

2. Who lacks proper parental care through the actions or omissions of the parent, guardian, or legal custodian;

3. Whose environment is injurious to his welfare;

4. Whose parent, guardian, or legal custodian fails or refuses to provide proper or necessary subsistence, education, medical care, or any other care necessary for his health, guidance, or well being;

5. Who is homeless, without proper care; or not domiciled with his parent, guardian, or legal custodian.

Neglect Petition

If anyone has questions regarding the legal allegations, ask the county
attorney and he will help determine the allegations which would be
appropriate on filings.

Steps to Filing a Neglect Petition

1. Consult with supervisor
2. Fill out Court Intake Sheet--it is extremely important to fully
   complete the Intake Sheet with facts, who has legal custody, and
   names and addresses
3. Give Intake Sheet to county attorney

In an emergency situation, an immediate custody or ex-parte order can
be obtained by phoning the Court. However, the Intake Sheet for Neglect Petition must be delivered to the Court within 24 hours. This
course of action should be used sparingly and only in emergencies.

Appendix D-2 (1)

TO: All Protective Service Units
FROM: Claudia Carroll, Supervisor
RE: Guidelines for Placement

The following are <u>guidelines</u> for the difficult decision around removal
of a child from his home, and the risk to the child in the parents'
home. These points are <u>some</u> of the factors to be considered in removing or leaving a child in his home. (As more resources are available and utilized by the family, the need for placement is reduced.)

1. Age of child. Be particularly cautious about taking chances with
    an infant--he is more vulnerable and less visible in terms of
    injuries and community observation.

2. Type of injury and severity. Broken bones, burns, head injuries,
    and severe multiple bruises imply more violent outbursts and less
    impulse control. Children with such injuries should always be
    examined by a physician. Was the injury a loss of control by the
    parents or a methodical torture of the child?

3. What is your assessment of the parents? Does the parent(s) appear
    psychotic or neurotic? What are we dealing with?

4. What precipitated the abuse? Children are abused during crisis
    situations. If the family is involved in a current crisis that
    has not been resolved, abuse might be more likely to continue.
    Was the abuse precipitated by the child's behavior that is likely
    to continue, such as the crying of an infant? Is this an isolated
    incident or ongoing problem?

5. Does the parent know when to ask for help, or take the child to
    someone for relief? Has he or she used such assistance?

6. Where are the parents "life-lines?" Who is meeting the needs of
    the parents? Is there someone readily available to the parent?

7. Compatibility of explanation. If the child has been injured, is
    the explanation compatible with the injury? Medical verification
    of the injury and if the parent's explanation of how it happened
    is compatible with the injury should be obtained.

8. Is the abusive parent blaming the child for having brought trouble
    to the family? This will indicate that the parents' anger over
    the intervention will be directed toward the child, and it could
    set the child up for further abuse when the social worker leaves.

9. Is the parent able to see the child as an individual separate from
    herself/himself, or is the parent unable to separate her own
    identify from that of the child or other family members? Lack of
    individualization indicates more danger to the child.

379

Guidelines for Placement

10. Does the parent think the abuse is necessary and justified to correct the child and his behavior?

11. Does the parent have a distorted view of the child? An extreme example would be seeing the child as evil, possessed by the devil. This would allow the parent to feel justified in abusing the child.

12. Bear in mind that intervention by the Department of Social Services or police is very threatening to parents and can precipitate a crisis, so if they react to crisis by battering, our presence can endanger the child.

13. Is the child in a particularly difficult developmental state (i.e., "the terrible two's") so that the parent is having added problems coping with the child? Does the child have special needs requiring additional time and attention which the parent is finding excessive?

Appendix D-3 (1)

TO: All Protective Service Units
FROM: Claudia Carroll, Supervisor
RE: Guidelines for Returning a Child Home and Case Closure

A. The following are guidelines for returning a child home and areas
   where change should take place to consider return of the child to
   the parents' home:

   1. Is there more open communication between parents, and is it
      sustained over a period of time, a number of weeks or months?

   2. Are the parents' expectations of the child more realistic,
      based on the child's age and developmental level?

   3. Are parents meeting each other's needs more appropriately?
      Particularly important, there should be less tendency on the
      part of the parents to look to the child to have their needs
      met. What is the need-meeting system of the family? Who is
      doing what for whom?

   4. Is the parents' view of the child realistic, not distorted?
      What is the perception of the child?

   5. Can the parent allow the child to develop his own identity?
      Can the parent see his emotions as separate from those of the
      child or others in the home?

   6. Reduction in family stress. Children are abused during crisis
      situations. If there are fewer crisis situations, there is
      less probability of continuing abuse of the child. Also, you
      can judge growth of the parents by their ability to cope with
      situations before they turn into crises, so that they actually
      have fewer crisis situations. Consider the coping and adapta-
      tion abilities of the family.

   7. Are the parents more able to understand and meet their
      children's needs?

   8. Often the child's behavior will provoke the parents' abuse.
      When this is the case, has the child's negative behavior im-
      proved? Can the parents use your help in dealing with this
      behavior in an effective way?

   9. If you were able to understand what interaction took place
      between the parents or family members that brought about the
      abuse of the child, look for a change in the behavior pat-
      terns of the family members.

381

Guidelines for Returning a Child Home and Case Closure

10. Are you seeing healthy interaction between the parent and child during visits?

11. Can the abusive parent ask for help when he or she needs it? Are they aware of potentially difficult times for them?

12. Can someone else in the family or home intervene successfully to protect the child? Is he or she helpful and supportive to the parent? Where are the support systems?

13. Is there a treatment relationship established with a helping person, so that when the parent has the impulse to act out (i.e., abuse), the parent will call the worker when in crisis?

14. Are the parents less isolated and do they feel better about themselves?

15. Have the parents learned an alternative way of discipline?

16. Is the parent ambivalent regarding the child? Is he saying one thing and his behavior indicating otherwise (i.e., verbalizing wanting the child back, yet not following through on treatment plan or missing arranged visitation)?

17. What are the observations and assessments of other agencies involved in the case? Are they consistent or inconsistent with our evaluation?

B. Case Closure

1. The above guidelines are the same factors to be considered in closing protective service cases.

   What is particularly significant in the decision to close a case is a sustained period of positive functioning on the part of the parents and child, coupled with a gradual diminishing of the Department of Social Services involvement.

2. When closing a case, always let the parents and other involved agencies know that "the door is open," that is, we are interested and available for re-referrals.

FAMILY SOCIAL STUDY

Date_____   Time Period Covered_____

I. Source and Date of Referral

Name:_____   Date:_____

_____ School_____
_____ Hospital_____
_____ Neighbor_____
_____ Police _____
_____ Court _____
_____ Other Welfare _____
_____ Self _____
_____ Within Department _____
_____ Other_____
_____ Employment_____

II. Demographic Information

	Father	Mother
Name of parent		
Address of parent		
Phone (work and home)		
Birthdate		

Children:

Name	Address	Birthdate	Custody

III. Statement of Problem

_____
_____
_____
_____
_____
_____
_____
_____
_____
_____

Appendix D-4 (2)

Family Social Study

IV. Attitude of Client to Agency Involvement

_____ Anger
_____ Denial
_____ Cooperative
_____ Resistent
_____ Requesting Counseling
_____ Passively Compliant

V. Home Situation

A.

	In the home (Yes/No)	Employ-ment	Income	Education Grade & Sch. District	Health (Good/Poor)	Adequate Medical Care (Yes/No)
Father						
Mother						
Child						
Child						
Child						

B. Living Conditions of the Home

_____ Adequate   Explain:_____
_____ Inadequate   _____
                        _____
                        _____

VI. Relationships of the Family

Primary Family: Parent-Child Relationships:

Family Social Study

_____ Adjusted   Parents sensitive to children?
_____ Protective   _____ Yes
_____ Supportive   _____ No
_____ Close-knit   Explain:_____
_____ Inconsistent   _____
_____ Hostile   _____
_____ Uninvolved
_____ Disorganized

Comments_____

_____

(2)_____

_____

Extended Family:

_____ Adjusted   Comments:_____
_____ Protective   _____
_____ Supportive   _____
_____ Close-knit   _____
_____ Inconsistent   _____
_____ Hostile
_____ Uninvolved
_____ Domineering
_____ Disorganized
_____ Unavailable

VII. Individual Functioning

A.

Child	Child	Child	Child	Child	Mother	Father	
							Secure
							Insecure
							Alert
							Lethargic
							Resourceful
							Dull
							Shy
							Active
							Pleasant
							Outgoing
							Suspicious
							Depressed
							Suicidal
							Passive
							Animated
							Aggressive
							Violent
							Withdrawn
							Controlling
							Manipulative
							Overprotective
							Acting-out
							Disoriented
							Appropriate
							Stable
							Angry
							Anxious
							Dependent
							Hostile
							Other

Appendix D-4 (5)

Family Social Study

B. School Adjustment -- Describe

Child	Attendance	Attitude	Potential	Performance

VIII. Interventions

A. Presenting Problems

(1)_____
(2)_____
(3)_____

B. Cause of Problems

(1)_____
(2)_____
(3)_____

B. Type of Interventions (Intervention should reflect attention to the cause of the problem.)

_____ Homemaker placed
_____ Day care secured
_____ Job training enrolled
_____ Job referral effected
_____ Group counseling (type)_____
_____ Individual counseling (focus) _____
_____ Family counseling (focus) _____
_____ Child rearing education (focus)_____
_____ Marital counseling (focus) _____
_____ Play therapy
_____ Referral to whom _____
_____ Vocational rehabilitation
_____ Education
_____ Other_____

C. Legal and Court Involvement, if applicable

_____ Neglect Petition filed_____
_____ CHINS Petition filed_____
_____ Delinquency Petition filed_____

387

Family Social Study

	Crimical action
	Voluntary placement-- Date:_____
	Relinquishment-- Date:_____

Disposition:

_____ Adjudicated date_____
_____ Non-adjudicated date_____

Custody_____
_____
_____

D. Collateral

	Identify Worker	Role (i.e., primary, secondary, support)	Phone
Mental Health			
Court			
Public Health			
Hospital			
Other			

IX. Placement, if applicable

A. Whether placement made: Which children placed   Where
    ____Yes--Date_____   _____   _____
    ____No   _____   _____
    _____   _____

B. Basis and Reasons on Which Placement Made

    1.
    2.
    3.
    4.

C. Visitation

    ____Yes
    ____No   Explain (i.e., reaction of child/parents to visits, current arrangement)_____
    _____
    _____

Family Social Study

    D.   Financial--Describe current agreement

    _____

    _____

X. Treatment Plan (Identify goals)

    _____

    _____

    _____

    _____

    _____

    _____

Comments

    _____

    _____

    _____

    _____

    _____

    _____

    _____

    _____

Supervisor	Social Worker

Appendix D-5 (1)

Addendum to Family Social Study

Type of Problem

A. Abuse   C. Neglect

____ Severe   ____ Severe
____ Ongoing   ____ Ongoing
____ Isolated incident   ____ Isolated incident
____ Emotional   ____ Emotional
____ Physical   ____ Physical
                                     ____ Lack of supervision

B. Potential Abuse   D. Level

____ Severe   ____ Serious
____ Ongoing   ____ Minor
____ Isolated incident   ____ Preventative
____ Emotional   ____ Requested involvement of
____ Physical   agency

Description of Problem

A. Describe Injury/Abuse/Neglect (Age of children, number of chil-
    dren, circumstances, detailed description, number of bruises,
    location, broken bones, etc.)

    _____
    _____
    _____
    _____
    _____
    _____

B. Recidivism of Abuse/Neglect

    ____ No
    ____ Yes--Explain_____
    _____
    _____
    _____
    _____
    _____

C. Injuries, if applicable
    ____ Accidental_____
    _____
    ____ Non-accidental_____
    _____
    _____

390

Addendum

_____ Explanation consistent with injury
_____ Medical verification

_____ Explanation inconsistent with injury
_____ Medical verification

D. Injuries Inflicted By

_____ Parent

_____ Mother
_____ Father

_____ Other--explain: _____

_____
_____
_____
_____

E. Attitude of Person Who Injured Child Toward Injury

_____ Denial
_____ Anger
_____ Remorse
_____ Concern for child

F. Dynamics Present

_____
_____
_____
_____
_____
_____
_____

Appendix D-6 (1)

FAMILY SERVICE RECORDING

Date_____

Time Period Covered_____

I. Name_____

Address_____ Phone_____

Number and type of contacts_____

II. Target Problems

Primary_____
_____

Secondary_____
_____

III. Treatment Techniques Used

____ Individual counseling
____ Family counseling
____ Marital counseling
____ Group therapy
____ Behavior modification
____ Play therapy
____ Transactional analysis

IV. Types of Intervention

____ Foster placement
____ Day care
____ Court action
____ Child rearing education
____ Money management
____ Medical care
____ Family planning counseling
____ Job referral
____ Job training
____ Crisis intervention

Referrals and Resources Utilized- Service Effectiveness

____ Mental health   ____ Complete
____ Public health nurse   ____ Substantial
____ Public assistance   ____ Partial
____ Legal aid   ____ Minimal
____ Housing   Explain_____
____ Homemaker   _____
____ Information giving   _____
____ Other

392

Family Service Recording

V.   Collateral Contacts

Name   Agency   Phone

_____   _____   _____
_____   _____   _____
_____   _____   _____
_____   _____   _____

VI.   Current Status of Family Functioning

_____
_____
_____
_____

VII.   Court Status _____Next Hearing_____

VIII.   Treatment Plan and Goals

_____
_____
_____
_____

IX.   Comments

_____
_____
_____
_____

X.   Closure, if applicable   (Disposition of case at time of
        closing--when and why?)

_____
_____
_____
_____

_____   _____
        Supervisor   Social Worker

INITIAL SOCIAL STUDY FOR CHILD IN FOSTER CARE

Date_____

Time Period Covered_____

I.   Child_____Birthdate_____

      Parents: Mother_____Address_____
                                            Phone_____
                 Father_____Address_____
                                            Phone_____

II.   Date, Source, and Reason for Referral_____
      _____
      _____
      _____

III. Basis and Reason on which Placement Made

      _____ Abuse
      _____ Neglect
      _____ Run-away
      _____ Family conflict
      _____ Lack of housing
      _____ Voluntary request
      _____ Abandoned
      _____ Incest
      _____ Relinquishment
      _____ Other_____

      Comments_____
      _____
      _____

IV.   Court Action   Yes_____ No_____

      When filed_____

      Type of Petition_____

      _____ Adjudicated   Date_____
      _____ Non-adjudicated   Date_____

      Custody to whom_____

      Next hearing _____

V.   Placement

      Date of Placement _____
      Where Placed _____
      Behavior of Child Around Removal_____
      _____

Child in Foster Care

      What child was told during placement process_____

      _____

      _____

      _____

      _____

VI.   Child's understanding of reason for placement and initial
       adjustment to placement

      _____

      _____

      _____

      _____

VII.   General Health
       Background_____

      _____

      _____

      _____

      Current_____

      _____

      _____

      _____

      Areas needing attention_____

      _____

      _____

      _____

VIII. Plans for Visitation _____

      _____

      _____

      _____

IX.   Plan for Child (i.e., special needs, anticipated length of
       placement, resources needed, etc.)

      _____

      _____

      _____

X.   Are Parents Contributing to Support of Child? Yes____ No_____

XI.   Comments_____

      _____

_____   _____
     Supervisor   Social Worker

CHILD PLACEMENT SERVICE RECORDING

Date_____

Time Period Covered_____

I. Changes in Placement   ____Yes ____ No

    Moved to Where_____

    Why _____

    _____

II. Current Adjustment in Placement

    ____ Good
    ____ Fair
    ____ Poor

    Comments_____

    _____

    _____

    _____

III. Health _____

    _____

    _____

IV. Social and School Performance

    ____ Accepted or rejected by others
    ____ Has friends
    ____ Working to capacity
    ____ Requires special help
    ____ Behavior problems

    _____

    _____

    _____

    _____

    Resources used _____

    _____

V. Visitation and Child's Reaction

    _____

    _____

    _____

VI. Current Legal Status

    _____

Child Placement Service Recording

VII.   Future Plans and Goals _____

       _____
       _____
       _____
       _____

VIII. Closure, if applicable

       Date Closed_____ Why closed_____
                              _____

       Returned to parents _____ When _____
       Referred to family caseworker for follow-up _____
       Termination of parental rights _____
       Adoption _____

_____   _____
     Supervisor   Social Worker

Appendix D-9 (1)

JUVENILE COURT PETITION--INTAKE/REFERRAL SHEET

Complainant___ Worker's Name - Adams County Dept. of Social Services
Address___ 4200 East 72nd Avenue, Commerce City, Colorado 80022
Phone___ 287-8831_____ Date _____

Children   Sex Age Birthdate Grade and School
1. List all minors in the family___ ___ _____ _____
2. *Asterisk those filing on___ ___ _____ _____
_____ ___ ___ _____ _____
_____ ___ ___ _____ _____

Race _____ Religion _____

Address of children _____ Phone_____

Guardian or Custodian _____

_____

Father _____ Mother _____
Stepmother _____ Stepfather _____
Address (must have, even if old)___ Address _____
Phone _____ Phone _____
     Home   Work   Home   Work
Employment_____ Employment_____
Hours _____ Hours _____

_____

Others interested or having knowledge of problems:

1. Possible resources: police, hospitals, physicians, school, mental
   health, tri-county, neighbors, referring party, and other agencies
   or departments or both.

2. Who should be subpoened (our attorney will handle this).

   (a) Discuss with our attorney to initiate action. He will take
       subpoena to court.

3. Who should be notified by letter--parents and other agencies.

4. Other workers having knowledge and why.

5. Attorneys involved and who they represent.

398

Juvenile Court Petition

6. Indicate no other agencies are involved if, to the best of our knowledge, this is the case.

INFORMATION

I. Evidence

   A. Are the allegations justified, so that the court can see why the action was filed?

   B. Clarify which children filing are on and why. Include legal status of each child.

   C. Describe specific injuries, circumstances regarding the safety of the child in the home, the parents' ability to care or protect child, etc.

   D. Indicate whether school, medical, police reports, or CWS-59 are attached to the Intake Sheet or will be included for merits hearing.

   E. Deal with facts, not impressions.

   F. Give indication of parents' attitude and their statement regarding the allegations.

II. Allegations (list allegations pertinent to case from among the five listed below). Under the Colorado Children Code a "neglected child" is defined as a child:

   A. Whose parent, guardian, or legal custodian has abandoned him or has subjected him to mistreatment or abuse; or whose parents, guardian, or legal custodian has suffered or allowed another to mistreat or abuse the child without taking lawful means to stop such mistreatment or abuse and to prevent it from recurring;

   B. Who lacks proper parental care through the actions or omissions of the parent, guardian, or legal custodian;

   C. Whose environment is injurious to his welfare;

   D. Whose parent, guardian, or legal custodian fails or refuses to provide proper or necessary subsistence, education, medical care, or any other care necessary for his health, guidance, or well-being;

   E. Who is homeless, without proper care, or not domiciled with his parent, guardian, or legal custodian.

Appendix D-9 (3)

Juvenile Court Petition

III. What the Department of Social Services is Requesting of Court

A. If requesting immediate custody, justify why it is essential at this time (i.e., are the parents demanding that the child be released from the hospital? What is the immediate danger to the child?) Once custody is granted, we are obligated to enforce it.

B. Other possible notes at time of forwarding the intake papers to Court:

1. Hearing (note any appropriate time, or if worker will be unavailable between certain dates.)

2. That the court take no action at this time, but hold intake sheet until further notice. (Indicate HOLD on top of intake sheet. Update the information if matter is held for a few days, and we want to go ahead with a filing. Notify Court if not going to file.)

3. We can request that the Court forward the respondent's summons to appear in Court to the worker for service. This means that the respondents, at our request, need not be served by the Sheriff's Department. The clients then sign a waiver of service, and the worker returns the appropriate papers to Court. This is an alternative way for the Court papers to be given to clients to be used at the discretion of the worker, and the Court papers should be used in those cases where we know the clients will sign the waiver of service. (A waiver of service means that the clients are waiving being served by the Sheriff's Department.)

Requests are not mandatory.

COURT REPORTS

The following are guidelines for court reports. They need not be followed line by line, but are intended to assist you in covering pertinent
information which the court needs in assessing a case. If, for example,
a worker prefers to send Court Reports in the form of a letter, this
is certainly acceptable as long as the information given is complete
and gives a clear picture of the case.

Court J# _____

Worker's Name _____

Hearing Date _____

ADJUDICATORY HEARING

I. Jurisdictional Facts
   Adjudicatory

   Concerning: Name, birthdate
                Mother: name and address
                Father: name and address
                (attorney for parents)
                (attorney for minor)

   Facts regarding allegation: Brief summary; enlargement of what
                                is on Intake Sheet and why case is
                                in court.

   Parents' statement: Their statements are to cover the allegations
                        of the petition only.

   Witnesses' statements: List only those witnesses who will be in
                           court to testify. Their statement in com-
                           plete detail is not necessary, but it
                           should reflect their own knowledge. In-
                           dicate to what they can testify, such as
                           "Mrs. G., neighbor of the J. Family, saw
                           Johnny J. spanked with a belt by his
                           mother."

DISPOSITIONAL HEARING

II. Social Information

   A. Observational Process

      1. Family History and Environment

         Father
         Mother

Court Reports

Social history of each parent; physical, emotional, and marital problems; child-rearing practices; view of child; view of court involvement; current personal or emotional crisis of the family; give the court an idea of the relationships of the family (e.g., run-away, arrests, criminal actions, and previous placements); strengths of family; and employment of parents.

The Children

Description and impressions; child's statement, if not a witness; psychosocial and motor development; well-child care; and brief history of custody, placements, physical problems, emotional problems, and special needs.

Other Reports

School, medical, and psychological or psychiatric

2. Treatment Plan

Identification of causes of problems necessitating court jurisdiction; description of plan, reason for particular plan, goals, and time frame of plan and goal; identification of what parents should be doing to remedy the problem; possible resources for special needs of child and parents; placement, why or why not placement proposed, type of placement (i.e., foster home, institution, relative, or remain with parents), and general idea of length of anticipated placement; parents' attitude toward plan, placement, etc.; and course of treatment for each family member and agencies to be involved and the role of each.

3. Financial Arrangement, if indicated

Mandatory in all cases where placement is a factor. What is the attitude of parents? Are they in agreement? Indicate whether payment should go directly to the Department of Social Services or through Court Registry.

4. Recommendations

Possible recommendations (Recommendation should primarily concern social work plan and what needs to be done.)

a. "It is respectfully recommended that (name of child) be declared a neglected child and made a ward of the court and temporary custody given to Social Services Department."

Court Reports

      b. Parents retain custody, Department of Social Services
          supervises.

      c. Custody to Department of Social Services, custodial
          care to parent, guardian, or other interested party.

      d. Any specific requirements for the parents.

_____

Worker's Signature

REVIEW REPORT

Indicate whether this is a report for a hearing (date), or if report is in lieu of a hearing.

A. Evaluation of Present Situation

    1. What has happened since last hearing? How often seen by worker?

    2. Progress

    3. What accomplished up to date? What approach has been used?

    4. Changes

    5. Current custody, financial, and visiting arrangement. (Where did visitation take place? Was it observed by the worker at any time? Where did the worker observe visitation (i.e., in office, in parents' home)?

    6. Attitudes of parents and child

    7. Cooperation

B. Plan

    1. Guidelines for future

    2. Reason for particular plan

    3. Where going--goals

    4. What specifically should parents be doing to remedy the problem

    5. What hope to accomplish

    6. Timetable

C. Recommendation

    1. Specific action for Court

    2. Worker(s) and agency attorney must be in agreement prior to hearing

    3. Specific alternative if plan does not work (i.e., termination if, after reasonable length of time, no progress made toward child's return home)

Appendix D-11 (2)

Review Report

4. Clients must be aware of recommendation and in agreement if no hearing scheduled and report suffices. Indicate in report if client is aware of recommendation and in agreement.

5. Requests (possible)

   a. Continuation--by report of hearing, specify which
   b. Terminate court action

_____
Worker's Signature

SAMPLE COURT REPORT

Review Hearing

REPORT TO COURT

Richmond, Karen--age 4
Richmond, Lindsay--age 7
Richmond, Kyle--age 9

The purpose of this report is to provide the court with information regarding the current involvement of the Adams County Department of Social Services with Mr. and Mrs. Ben Richmond. At the adjudicatory and dispositional hearing three months ago, Karen, Lindsay, and Kyle Richmond were declared neglected and dependent children based on the evidence given that there was physical and emotional abuse present in the home. Lindsay and Kyle were left in the care of their parents, and Karen was placed in temporary foster care because of numerous inflicted bruises.

Evaluation of Present Situation. Since the last hearing, the Richmonds and I have been able to arrive at some mutually agreeable plans. Mrs. Richmond has begun individual therapy with me, and she is actively participating in this. Mr. Richmond has begun individual therapy at Adams County Mental Health Center, and, additionally, Mr. and Mrs. Richmond are being seen there for marital problems. My contacts with the Richmonds have included four home visits, eight office visits, and frequent phone calls in which Mrs. Richmond has felt comfortable in calling me when stressed. In addition, Mr. and Mrs. Richmond have had regular visitations with Karen, and they are current in their child support payments.

Karen's visits home have gone well with a gradation of time being spent in the home. During my visits to the Richmond home, I have been impressed with Karen's gregarious nature and high level of activity and energy. She appears to be quite bright and somewhat provocative. The interaction between Karen and the family was basically positive, and, of particular importance, was the warmth between Karen and her mother. Whereas Mrs. Richmond previously felt a lack of closeness between herself and her daughter, I believe their relationship can be now characterized as more positive and giving.

Both Mr. and Mrs. Richmond have continued to be employed during this period. Mrs. Richmond feels that working out of the home is good for her, and I have supported her in this.

Lindsay continues to do well in school, and it appears that Kyle has made some progress, having received satisfactory and above grades. I have talked with the Richmonds about their allowing Kyle to be seen by a school counselor for individual counseling for his depressed and withdrawn behavior, and they are willing to proceed with this step.

Sample Court Report

Plan. 1. For Karen to return to the Richmond home with continued supervision by Adams County Department of Social Services. It is my opinion that both Mr. and Mrs. Richmond very much want her home. Indicators supporting the return of Karen to the home are as follows: (1) the self-image of each of the parents seems to have improved through the therapy they are receiving, (2) there is a more realistic and empathetic perception of the child by both parents, and (3) there is a meaningful relationship existing between myself and the Richmonds, which they have used very appropriately to deal with problems. The Richmonds are in agreement with my continuing involvement with them. They are asking for help with specific "what to do" situations, and we plan to discuss alternative ways of discipline and more realistic expectations of their children.

2. Mr. and Mrs. Richmond will continue their joint therapy with a social worker at Adams County Mental Health Center regarding marital issues (this report is attached).

3. Karen's social worker of Adams County Department of Social Services has been seeing her regularly in play therapy for the past three months and will continue to do so after her return home.

Recommendations. This situation is not without problems--that is, financially, the Richmonds are still under pressure and individually, both Mr. and Mrs. Richmond appear to have a propensity toward depression. They recognize their need to be more supportive of each other in such areas as child rearing. However, it is my opinion that we have made a beginning. I see that it will be necessary for our department to be involved, and the concerted efforts of the Richmonds, Adams County Mental Health, and Adams County Department of Social Services to continue for a period of several months. Significant areas that will be a part of my ongoing evaluation and work with the Richmonds include: (1) looking at their coping abilities to current stress, (2) their individual and marital stability, and (3) their perception and individualization of each child.

It is my recommendation that Karen be returned to the home of Mr. and Mrs. Ben Richmond, and that her custody also be returned to them. It is further recommended that these three children remain under the jurisdiction of the Court.

Claudia Carroll, M.S.W.
Casework Supervisor III

Index